Rebound 1995

The Art
of
Short Fiction

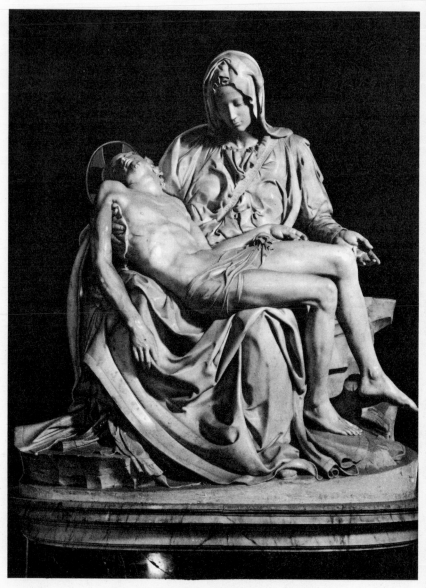

The *Pieta* by Michaelangelo (See p. 13)

The Art
of
Short Fiction

Barbara Pannwitt
Evanston Township High School

GINN AND COMPANY
Boston
New York · Chicago · Atlanta · Dallas · Palo Alto · Toronto

ACKNOWLEDGMENTS

Grateful acknowledgment is due to the following publishers, authors, and other holders of copyright material for permission to use selections from their publications.

THE AMERICAN-SCANDINAVIAN FOUNDATION: "The Father," from *Stories,* by Björnstjerne Björnson. Reprinted with the permission of the American-Scandinavian Foundation.

THE ATLANTIC MONTHLY: "Holiday," by Katherine Anne Porter. Copyright 1960, by The Atlantic Monthly Company, Boston 16, Massachusetts.

BRANDT & BRANDT: "So Much Unfairness of Things," by C. D. B. Bryan, © 1962 The New Yorker Magazine, Inc. Reprinted by permission of Brandt & Brandt.

CHATTO & WINDUS LTD: "The Lottery Ticket," from *The Wife and Other Stories,* by Anton Chekhov. Translated by Constance Garnett. "Action," from *Action and Other Stories,* by C. E. Montague.

J. M. DENT & SONS, LTD: "Youth: A Narrative," from *Youth: A Narrative and Two Other Stories,* by Joseph Conrad. "Patricia, Edith and Arnold," from *Portrait of the Artist as a Young Dog,* by Dylan Thomas.

EYRE & SPOTTISWOODE LTD: "Autumn Mountain," by Ryūnosuké Akutagawa, as it appeared in *Modern Japanese Stories: An Anthology,* edited by Ivan Morris. Copyright 1962, UNESCO Collection of Representative Works, Japanese Series.

FARRAR, STRAUS & CUDAHY, INC.: "Charles," reprinted from *The Lottery,* by Shirley Jackson, by permission of Farrar, Straus & Cudahy, Inc. First appeared in *Mademoiselle.* Copyright 1948 by The New Yorker Magazine, 1949 by Shirley Jackson. A critical evaluation of "The Sisters," reprinted from *A Reader's Guide to James Joyce,* by William York Tindall, by permission of Farrar, Straus & Cudahy, Inc. Copyright © 1959 by William York Tindall.

ALFRED A. KNOPF, INC.: "The Guest," reprinted from *Exile and the Kingdom,* by Albert Camus, translated by Justin O'Brien, by permission of Alfred A. Knopf, Inc. Copyright, 1957, 1958 by Alfred A. Knopf, Inc. "The Fair Young Willowy Tree," reprinted from *The Collected Tales of A. E. Coppard,* by permission of Alfred A. Knopf, Inc. "The Upturned Face," reprinted from *Stephen Crane: An Omnibus,* edited by Robert Wooster Stallman, by permission of Alfred A. Knopf, Inc. Published 1952 by Alfred A. Knopf, Inc. "Feuille d'Album," reprinted from *The Short Stories of Katherine Mansfield,* by Katherine Mansfield, by permission of Alfred A. Knopf, Inc. Copyright, 1920, 1937 by Alfred A. Knopf, Inc. "Pigeon Feathers," reprinted from *Pigeon Feathers and Other Stories,* by John Updike, by permission of Alfred A. Knopf, Inc. Originally published in *The New Yorker.* Copyright, 1961 by John Updike.

THE MACMILLAN COMPANY: "The Lottery Ticket," reprinted with permission of the publisher, from *The Wife and Other Stories,* by Anton Chekhov. Copyright 1918 by The Macmillan Company, copyright 1946 by Constance Garnett.

McINTOSH AND OTIS: "The Affair at 7, Rue de M——," by John Steinbeck. Copyright © 1955 by John Steinbeck. Appeared originally in *Harper's Bazaar.* Reprinted by permission of McIntosh and Otis, Inc.

HAROLD MATSON COMPANY: "The Golden Kite, The Silver Wind," from *The Golden Apples of the Sun,* by Ray Bradbury. Copyright © 1952 by Ray Bradbury. Reprinted by permission of Harold Matson Company.

THOMAS NELSON & SONS: "The New Testament, Luke 15:11-32," from The Revised Standard Version of the Holy Bible, copyrighted 1946 and 1952 by the Division of Christian Education of the National Council of Churches, and used by permission.

NEW DIRECTIONS: "Patricia, Edith and Arnold," from *Portrait of the Artist as a Young Dog,* by Dylan Thomas. Copyright 1940 by New Directions. Reprinted by permission of New Directions, Publishers.

THE NEW YORKER: "Benediction," by Patricia Collinge. Reprinted by permission of the author; copyright © 1957 The New Yorker Magazine, Inc.

NEW YORK UNIVERSITY PRESS: "The 'Sisters' of Joyce" from *Joyce: The Man, The Work, The Reputation,* by Marvin Magalaner and Richard M. Kain. Copyright © 1956 by New York University.

A. D. PETERS: "The Fair Young Willowy Tree," from *The Collected Tales of A. E. Coppard.*

SCHOCKEN BOOKS INC.: "The Burrow," reprinted by permission of Schocken Books Inc., from *The Great Wall of China,* by Franz Kafka. Copyright 1946, 1948 by Schocken Books Inc., New York; translated by Willa and Edwin Muir.

SCHOLASTIC MAGAZINES, INC.: "Leatherback," by Katherine Kittleman. Reprinted by permission of Scholastic Magazines, Inc. "The Noontide of the First Day," by Jean Weir, from *Practical English.* Copyright © 1955 by Scholastic Magazines, Inc. Reprinted by permission.

To
Perle G. Taylor

Contents

Stories by Students of Short Fiction

Foreword

WHAT IS MAN? The long, long search for an answer to this question has raised yet further questions: What is man's responsibility to himself? What is his relationship to nature? to his fellow man? to God? How does he adjust to the seven ages of man that he must go through if he lives a normal span? How does he resolve the conflicts among those seven ages? Above all, why must man die? And how can he hope to achieve some kind of immortality? All these searchings are the subject matter of the humanities: art, dance, drama, music, philosophy, sculpture, theology, and literature.

These vital concerns of man are emphasized in this collection of short stories. Through the study of one kind of art, a genre of literature —in this case, short fiction—we can attempt an understanding of the meaning of life. Such a study may help to show young people ways of meeting and responding to the ambiguity, comedy, tragedy, and triumph of human existence.

These unsettled times make us cry out for such help. The threat of nuclear attack and the high worth that society places on material technology shake our emotional and moral stability. Increased automation, what seems to be the control of life by machines, and the mediocre models of the "good life" that assail the senses through the mass media make us fear depersonalization of the individual. The tawdriness of large urban areas and the conformity of people in suburban communities are intensifying the individual's loneliness and personal frustration. While man looks to the stars for the conquest of space and of those he thinks are his enemies, does he risk losing the vision and perspective with which to marvel at the wonder of those stars? In short, without rejecting the facts of science, the insights of social science, and the technological monuments to man's ingenuity, we need to emphasize our concern, not only for knowledge but also for wisdom and beauty. Man needs to balance his control over matter with a deeper investigation into the mysteries of the human spirit.

These mysteries—the proper studies of mankind—comprise the stuff of literature. The stories selected for this volume represent a variety of ways in which artists of the past and present have probed the restless, creative nature of man. The selections are grouped according to some topics about which man has always asked questions: Love and Hate, Youth and Age, Man and Nature, Man Alone, and Mortality and Imagination. Illustrating these topics are selections as old as a parable from the New Testament and as new as John Updike's "Pigeon Feathers"; as well established in literature as Maupassant's "old master," "The Piece of String," and as fresh as some high school students' contributions. Nobel prize winners and other American, British, and European authors, as well as the Japanese Ryūnosuké Akutagawa, are represented. Each story has been chosen because of its humanistic value, its appeal to the interests of youth, and its illustration of the art of short fiction.

The techniques of artistic expression are explained in the section "The Art of Short Fiction," in the editor's commentaries on some stories, and in guest commentaries. These interpretations are designed to aid students and teachers in their own analyses. The commentaries are not intended to be exhaustive but rather to be provocative of further thought. Indeed, readers are encouraged to disagree with the interpretations. No commentaries are provided for a number of the stories in order that readers may come to understand them through their own close reading. Questions following the stories and thematic divisions of the book are designed for either discussion or written assignment. Both commentaries and questions are meant to be aids in the close reading of the stories and the consequent development of responsible, critical taste.

The editor believes that a student should concentrate on the stories themselves and that literary analysis should not depend on such external factors as the authors' lives or the social milieus that produced or inspired their stories' art. Having interpreted a story on the basis of what can actually be *pointed to* in it, however, a reader may derive additional enrichment and understanding by knowing some of the external factors. For that reason, and as a further aid to both student and teacher, brief biographies of the authors and critical bibliographies of the stories are supplied. A glossary of literary terms is also offered as a supplementary aid to the study and appreciation of the literary art of short fiction. For additional reading of short fiction, the student and teacher may wish to use the lists of titles at the end of each thematic section.

No book, though, can possibly take the place of discussion nor of the interchange of ideas under the inductive leadership and guidance of a teacher. This book, therefore, is offered with the hope that it will be useful to young people and their instructors and with appreciation to those who helped to make its publication possible.

The editor suggests two ways in which the student of short fiction may use this book. First, he may read the chapter on "The Art of

Short Fiction" fairly quickly in order to achieve a frame of reference for the commentaries and discussion questions that follow the stories and to note the underlying philosophy upon which the book is organized. Then, after reading some or all of the stories, the student may return to the chapter on theory and technique for closer study and understanding. The second way that a student may use this book is to follow the chronological order, depending on the cross references (in parentheses throughout) to explanations of terms and principles in the chapter "The Art of Short Fiction."

Besides the artists who wrote the stories, a number of other people have helped to make this book a reality, and special acknowledgment is due them. These comprise all the teachers who played a part in developing the editor's own interest in the humanities, including those unseen teachers who wrote influential textbooks that the editor has read. The guidance of fellow teachers at Evanston Township High School—especially Mr. Clarence W. Hach and Mr. Malcolm F. Mosing—and of the boys and girls who, as pupils, very often taught more than they may have learned, is appreciated. The interest and tolerance of the editor's family during the compilation of this book also have made it possible. Helpful criticism and encouragement have been the valuable contribution of Dr. Robert L. Page, Dr. Harold Keables, Mr. Fred J. Pannwitt, and Mr. William B. Rood, Jr.

Barbara Pannwitt

The Art of Short Fiction

Before we can discuss short fiction as art, we must ask a question: What do we mean by art? Art is Van Cliburn playing Beethoven's *Emperor Concerto,* Miles Davis playing a jazz trumpet solo of "Prayer" from Gershwin's *Porgy and Bess,* and Laurence Olivier portraying Hamlet. Art is Shakespeare's *Romeo and Juliet,* Leonard Bernstein's *West Side Story,* Leonardo da Vinci's *Mona Lisa,* Picasso's *Guernica,* Michelangelo's *Pieta.* It is the Taj Mahal and the chapel at the United States Air Force Academy. It is Fred Astaire's or Pavlova's dancing, John Keats's "Ode on a Grecian Urn," Wallace Stevens's "Sunday Morning," Mark Twain's *The Adventures of Huckleberry Finn.* It is the Bible—and the short stories in this book.

All these works of art are harmonious expressions of man's thought and feeling for the purpose of giving aesthetic pleasure. They are all communications that imitate and interpret what man has observed, thought about, imagined, and reacted to emotionally. Art, in this sense, includes the spatial arts of architecture, sculpture, and painting and the temporal arts of music, drama, the dance, and literature.

Why does man create art? Many theories have evolved to answer this question. Some people believe that man's natural love of rhythm and harmony makes him create things that are also rhythmic and harmonious. Today many aesthetic theories are based on the belief that the artistic impulse springs from man's fear of the unknown, especially death. In his best-known poem, "Sunday Morning," for instance, Wallace Stevens has expressed this thought:

> Death is the mother of beauty; hence from her
> Alone, shall come fulfilment to our dreams
> And our desires.

In other words, if man knew what lies beyond the grave, or if man did not know that he is mortal, he would have no impetus to leave something lasting of his own creation behind.

One of the questions that the humanities, including the arts, seek to answer is, How can man achieve immortality? One of the answers man has found is in the creation of art.

Two Works of Art

Here now are two works of the art of short fiction. Each is a harmonious expression of man's thought and feeling for the purpose of giving aesthetic pleasure, communicated through the medium of language, imitating and interpreting what man has observed, imagined, and reacted to emotionally. The parable of "The Prodigal Son" from the New Testament is a very old work of art, and "The Piece of String" by Guy de Maupassant is a relatively modern work of art.

The Prodigal Son

Luke 15:11-32

And he said, "There was a man who had two sons; and the younger of them said to his father, 'Father, give me the share of property that falls to me.' And he divided his living between them. Not many days later, the younger son gathered all he had and took his journey into a far country, and there he squandered his property in loose living. And when he had spent everything, a great famine arose in that country, and he began to be in want. So he went and joined himself to one of the citizens of that country, who sent him into his fields to feed swine. And he would gladly have fed on the pods that the swine ate; and no one gave him anything. But when he came to himself he said, 'How many of my father's hired servants have bread enough and to spare, but I perish here with hunger! I will arise and go to my father, and I will say to him, "Father, I have sinned against heaven and before you; I am no longer worthy to be called your son; treat me as one of your hired servants." ' And he arose and came to his father. But while he was yet at a distance, his father saw him and had compassion, and ran and embraced him and kissed him. And the son said to him, 'Father, I have sinned against heaven and before you; I am no longer worthy to be called your son.' But the father said to his servants, 'Bring quickly the best robe, and put it on him; and put a ring on his hand, and shoes on his feet; and bring the fatted calf and kill it, and let us eat and make merry; for this my son was dead, and is alive again; he was lost, and is found.' And they began to make merry.

"Now his elder son was in the field; and as he came and drew near to the house, he heard music and dancing. And he called one of the servants and asked what this meant. And he said to him, 'Your brother has come, and your father has killed the fatted calf, because he has received him safe and sound.' But he was angry and refused to go in. His father came out and entreated him, but he answered his father, 'Lo, these many years I have served you, and I never disobeyed your command; yet you never gave me a kid, that I might make merry with my friends. But when this son of yours came, who has devoured your living with harlots, you killed for him the fatted calf!' And he said to him, 'Son, you are always with me, and all that is mine is yours. It was fitting to make merry and be glad, for this your brother was dead, and is alive; he was lost, and is found.' "

The Piece of String

Guy de Maupassant

It was market-day, and over all the roads round Goderville the peasants and their wives were coming towards the town. The men walked easily, lurching the whole body forward at every step. Their long legs were twisted and deformed by the slow, painful labors of the country: —by bending over to plough, which is what also makes their left shoulders too high and their figures crooked; and by reaping corn, which obliges them for steadiness' sake to spread their knees too wide. Their starched blue blouses, shining as though varnished, ornamented at collar and cuffs with little patterns of white stitch-work, and blown up big around their bony bodies, seemed exactly like balloons about to soar, but putting forth a head, two arms, and two feet.

Some of these fellows dragged a cow or a calf at the end of a rope. And just behind the animal, beating it over the back with a leaf-covered branch to hasten its pace, went their wives, carrying large baskets from which came forth the heads of chickens or the heads of ducks. These women walked with steps far shorter and quicker than the men; their figures, withered and upright, were adorned with scanty little shawls pinned over their flat bosoms; and they enveloped their heads each in a white cloth, close fastened round the hair and surmounted by a cap.

Now a char-à-banc passed by, drawn by a jerky-paced nag. It shook up strangely the two men on the seat. And the woman at the bottom of the cart held fast to its sides to lessen the hard joltings.

In the market-place at Goderville was a great crowd, a mingled multitude of men and beasts. The horns of cattle, the high and long-napped hats of wealthy peasants, the head-dresses of the women, came to the surface of that sea. And voices clamorous, sharp, shrill, made a continuous and savage din. Above it a huge burst of laughter from the sturdy lungs of a merry yokel would sometimes sound, and sometimes a long bellow from a cow tied fast to the wall of a house.

It all smelled of the stable, of milk, of hay, and of perspiration, giving off that half-human, half-animal odor which is peculiar to the men of the fields.

Maître Hauchecorne, of Bréauté, had just arrived at Goderville, and was taking his way towards the square, when he perceived on the ground a little piece of string. Maître Hauchecorne, economical, like all true Normans, reflected that everything was worth picking up which could be of any use; and he stooped down—but painfully, because he suffered from rheumatism. He took the bit of thin cord from the ground, and was carefully preparing to roll it up when he saw Maître Malandain, the harness-maker, on his door-step, looking at him. They had once had a quarrel about a halter, and they had remained angry, bearing malice on both sides. Maître Hauchecorne was overcome with a sort of shame at being seen by his enemy looking in the dirt so for a bit of string. He quickly hid his find beneath his blouse; then in the pocket of his breeches; then pretended to be still looking for something on the ground which he did not discover; and at last went off towards the market-place, with his head bent forward, and a body almost doubled in two by rheumatic pains.

He lost himself immediately in the crowd, which was clamorous, slow, and agitated by interminable bargains. The peasants examined the cows, went off, came back, always in great perplexity and fear of being cheated, never quite daring to decide, spying at the eye of the seller, trying ceaselessly to discover the tricks of the man and the defect in the beast.

The women, having placed their great baskets at their feet, had pulled out the poultry, which lay upon the ground, tied by the legs, with eyes scared, with combs scarlet.

They listened to propositions, maintaining their prices, with a dry manner, with an impassible face; or, suddenly, perhaps, deciding to take the lower price which was offered, they cried out to the customer, who was departing slowly:

"All right, I'll let you have them, Mâit' Anthime."

Then, little by little, the square became empty, and when the *Angelus* struck midday those who lived at a distance poured into the inns.

At Jourdain's the great room was filled with eaters, just as the vast court was filled with vehicles of every sort—wagons, gigs, char-à-bancs, tilburys, tilt-carts which have no name, yellow with mud, misshapen, pieced together, raising their shafts to heaven like two arms, or it may be with their nose in the dirt and their rear in the air.

Just opposite to where the diners were at table the huge fireplace, full of clear flame, threw a lively heat on the backs of those who sat along the right. Three spits were turning, loaded with chickens, with pigeons, and with joints of mutton; and a delectable odor of roast meat, and of gravy gushing over crisp brown skin, took wing from the hearth, kindled merriment, caused mouths to water.

All the aristocracy of the plough were eating there, at Maît' Jourdain's, the innkeeper's, a dealer in horses also, and a sharp fellow who had made a pretty penny in his day.

The dishes were passed round, were emptied, with jugs of yellow cider. Every one told of his affairs, of his purchases and his sales. They asked news about the crops. The weather was good for green stuffs, but a little wet for wheat.

All of a sudden the drum rolled in the court before the house. Every one, except some of the most indifferent, was on his feet at once, and ran to the door, to the windows, with his mouth still full and his napkin in his hand.

When the public crier had finished his tattoo he called forth in a jerky voice, making his pauses out of time:

"Be it known to the inhabitants of Goderville, and in general to all—persons present at the market, that there has been lost this morning, on the Beuzeville road, between—nine and ten o'clock, a pocket-book of black leather, containing five hundred francs and business papers. You are requested to return it—to the mayor's office, at once, or to Maître Fortuné Houlbrèque, of Manneville. There will be twenty francs reward."

Then the man departed. They heard once more at a distance the dull beatings on the drum and the faint voice of the crier.

Then they began to talk of this event, reckoning up the chances which Maître Houlbrèque had of finding or of not finding his pocket-book again.

And the meal went on.

They were finishing their coffee when the corporal of gendarmes appeared on the threshold.

He asked:

"Is Maître Hauchecorne, of Bréauté, here?"

Maître Hauchecorne, seated at the other end of the table, answered:

"Here I am."

And the corporal resumed:

"Maître Hauchecorne, will you have the kindness to come with me to the mayor's office? M. le Maire would like to speak to you."

The peasant, surprised and uneasy, gulped down his little glass of cognac, got up, and, even worse bent over than in the morning, since the first steps after a rest were always particularly difficult, started off, repeating:

"Here I am, here I am."

And he followed the corporal.

The mayor was waiting for him, seated in an arm-chair. He was the notary of the place, a tall, grave man of pompous speech.

"Maître Hauchecorne," said he, "this morning, on the Beuzeville road, you were seen to pick up the pocket-book lost by Maître Houl-brèque, of Manneville."

The countryman, speechless, regarded the mayor, frightened already by this suspicion which rested on him he knew not why.

"I, I picked up that pocket-book?"

"Yes, you."

"I swear I didn't even know nothing about it at all."

"You were seen."

"They saw me, me? Who is that who saw me?"

"M. Malandain, the harness-maker."

Then the old man remembered, understood, and, reddening with anger:

"Ah! he saw me, did he, the rascal? He saw me picking up this string here, M'sieu' le Maire."

And, fumbling at the bottom of his pocket, he pulled out of it the little end of string.

But the mayor incredulously shook his head:

"You will not make me believe, Maître Hauchecorne, that M. Malandain, who is a man worthy of credit, has mistaken this string for a pocket-book."

The peasant, furious, raised his hand and spit as if to attest his good faith, repeating:

"For all that, it is the truth of the good God, the blessed truth, M'sieu' le Maire. There! on my soul and my salvation I repeat it."

The mayor continued:

"After having picked up the thing in question, you even looked for some time in the mud to see if a piece of money had not dropped out of it."

The good man was suffocated with indignation and with fear:

"If they can say!—if they can say . . . such lies as that to slander an honest man! If they can say!—"

He might protest, he was not believed.

He was confronted with M. Malandain, who repeated and sustained his testimony. They abused one another for an hour. At his own request Maître Hauchecorne was searched. Nothing was found upon him.

At last, the mayor, much perplexed, sent him away, warning him that he would inform the public prosecutor, and ask for orders.

The news had spread. When he left the mayor's office, the old man was surrounded, interrogated with a curiosity which was serious or mocking as the case might be, but into which no indignation entered. And he began to tell the story of the string. They did not believe him. They laughed.

He passed on, button-holed by every one, himself button-holing his acquaintances, beginning over and over again his tale and his protestations, showing his pockets turned inside out to prove that he had nothing.

They said to him:

"You old rogue, *va!*"

And he grew angry, exasperated, feverish, in despair at not being believed, and always telling his story.

The night came. It was time to go home. He set out with three of his neighbors, to whom he pointed out the place where he had picked up the end of string; and all the way he talked of his adventure.

That evening he made the round in the village of Bréauté, so as to tell every one. He met only unbelievers.

He was ill of it all night long.

The next day, about one in the afternoon, Marius Paumelle, a farm hand of Maître Breton, the market-gardener at Ymauville, returned the pocket-book and its contents to Maître Houlbrèque, of Manneville.

This man said, indeed, that he had found it on the road; but not knowing how to read, he had carried it home and given it to his master.

The news spread to the environs. Maître Hauchecorne was informed. He put himself at once upon the go, and began to relate his story as completed by the *dénouement.* He triumphed.

"What grieved me," said he, "was not the thing itself, do you understand; but it was the lies. There's nothing does you so much harm as being in disgrace for lying."

All day he talked of his adventure, he told it on the roads to the people who passed; at the cabaret to the people who drank; and the next Sunday, when they came out of church. He even stopped strangers to tell them about it. He was easy, now, and yet something worried him without his knowing exactly what it was. People had a joking manner while they listened. They did not seem convinced. He seemed to feel their tittle-tattle behind his back.

On Tuesday of the next week he went to market at Goderville, prompted entirely by the need of telling his story.

Malandain, standing on his door-step, began to laugh as he saw him pass. Why?

He accosted a farmer of Criquetot, who did not let him finish, and, giving him a punch in the pit of his stomach, cried in his face: "Oh you great rogue, *va!*" Then turned his heel upon him.

Maître Hauchecorne remained speechless, and grew more and more uneasy. Why had they called him "great rogue"?

When seated at table in Jourdain's tavern he began again to explain the whole affair.

A horse-dealer of Montivilliers shouted at him:

"Get out, get out you old scamp; I know all about your string!"

Hauchecorne stammered:

"But since they found it again, the pocket-book!"

But the other continued:

"Hold your tongue, daddy; there's one who finds it and there's another who returns it. And no one the wiser."

The peasant was choked. He understood at last. They accused him of having had the pocket-book brought back by an accomplice, by a confederate.

He tried to protest. The whole table began to laugh.

He could not finish his dinner, and went away amid a chorus of jeers.

He went home, ashamed and indignant, choked with rage, with confusion, the more cast-down since from his Norman cunning, he was, perhaps, capable of having done what they accused him of, and even of boasting of it as a good trick. His innocence dimly seemed to him impossible to prove, his craftiness being so well known. And he felt himself struck to the heart by the injustice of the suspicion.

Then he began anew to tell of his adventure, lengthening his recital every day, each time adding new proofs, more energetic protestations, and more solemn oaths which he thought of, which he prepared in his hours of solitude, his mind being entirely occupied by the story of the string. The more complicated his defence, the more artful his arguments, the less he was believed.

"Those are liars' proofs," they said behind his back.

He felt this; it preyed upon his heart. He exhausted himself in useless efforts.

He was visibly wasting away.

The jokers now made him tell the story of "The Piece of String" to amuse them, just as you make a soldier who has been on a campaign tell his story of the battle. His mind, struck at the root, grew weak.

About the end of December he took to his bed.

He died early in January, and, in the delirium of the death-agony, he protested his innocence, repeating:

"A little bit of string—a little bit of string—see, here it is, M'sieu' le Maire."

Universality and Individuality

"The Prodigal Son" and "The Piece of String" are works of art which have the qualities of universality and individuality. To be able to recognize the familiar and to be able to discover the new are two basic human needs. Universality in a work of art satisfies man's need to recognize the familiar, and individuality in a work of art satisfies man's need to discover the new. Satisfaction of these needs gives man pleasure. Essential, then, to a work of art are the qualities of universality and individuality.

"The Prodigal Son" produces a pleasurable response in readers because in the story we recognize the familiar. The story is about a father and his two sons; it is about the love of the father, the waywardness of one son, the jealousy of the brother, and the forgiveness of their father.   Father-and-son relationships, parental sacrifice, and family quarrels and rivalries are common to all mankind.   "The Prodigal Son" has the quality of universality.

There is also universality in "The Piece of String."   Each of us has had or known of an experience in which some apparently insignificant act or incident changed the course of someone's life.   Each of us has done or said things that have been misinterpreted, and each of us has misinterpreted what others have said or done.   Drawing upon these universal experiences, therefore, we recognize how the misunderstanding between Maître Hauchecorne and the other characters changed the course of his life.

Not only do "The Prodigal Son" and "The Piece of String" satisfy our desire to recognize the familiar through their universality, but they also satisfy our desire to discover the new through their individuality. The way in which an artist makes his work of art different from any other work of art gives it the quality of individuality.   The authors of "The Prodigal Son" and "The Piece of String" have presented the familiar in a new, individual way.   In "The Piece of String" Hauchecorne represents any man in a universal situation, but Maupassant has also made Hauchecorne a particular man, one whom we have not known before.   He is like other men in a number of ways, but in other ways he is unique.   It is his uniqueness that makes him new or different to us.   How Maupassant makes Hauchecorne different from other men contributes to the way in which Maupassant presents a universal theme; it is one of the ways by which he gives his whole story individuality.

The new way in which the author of "The Prodigal Son" presents the familiar or universal, however, is not achieved through the way he presents his characters.   The characters are not identified as particular people; they do not even have names, which often help to identify men as particular individuals.   The characters in this story are universal characters, but the brief, simple, and direct method with which the author has presented the unqualified love of a father gives this parable its unforgettable individuality.

Every work of art worthy of the name has the qualities of universality and individuality.   Without universality, it is not recognizable and is not comprehensible.   Without individuality, it is not new; it is stereotyped.

Harmonious Expression

The universality and individuality of art give men pleasure, but art must also be a harmonious expression of universality and individuality. To produce harmony or wholeness, the parts of a work of art must be organically interrelated. These parts are 1) the content or universal thought or feeling the artist wishes to communicate, 2) the material or medium whose manipulation by the artist gives his work of art individuality, and 3) the form or unifying principle that gives shape to the material so as to express the content. Form is not only the unifying principle that blends content and material, but it is also the result or harmony of that blend. Form is both unifier and result; both part and whole. Content could not be expressed without material, but material itself could not express without being given form. The work of art could not exist without form, the union of content and material. Hence the work of art *is* the form, and the form of the work of art is the work of art itself.

Man thinking, man feeling, and man acting are harmoniously interrelated to produce the whole of man. Since art is an expression of man —of his thoughts, his feelings, and his actions—it is appropriate that the parts of art are harmoniously interrelated in a similar organic way.

In sculpture, the universal idea to be expressed is the content; the stone or marble or clay which the sculptor has manipulated in his own individual way is the material; and the statue that results from the blend is the form. The content of Michelangelo's statue, the *Pieta,* for example (see the frontispiece), is the pity and sorrow of a grieving mother holding her dead son as though he were peacefully sleeping on her lap. The form of the statue, however, is not the same as the flesh-and-blood son and mother. The form is an individualized representation or imitation of a particular dead son, Jesus, and a particular grieving mother, Mary. The unifying principle of art, its form, is its representation of content, its universality, but it is something more: it is also its beauty, its individuality, the unique interpretation of a particular artist. The beauty or individuality of the *Pieta* is Michelangelo's particular interpretation of the grieving Mary and dead Jesus: a very young and sensitive Mary, strong enough to hold her thirty-three-year old son on her lap, and a lean Jesus in repose, strong even in death. For many people the beauty of Michelangelo's *Pieta* is heightened because of their religious beliefs. Many other sculptors and painters have represented Mary and Jesus in *Pietas,* but no one else has ever done so in the particular way that Michelangelo has.

Michelanglo was able to blend the content and form of his master-piece by skillfully manipulating the material he used, white Carrara marble. The form of a work of art is not only the universality of the content, but it is also the material out of which the form has given individuality to its content. How Michelangelo molded the marble, "releasing" the form from it, as he himself said, to express with beauty and harmony his thoughts and feelings about the content, is his im-mortal art, which has been giving pleasure to people ever since. The *Pieta* itself *is* the form.

In fiction, content is the idea or theme produced by character in action. The material is the language which the author manipulates to give individuality to the universal theme, characters, and action; and the form is not only the way in which he unites content and material, but also the result of the union: the unity, the story itself.

In "The Piece of String" the content is Hauchecorne and the people involved with him; the things that happened to him, why they happened, and what their consequences were; and the meaning for us, the universal quality, or the theme of the story—how an in-significant act, misinterpreted, can change the course of a man's life. The material is the language Maupassant used to express the ex-periences he selected and arranged to tell the story. And the form? Well, to explain the form would be to tell the whole story, because the form *is* "The Piece of String."

The Communicative Function of Art

If the purpose of art is to communicate a harmonious expression of universality and individuality to give pleasure, there must be not only an artist who creates the art but also someone to whom he communicates and gives pleasure. We need to consider the rela-tionship of artist and viewer or listener or reader and what the responsibilities of each are. To analyze and to appreciate what the artist has done to effect his work of art is the responsibility of the one who wishes to derive pleasure from the work of art. To fulfill the requirements of art and to master the particular techniques of manipulating his material are the responsibility of the artist.

Our chief concern here is to relate the criteria of art to the particular art of short fiction and thence to appreciate the responsibility of the author. We can so relate and appreciate by examining the techniques involved in writing short fiction in order that we can responsibly analyze and derive pleasure from short fiction.

Before we do so, however, we need to emphasize the distinction between fiction that is art and fiction that is not. Many stories are written which do not qualify as art. Not all that we read for pleasure must be art. Light entertainment for purposes of relaxation, for the passing moment, not to be remembered particularly, has its place in our lives. It is amusing—but in a fleeting sense. It lacks universality or individuality or both. It is not art. That does not mean we do not like it or cannot enjoy it. There is room in our lives for the merely amusing. But there is a vast difference between reading a story "just for fun" and reading a story to search for a truth about life, be the truth comic or tragic, pleasant or unpleasant, or an author's interpretation of truth with which we agree or disagree.

Many readers, it is true, who appreciate fiction "just for fun," say they do not enjoy a story that has an "unhappy ending." They do not derive pleasure from reading a story that portrays a tragic or unpleasant truth about life or that contains an author's interpretation of life with which they disagree. Students who are just beginning to appreciate reading as a search for truth about human experience also often wonder why so many stories purported to be "great literature" have to be "so depressing." And indeed, many works of literature may *seem* depressing. However, as a reader matures in his appreciation of art as a mirror of life, and as he develops a more discriminating aesthetic taste, he will recognize that much of life itself may *seem* depressing. But is it really *life* that is depressing? Is it really the author's artistic imitation and interpretation of life that is depressing? Is it not, rather, a person's own attitude toward reality that makes him regard an experience as depressing, that makes him regard a work of fiction as depressing?

The pleasure we derive from a work of art depends on how much of ourselves we are willing to put into appreciating it. The pleasure of reading literature depends on how much we are willing to invest of our time and thought to read closely and analytically. The more we learn about how an author creates his art, the more we will be able to find meaning in his story. The universality and individuality that we find in the story will give us enjoyment that will outlast the momentary pleasures of so-called "light" fiction, which does not purport to be art.

Fiction

Having considered what we mean by art when we speak of the art of short fiction, we need also to consider what we mean by the *art of fiction*. (The word *fiction* comes from the Latin word that means "to fabricate.") Both "The Prodigal Son" and "The Piece of String" are stories that are fabricated, are made up. Fiction is about people who may never actually have existed and about events that may never actually have happened. The stories of fiction are not true in the same sense that a historical account or a newspaper account is factually true. But the stories of fiction are true to life in that they *could* be true if they were about real people and real events.

The difference between fiction and factual accounts of what actual people have actually done is that fiction intends to abstract the universal meaning of the situation. Fiction which qualifies as art gives us a picture of life—not the kind of picture that science or history or objective reporting gives us, but the kind of picture that shows a way—a particular author's way—of looking at life. The truth of fiction is *verisimilitude;* fiction is metaphor—fiction is *as if* it were true. Like the other arts, fiction imitates and *interprets* human action, character, thought, and feeling in order to evoke a pleasurable aesthetic response in the reader or to provide the emotional pleasure that results from a satisfying understanding of the meaning of a story.

Historical and biographical fiction are about events that really happened and about people who really existed, though some of the events and characters may be made up. It is in the imaginative interpretation of the universal meaning of what happened to these historical characters that the difference between a factual account and a fictional narrative lies. For example, *All the Living,* by Henrietta Buckmaster, is a novel that tells the story of one year in the life of Shakespeare, the year in which he wrote his enigmatic masterpiece, *Hamlet.* Some of the things that happened to Shakespeare that year, as recounted by Miss Buckmaster, really did happen, and both he and some of the historical personages mentioned really did exist. But in her story Miss Buckmaster has imagined many of the statements and thoughts she attributes to Shakespeare. Her interpretation of the universal meaning of what happened to him that year and how that meaning is reflected in *Hamlet* (itself a fictional interpretation of a historical figure) is what gives her novel fictional truth.

Irving Stone has also given a fictional interpretation of a real person, Michelangelo, in *The Agony and the Ecstasy;* and in his short story "The Devil and Daniel Webster," Stephen Vincent Benét has given a fictional interpretation of a historical figure.

What makes all these works of fiction true, in the literary sense, is not that the characters really lived and events really happened, but that the stories present the truth about life, *as the authors see it.*

The truth of fiction is also found in fables and fantasies. A *fable,* or *apologue,* was aptly defined by Dr. Samuel Johnson, English literary personality of the 18th century, who wrote one of the first English dictionaries. He said that a fable or apologue (note the subtitle of Nathaniel Hawthorne's story on page 328) is "a narrative in which beings irrational and sometimes inanimate, are, for the purpose of moral instruction, feigned to act and speak with human interests and passions." Between the *parable* and the fable the most obvious difference is that in a fable the human qualities of the characters are manifested by animals. Another difference is that a parable has a more spiritual connotation than does the fable. The truth of fiction in both fable and parable lies in the moral each intends to convey: the lesson in conduct for human beings. As La Fontaine, 17th-century French poet and writer of fables, put it, ". . . the apologue is composed of two parts, body and soul. The body is the story, the soul is the morality." Webster defines the parable as "a comparison; a short fictitious narrative from which a moral or spiritual truth is drawn; as, the *parables* of Christ."

Science fiction is another kind of fiction in which the characters and events would appear to be improbable in the everyday world in which we live. But the science fiction stories that qualify as art present us with their author's way of looking at life and finding in it universal truths, no matter how fantastic the characters and events may seem to us.

Fantasy in fiction, as in other kinds of literature, is the term we use to describe unreal and improbable situations. Human experience, as we know it, is distorted or ignored in fantasy, which may deal in mental disorders, imaginative jokes, or political satire. But fantasy says something serious about life in a fresh, new way. Steinbeck's "The Affair at 7, Rue de M——" and Poe's "Metzengerstein" are examples of fantasy in this volume.

Realistic or romantic fiction, historical or biographical fiction, science fiction, parable, fable, fantasy—all, to qualify as fictional art, must present truth in the literary sense.

Besides being true-to-life, fiction is also characterized by the language of prose as distinguished from the verse of ballads and epic poetry, which also tell stories. Fiction may vary in length from the long narrative known as the novel to the very short narrative known as the short-short story. What constitutes "length" and "shortness" of fiction is debatable. Edgar Allan Poe defined the proper shortness of a short story as the length of time that it takes to read an entire story in a single sitting. (It is also debatable how long different people can sit at one time!) Another way of defining the length of a work of fiction is as modern magazine publishers generally do: The *short-short story* is about 500 to 2500 words, the *novelette* is about 10,000 to 20,000 words or fifty pages, and the *short story* is somewhere in-between in length.

Development of the Short Story

The short story, in one sense, is probably the oldest kind of fiction, but at the same time, in another sense, it is also the newest kind to be distinguished as a separate literary genre. Man has been writing narrative prose stories since he first learned to express himself in a written language. Long before, he had told stories, first in the spoken language, and then in picture language. Poetry and drama also began in primitive ways, but each became formalized, defined, long before fiction did. The novel was the first kind of prose fiction to be designated as a particular literary genre—in the 18th century. The short story, as we know it today, however, was not consciously called that or defined until the 19th century.

"The Prodigal Son" is a very old prose tale used by Jesus to illustrate a truth about life by pointing out a lesson or moral. Perhaps this parable might better be called "The Forgiving Father" because the moral it teaches is that a father's love is simple and unqualified, strong enough to forgive a son who has wasted his time and the property the father had shared with him. The parable was told long before man ever developed a definition of a short story. Even so, it has all the essentials of the art of short fiction: universality of content (character, action, and theme) and individuality through form.

The writers most generally credited with laying foundations for the defined, modern short story are Edgar Allan Poe, Nathaniel Hawthorne, and Guy de Maupassant, all of whom lived in the 19th century. Maupassant learned from Gustave Flaubert, the French novelist and short-story writer, that use of concrete detail or imagery or sense impressions is one of the ways to give a story its individuality. Edgar Allan Poe, reviewing the stories of Hawthorne, gave us some rules for writing and judging short stories. He said that a short story must give a singleness of impression; it must be told with an "economy of means"—short enough to be read at a single sitting; it must have unity of tone—everything in it must be consistent with and relevant to the central effect; its background must be a fitting one; and there must be truth in the portrayal of its characters.

Since Poe pointed the way, other writers have understood and developed the art of short fiction even more fully. Henry James, an American novelist and short-story writer, influenced the art of fiction through his stories and criticism, especially in the prefaces to some of his novels. Many of his ideas have become rules to fiction writers. Two rules are especially important. One is that fiction must have "the air of reality (solidity of specification)," which is a refinement of what Maupassant learned from Flaubert: concrete details individualize a story and make it convincing. The other rule James taught is that character determines incident, which, in turn, illuminates character. Another of the important aspects of the art of writing a story is what James called "the post of observation," or the point of view or authority from which a story is told. This particular technique is discussed later in this chapter.

But long before storytellers were conscious of technique, many were managing their materials in such a way as to effect the harmony of parts we now recognize as the content of fiction: character, action, and theme, related to each other in such a way as to produce universality and individuality.

The oldest recorded prose fiction is an Egyptian collection, *Tales of the Magicians,* which, historians believe, dates back to 4000 B.C. These stories were told by his sons to entertain the pyramid builder King Cheops. "The Shipwrecked Sailor" and "The Doomed Prince" are the best known of these tales. Another storyteller was Scheherazade, who entertained her husband, the Sultan of the Indies, by telling him stories every night so that he would not continue his custom of selecting a new wife each day and having her put to death the next morning. Scheherazade's stories are collected in *The Arabian Nights Entertainment: The Thousand and One Nights.* Dating back to A.D. 987, these stories include such favorites as "Aladdin and His Wonderful Lamp" and "Ali Baba and the Forty Thieves."

The Hebrews also told stories, but their narratives had a purpose beyond entertainment. Their stories teach religious lessons, as do "The Prodigal Son" and other of Jesus's parables in the New Testament. The Hebrews' stories are the parables of the Old Testament, such as the Book of Ruth and the Book of Jonah.

Ancient Hindu fables, collected in the *Panchatantra* and appearing as independent episodes in two epics, the *Rāmāyana* and the *Mahābhārata,* also are primitive short stories. Early Greek and Roman tales and a Latin book written in England, *Gesta Romanorum* ("Deeds of the Romans"), in about 1300, also contributed to the development of

the short story. Beast fables by Aesop and Pilpay and picaresque
tales (satiric accounts of the adventures of rogues), such as the
German *Tyll Eulenspiegel,* the Spanish *Little Lazarus of Tormes,*
and the English adventure tales of Sir John Mandeville, are examples
of short fiction from the Middle Ages. These tales and various
episodes in long works of fiction that were precursors to the novel—
Boccaccio's *Decameron,* Chaucer's *Canterbury Tales,* Cervantes's *Don
Quixote,* and Bunyan's *Pilgrim's Progress*—inspired short-fiction writers
of the early 19th century.

Besides episodes in longer stories, another kind of tale which has
contributed to the development of the short story is the 18th-century
literary essay. As printing became less expensive and as more people
became able to read, periodical publications grew. Such English
precursors of modern newspapers and magazines as *The Spectator*
and *The Tatler* of Addison and Steele and *The Rambler* of Samuel
Johnson contained news and social comment. These were written
in the style of the essay, which, therefore, flourished in these early
journalistic efforts. Some of the essays, light in tone, were presented
in the form of a fictitious tale, in which characters were vividly
portrayed. Addison's Sir Roger de Coverley sketches showed a fictitious character, typical of a country squire of the times.

Besides Flaubert, Maupassant, Poe, Hawthorne, and James, who,
as we have seen, contributed to the development of the modern
short story, other 19th-century authors who played an important
part too were Washington Irving, Herman Melville, Bret Harte,
Ambrose Bierce, and Stephen Crane in the United States; E.T.W.
Hoffmann, Jacob and Wilhelm Grimm, and Johann Ludwig Tieck in
Germany; Alexander Pushkin, Anton Chekhov, and Nikolai Gogol in
Russia; Prosper Mérimée, Honoré de Balzac, and Théophile Gautier
in France; and Robert Louis Stevenson and Rudyard Kipling in
England.

The influence of Chekhov has been felt in England and America
in the 20th century. The highly structured stories of action by
Maupassant and Poe were forerunners of stories by O. Henry and
Jack London, but the stories of Chekhov emphasize revealing moments
in the lives of characters rather than structure of action. Chekhov
believed that the internal unity of character revelation is
more important than the external resolution of complicated action. This contribution of Chekhov's to the modern short story
and the organic interrelationship of character and action, which
was both propounded and practiced by Henry James, have been

adapted and furthered by the most important 20th-century writers of fiction.

With the conscious awareness of technique that 19th- and 20th-century authors have manifested, the short story has come a long way from the caveman's simple tales toward the concept we now have of a dynamic art which will continue to develop as the many new and promising young authors of our time achieve success in their experiments with form.

Analyzing a Short Story

Now that we have considered the development of short fiction as an art, how fiction is distinguished from the other arts, and how it is like the other arts in respect to the purpose and function of art, let us consider how we go about analyzing a work of short fiction.

That we cannot separate the form, content, and material of a work of art without destroying all three does not mean that making distinctions among them is not useful. We cannot avoid making the distinctions if we are to appreciate the art as a harmonious whole. We need to look at a short story, for example, as a harmonious sum of its parts, but in order to appreciate the harmony of the parts, we need to examine each part. This examination is analysis. Following analysis, we synthesize the parts back into the whole to arrive at a new, enriched interpretation and appreciation of the whole.

Reading a Short Story as a Whole

A short story, to be studied and appreciated as an organic work of art, should be read at least twice. The first reading attends to the wholeness of the story, and for this kind of reading, the following suggestions should be helpful:

1. Read for pleasure. Get to know the characters as people, responding favorably or unfavorably to them, fearing for them, enjoying their success, sympathizing with their defeats, approving or disapproving of their actions.
2. Notice what is happening and try to remember as many of the details as possible.
3. Inhabit the world of the story, where and when it is taking place (both physically and psychologically), and adapt to its atmosphere and timing.
4. Look at your own attitudes and expectations. Consider how you *feel* about the story.

5. Consider what is the important impression you have received. It may or may not be what the author hoped it would be, but it is your right to determine it on the basis of the evidence.

Close Reading

The first reading of a story is an over-all consideration of the "what" of the story. The "how" and "why"—*analysis* and *interpretation*—are what we should be concerned with during the second reading. Until we first read a story with an open mind and then read it with a critical mind, we really have no right to make a judgment about it. It is not fair, any more than it is fair to judge a human being only by "what" he is without considering also the "why" and "how" of what he is. An impressionistic appraisal is not a valid criticism of a work of art, but an evaluation based on analysis and interpretation substantiated by evidence *is* a valid criticism.

The first reading of a short story leads to an understanding of the first level of meaning, an acquaintance with the characters, and a grasp of the order and progress of the action.

For the second reading, the following three principles of attitude should be helpful:

1. Concentrate upon the work itself. Discard preconceived ideas as to what the story *should* do, such as teaching a moral, revealing the author's intention, agreeing with your own view of the subject, or forcing a specific conclusion.
2. Take it for granted that the story has form, a unifying principle, that nothing in it is irrelevant to its total effect—until you can prove otherwise. If it is a generally accepted work of art and you have not found it so unified, perhaps its kind of unity is more subtle than you realize.
3. Remember that the purpose of art includes the creation of an emotional effect. The ultimate effect of the story may be more intellectual than emotional, but if the intellectual stimulus is enjoyable, that very enjoyment is an emotional response. If the effect is that of giving the reader an insight into himself, the story will achieve the highest type of aesthetic response; it will be a work of art.

Analyzing the Content of a Short Story

Just as the content, form, and material of a work of art are organically interrelated to produce a harmonious whole, so are the parts of the content of a short story—*character, action,* and *theme*—inextricably intertwined. Character determines action, action reveals character, and character *in* action illuminates the theme of the story.

Character Character is an integral part of the content of a short story. In "The Prodigal Son" we do not find a full development of character. We simply recognize the universality of the father who had two sons: the younger son, who "took his journey into a far country" and "squandered his property in loose living," suffered, returned home, and was welcomed with love; and the elder son, who was overcome with jealousy. Further development of the characters as individual personalities would require lengthening the story. Since its theme is the simplicity of a father's forgiveness, however, lengthening the story would make it more complex. The simplicity of the language and the brevity of the narrative are consistent with the simplicity of the lesson of the parable. It does not need fuller characterization to make its point.

On the other hand, in "The Piece of String" a more complex revelation of character is necessary. In examining this story, we can see how important character is to the theme and action.

Characters in fiction are revealed when an author adapts the ways that real people get to know each other. One of the first things we learn when we meet someone is his name. Frequently it tells us something about him, possibly his nationality. In a story, the name usually establishes whether we are going to become acquainted with a man or woman. A nickname may tell us more about the character if it is associated with a personal characteristic such as "Freckles" or "Shorty." "Maître Hauchecorne of Bréauté" tells us that the central character of "The Piece of String" is a Frenchman, not of a titled class, and an adult. In "Feuille d'Album," by Katherine Mansfield, the first name of the central character, Ian, is a characteristically British one, but the surname is the name of the language of the title. This association is an emphasis by the author that not only tells us something about the character but also suggests that something characteristically French is going to happen to him.

Names of characters help to define personality, sometimes by the way they sound. The name Bartleby, for example, has a euphony that makes it easy to remember. But it is also an unusual name for an American. The title character of "Bartleby the Scrivener" is an unusual person, and the unusualness of his name contributes to Melville's development of the character. In terms of the theme and action of that story, it is important that we see Bartleby as a character so unusual that he is abnormal.

Besides his name, a person's appearance is another thing we notice about him when we meet him.   In a story, a description of a character's physical appearance is a further development that contributes to our understanding of his personality.   The author's description of a character's physical appearance may include the character's physique and facial features, his clothes, mannerisms, gestures, or way of speaking. Maître Hauchecorne, for instance, stoops "painfully, because he suffered from rheumatism." His stooping is important, not only because it further acquaints us with his personality, but also because it explains how he happened to be looking at the ground where he "perceived . . . a little piece of string" (action), which was to change his whole life (theme).   We learn further that he wears a blouse and breeches, typical garb of the peasants on the road to Goderville. He is one of them, the "aristocracy of the plough." We also learn that Maître Hauchecorne, like most human beings, wants people to think well of him and worries lest they will not. He has to stop everyone he meets and tell him, whether or not interested, that it was a piece of string and not someone's lost purse he had picked up. We know also that he must be poor and frugal if he would bother to pick up a piece of string. He is a little ordinary person that people in authority pick on, that other people laugh at. He has "Norman cunning" and might, therefore, have been guilty of the crime of purse-snatching, though he was not: "His innocence dimly seemed to him impossible to prove, his craftiness being so well known." He is sensitive, overly so. Through his extreme obsession with what happened to him, he makes himself sick and dies.

We have learned a great deal about Maître Hauchecorne from descriptions of his physical person, how he acts and moves, what other people have said to and about him and have done to him, and his manner of speech. These are all methods by which an author creates, develops, and reveals character. Still another way is to show the emotional reactions of a character. Maître Hauchecorne feels shame, gets "angry, exasperated, feverish, in despair at not being believed."

Also useful in characterization is information about a character's attitude toward life, his faith, his standards of right and wrong, his beliefs regarding man's relationship to society, to God, to the universe, to his physical and psychological environment. What other characters think of him is a clue to his personality, too. Maître Hauchecorne's associates think him a fool, a bore, and hence, so do we, even though we feel sorry for him.

By analyzing a character in a story and noting these methods that an author uses, we can determine how believable, how vital the character is. Character, the complex of traits displayed by a person in the world of a story, is also revealed by the choices he makes, what he habitually would or would not do, how conscious he is of his choices, and how intelligent and how intuitive he is.

In a short story the number of characters is necessarily limited, and the story usually develops fully only one *central character*. Development of other characters is determined by how they will contribute to a further revelation of the central character, of his motivations and the changes that take place in him. The central character usually changes in some way for better or worse during the course of a story. Some modern stories do not show such a change in a character, but this is not necessarily a flaw, since the inability of a character to change may be the point of the story. But if the central character does not change, something else must: either another character dependent on the central character, or the course of the action. If, on the other hand, the static nature of the action is essential to the theme, then the change will have to be in the central character. Whether in character or action, or in both, there must be some kind of *change* if the story is to have some kind of point, which it must have. A change or a solution to a problem or a realization of its unsolvability is as necessary to a short story as the conflict or problem that precipitates the change or solution or realization. This principle of change is what unites character and action to effect theme. Without the change of some sort, a narrative is merely a happening and not a short story.

Action Next to analyzing how character is revealed, a responsibly critical short-story reader needs to analyze how action is developed. Action is what happens to the characters. Action helps to reveal character, but it is also determined by character, and character in action illuminates theme.

There are two fairly common but differing conceptions, in literary criticism, of what the word *plot* means, as applied to the short story. One meaning of plot is that it is the author's plan for and method of telling his story. In this book, this meaning of plot is intended by the word *form*. The other common meaning of plot is simply what happens in a story. In this book, the word *action* is used to describe what happens to the characters of a story.

The action may be *external,* the things that happen to a character as a result of forces outside himself—other characters or his environment or his fate; or it may be *internal*—the forces that cause conflict within his own personality. In most stories the action is both external and internal, but in some it may be one or the other.

The beginning of the action in a short story is the *initial incident,* or *episode,* the middle of the action is the *development,* and the end of the action is the *denouement.* Each of these phases of the action takes place in *episodes,* or *incidents.* An episode may be a report of a physical happening, a description of a character's mood, a conversation between characters, or a process of thinking or reacting on the part of a character. Between the development of the action and its denouement, a change takes place, either in the central character, another character, or the direction of the action. The moment of actual change is the *turning point,* or *climax.* The end of the action may coincide with the climax (as in short-short stories with surprise endings, such as O. Henry's) or it may coincide with the end of the narrative. In some short stories, the "end" may even occur after the close of the narrative because the author wishes the reader to figure out for himself how it all turned out. A story with this kind of ending is Katherine Mansfield's "Feuille d'Album."

The beginning of the action is the first thing that happens that will lead to a change; it creates or poses a *problem* or a *conflict.* The end of the action is what happens as a result of the solution of the problem or the resolution of the conflict. The end is irreversible since the change cannot be undone without introducing new elements that have not been present in the story.

Different kinds of change occur in fiction. Change may be in a character's fortunes—a gain or loss of what he values. It may be an alteration in the nature of his complex of character traits. Or it may be a *reversal* or *discovery* in his thoughts, feelings, or attitudes. In any event, for the change to take place, there must be a problem or conflict. The art of most stories is the expression of the *tensions* that create the problem and pursue the problem to its solution, or the conflict to its resolution. The development of these tensions provides the reader with the emotional pleasure of *suspense.* Wanting to know what happens next and how it all turns out, being held in suspense and then being satisfied by the outcome give a reader pleasure. Reader interest in change is heightened by the climax of a story, the point at which the opposing forces that created the conflict are unbalanced and one of them wins. The action from then on is the inevitable denouement.

Action that preceded the "now" of the story is explained in the *exposition,* or background, of the action of the story. This reference to past happenings, necessary for the reader to know in order to understand what is happening in the story, may be made at the beginning of the narrative and during subsequent episodes.

To illustrate these principles, let us analyze the action of Maupassant's story.

In "The Piece of String" the action begins on market day when the peasants of Goderville are on their way to town. One of them is Maître Hauchecorne, who finds a piece of string and picks it up. During this *initial incident* or *episode* the exposition or background for the action is also presented. We learn the time and place of the action—*setting*—and we meet the central character and learn quite a lot about him. Also, the complication that will provide the conflict has been presented.

The development of the action starts with the second incident or episode, in which the old man is arrested for having picked up a purse. He had not done so, but his picking up the string in the first scene had been observed and misconstrued. The second incident is the first step toward the breaking of the old man's spirit, which is the internal action of the story. In the third episode he makes a futile explanation to the judge, and in the next one the neighbors show their mistrust of Maître Hauchecorne. The fifth incident tells how the purse is found and returned to its owner, and the old man believes his trouble has ended.

However, in the sixth episode, Malandain, the harness-maker, laughs at Hauchecorne, indicating he does not believe in the latter's innocence. Hauchecorne's failure to convince his neighbor makes the old man go to pieces. This episode is the climax, or turning point. The concluding episode, or denouement, is the old peasant's increasing despair, illness, and consequent death.

If the change in the action or character of a short story is to be credible, there must be reasonable cause for the events that take place and *motivation* for the characters who take part in the events. The believability depends not only on whether these things could happen in real life but also on whether they might logically be expected to happen in the world of the story as the author has presented that world to us. Consequently, at the beginning of a story certain facts of its world are given the reader: the setting, the kinds of characters, and the like. The reader is led into the world of the story in such a way that he will agree to suspend some part of his disbelief. The author must make the reader believe that the events in the world of the story really could happen. Once the world of the story has been established, the probability of subsequent events must be logical and therefore believable in the context of that world.

Foreshadowing is the term used for the information given from time to time during the story so that later events will be probable, characters' motivations will be clear, and the reader's curiosity and suspense will be heightened. In order to sustain suspense and contribute to the reader's pleasure of surprise and recognition at the end of the story, however, foreshadowing should not be too frequent or obvious.

In "The Piece of String" the foreshadowing of the climax, for example, is done quite early in the story:

He took the bit of thin cord from the ground, and was carefully preparing to roll it up when he saw Maître Malandain, the harness-maker, on his door-step, looking at him. *They had once had a quarrel about a halter, and they had remained angry, bearing malice on both sides.* Maître Hauchecorne was overcome with a sort of shame at being seen by his enemy looking in the dirt so for a bit of string. He quickly hid his find beneath his blouse; then in the pocket of his breeches; then pretended to be still looking for something on the ground which he did not discover; and at last went off towards the market-place, with his head bent forward, and a body almost doubled in two by rheumatic pains.

Seeing Hauchecorne behave in a guilty fashion, Malandain logically would be suspicious, and, since the two have been on bad terms, it should be no surprise to us later to find him the one who reported Hauchecorne to the police, and in the climactic scene, to find the harness-maker one who still believes Hauchecorne guilty even after the police have vindicated him. Hauchecorne's reaction to Malandain's looking at him while Hauchecorne was looking in the dirt for the piece of string is a manifestation of Hauchecorne's hypersensitivity and therefore is a foreshadowing of the hypersensitivity which later ruins him.

In this story we have noted both *external and internal action.* The external action ends upon the recovery of the purse, but the internal action continues because the spirit of the old peasant breaks under his compulsion to convince his neighbors of his innocence.

The world of a story is not only geographical and its happenings physical, but the world of the story is also emotional and its happenings psychological. Even if a character should be an animal or, as in the case of Kafka's "The Burrow," an unidentified biological species, or, as in Poe's "Metzengerstein," not only an animal but a supernatural one at that, the characters are personified in terms of human traits, including human emotions. Remembering that a work of art involves an emotional communication, we can see that the emotions of the reader and the emotions of the author meet in the *emotional atmosphere* of the story.

The emotional atmosphere may be comic, tragic, pathetic, sad, fearful, horrible, gay, joyful, apathetic, or eerie. By the time we have finished reading a story it is easy to label the emotional atmosphere by noting how we feel. But looking for the first clues to its atmosphere is part of the function of analyzing the story and discovering its meaning.

Theme   The meaning of a story is what is generally referred to as the theme. The theme may be the central emphasis, as it is in "The Prodigal Son" and "The Burrow," or figure less prominently than character and action, as in "The Piece of String" and "Pigeon Feathers." Theme may be explicitly stated by the author, as it often is in a parable or fable, but in modern short stories theme is usually implied. In the most experimental stories, the implication is so subtle that the reader's powers are challenged considerably, as in Joyce's "The Sisters," whose theme is that of a boy's loss of innocence through his disillusionment over someone he had trusted.

In "The Man of Adamant," Hawthorne, on the other hand, explicitly states the theme of the unpardonable sin of bigotry. Few authors, including Hawthorne, however, want to make their stories simply object lessons to improve their readers' morals. "The Prodigal Son" teaches us a lesson by showing that a loving father forgives his sons. The story does not state, "If you are a father, you *must* love your sons enough to forgive them." When Jesus tells the story of "The Prodigal Son," his purpose is to show that the forgiving nature of a father who loves his sons is like the forgiving nature of God, who loves His sons of men. Jesus is reassuring man, not issuing an injunction.

The theme of a story is an abstraction of the universal from the concrete situation of a particular character in a specific structure of action. The theme is not merely the topic of a story, but rather its core of meaning. The topic of Conrad's "Youth" is the contrast of youth and age, but its core of meaning is the strength, romance, and unawareness of youth as remembered by disenchanted age. Isolation is the topic of both "The Burrow" and "Bartleby the Scrivener," but the theme of each is the search for security against the riskiness of life and the inevitability of death.

Themes may deal with the great universal events of human life like those just mentioned, or they may deal with the equally universal but little things of life. A theme may be the simplest impression

of "a slice of life," like that of men at war in "The Upturned Face."
Theme may exhibit a natural law or the harshness of nature, as in
"Noontide of the First Day" and "To Build a Fire." It may deal
with a human passion in a particular situation, such as revenge in
"Metzengerstein"; or the delineation of unusual, striking, or memorable
character, such as the adolescent's in "Pigeon Feathers"; or the development or disintegration of character under the influence of a particular
emotion or circumstance, such as in "What Mistake?"

Determining theme in a story in which it is skillfully implied rather
than stated is sometimes difficult for an inexperienced reader. Before
they attempt to make a statement of the theme, most experienced
readers analyze characters and action and then the material or
literary devices an author has used.

To analyze the theme of a short story, a reader needs to ask himself
not What is this story about? but

1. What have I discovered as a result of reading this story?
2. What made the author feel that this story was worth writing?
3. How does every prominent detail of character and incident of
   action add up to something?
4. Is there evidence in the story itself to substantiate any generalization
   I have made?
5. Does any detail of the story contradict the generalization I am
   making? If so, is it a weakness in the story, or am I failing to
   take it into proper focus?
6. Why does the author repeat certain details? Is there a significant
   pattern of details?
7. What emotion do I feel, and why has the author sought to arouse
   this particular emotion in me?

Answering these questions will usually help to define the theme,
which the reader is then free to accept or reject as a commentary on
life as he knows it.

Analyzing Form—the Union of Content and Material

The material which an author manipulates to blend content and
form is language. The way he uses language and the way he selects
and arranges the details he expresses in language in order to display
his content determine the success or failure of his art. His plan for
revealing content and the method or way that he does it—his art—is
the form that gives his story its individuality. The different ways

that he gives shape to his material of language are known as literary devices. These include point of view, imagery, symbolism, and irony.

Point of View   One of the most important literary devices is point of view. It is the author's selection of a *narrator*, who tells the story. The relationship of the narrator to the story is determined by the "post of observation" (Henry James's term), or authority, from which the story is told. The narrator may be the author himself speaking directly to the reader, or the author may assume the mask or *persona* of one of the characters in the story.

There are many kinds of point of view from which an author may choose to narrate a story; the most commonly used are *first-person central, first-person minor, third-person limited, third-person omniscient,* and *third-person central.*

1. *First-person central* is the "I" point of view of the central character. He tells his story in his own words; he tells what he thinks, feels, and does, and what and whom he observes; for example:

I went in on tiptoe.   The room through the lace end of the blind was suf-fused with dusky golden light amid which the candles looked like pale thin flames.   He had been coffined.   Nannie gave the lead and we three knelt down at the foot of the bed.   I pretended to pray but I could not gather my thoughts because the old woman's mutterings distracted me.   I noticed how clumsily her skirt was hooked at the back and how the heels of her cloth boots were trodden down all to one side.   The fancy came to me that the old priest was smiling as he lay there in his coffin.

from "The Sisters" by James Joyce

In this example, the first-person-central narrator is a boy, who describes his action of tiptoeing and kneeling; his observations of how the room, candles, and Nannie's skirt and boots looked; the effect her mutterings had on him; how he pretended to pray but could not, and how he imagined that the corpse was smiling at him.

2. *First-person minor* is the "I" point of view of a minor character who tells the central character's story; the narrator may or may not be regarded as important to or by the central character; for example:

We were sitting round a mahogany table that reflected the bottle, the claret-glasses, and our faces as we leaned on our elbows.   There was a director of companies, an accountant, a lawyer, Marlow, and myself. . . . We all began life in the merchant service.   Between the five of us there was the strong bond of the sea, and also the fellowship of the craft, which no

amount of enthusiasm for yachting, cruising, and so on can give, since one is
only the amusement of life and the other is life itself.

Marlow (at least I think that is how he spelt his name) told the story, or
rather the chronicle, of a voyage.

from "Youth" by Joseph Conrad

In "Youth," the narrative starts with the story being told from the
first-person-minor point of view, as in the quoted passage. However,
this narrator merely sets the stage for the main part of the story,
which is a story within a story. In the story within the story, Marlow
takes over as first-person-central narrator:

Yes, I have seen a little of the Eastern seas; but what I remember best is
my first voyage there. You fellows know there are those voyages that seem
ordered for the illustration of life, that might stand for a symbol of existence.
You fight, work, sweat, nearly kill yourself, sometimes do kill yourself, trying to accomplish something—and you can't. Not from any fault of yours.
You simply can do nothing, neither great nor little—not a thing in the world
—not even marry an old maid, or get a wretched 600-ton cargo of coal to its
port of destination.

The narration in "Youth" proceeds with the first-person-central
narrator reporting his memory of what he had thought, felt, done,
and observed as a youth; he also evaluates the experiences he remembers.

First-person narration has a number of advantages. It has the
authority of the eyewitness and can give the reader close-ups, scenic
effects, immediacy, intimacy, and reality. It is convincing because it is
natural, like life; the reader can easily identify with the "I" of the
story, seeing with that "I." Because the narrator usually is not telling
the story as it happens but as it happened in the past, the narrator
can summarize events, focusing on the most important; he can meditate
on the fortunes of himself and the other characters and reflect upon
the significance of what happened.

On the other hand, there are some disadvantages to firsthand
narration. Whether he is the central or minor character, if the narrator
is sufficiently involved in the action, we cannot expect his report
to be completely unbiased. If he remains outside the action enough
to be completely objective, we may wonder why he is there at all.
Furthermore, the use of "I" may give the impression that the narrator
is a boastful egoist. Of course the disadvantages of this method could
be turned to advantage if the author's purpose, for instance, were

to develop an egotistical character such as Carleton Esch in "What Mistake?"

The following diagrams show how an author uses first-person narration to lead the reader into the world of the author's story. In each diagram, the large circle represents the world of the story. N is the Narrator, R the Reader, C the Central character, M a Minor character, the characters being represented by the small circles. The lines represent the relationships among Reader, Narrator, and Central and Minor characters. When a line penetrates a small circle, it indicates that the Reader has been led into the very thoughts of the character represented by the circle.

FIRST-PERSON CENTRAL

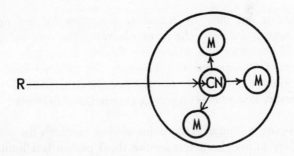

The Reader is led into not only the world of the story but also the mind of the first-person Narrator, who is the Central character. The Central character's thoughts, feelings, actions, and observations of what is happening around him and of Minor characters' actions supply all the evidence of the story. This kind of narration may be objective, external, and dramatic, if it is limited only to what the Central character tells of what he does and observes. It can, in addition, be subjective, internal, and analytic, if the Central character also discloses his thoughts and feelings, imaginings, and evaluations.

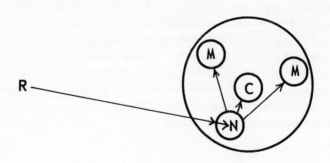

The Reader is led into the world of the story by the first-person Narrator, who is a Minor character observing the external actions of the Central character and telling the Central character's story. The first-person-minor Narrator also observes the external actions of the Minor characters with whom the Central character comes in contact. This method of narration is objective, external, and dramatic.

3. *Third-person limited* is the point of view in which the unidentified author refers to his characters in the third person but limits himself by telling only what can be seen or heard from inside the world of the story. Speaking impersonally, not entering the minds of the characters, the author is like a television camera making an objective report; for example:

For three days and three nights people saw the father rowing round and round the spot, without taking either food or sleep; he was dragging the lake for the body of his son. And toward morning of the third day he found it, and carried it in his arms up over the hills to his farm.

It might have been about a year from that day, when the priest, late one autumn evening, heard someone in the passage outside of the door, carefully trying to find the latch. The priest opened the door, and in walked a tall, thin man, with bowed form and white hair. The priest looked long at him before he recognized him. It was Thord.

from "The Father" by Björnstjerne Björnson

The passage from "The Father" shows how the narrator is not a character in the story. He is an unidentified third-person voice reporting the action, refraining from comment about it, and not stating what the thoughts or feelings of the characters are.

The chief advantage of third-person limited is that it enables the author to present his story in a completely objective, dramatic way, leaving the interpretation and inferences of the characters' actions up to the reader. A limitation, however, is that the reader is not permitted the depth of understanding that a revelation of a character's thoughts and feelings might give.

The following diagram illustrates how this point of view works:

THIRD-PERSON LIMITED

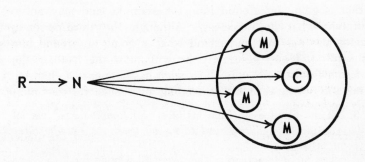

The Reader is led by the third-person-limited Narrator into the world of the story to observe objectively with the Reader only the external actions of the Central and Minor characters.

4. *Third-person central* is the point of view in which the author refers to his characters as "he" or "she" but limits himself to narrating only what the central character thinks, feels, does, and what and whom the central character can observe. The central character also records and evaluates everything that happens around him, to him, and within himself.

This method, extremely popular among modern authors, has the advantages of first-person narration, with the additional advantage that there is no danger of an impression of egoism on the part of the narrator. Furthermore, the method confines the reader's knowledge to only what the central character can know and understand and thus gives the reader the pleasure of drawing his own inferences and enjoying the suspense of wondering if he is right in his conjectures. Third-person central does not give quite the same degree of intimacy that is possible in first-person narration; however, in the hands of a skillful author, this limitation may of itself be the very thing he needs to produce an aura of mystery or distance which he may want his central character to have.

Henry James called this kind of point of view "the method of the Central Intelligence." He believed that action in fiction should be analyzed and interpreted by a single superior mind. The method seems to have most of the advantages of first-person narration and none of the disadvantages. The first-person narrator may not understand all that is going on around him, for example, and may not report accurately what he perceives. Although the third-person-central narrator also may not understand what is going on around him and also may not report accurately, he will know the truth in the end because his story is not only about what has happened to him but also a dramatic portrayal of his developing awareness; for example:

P.S. felt the blood drain from his face. *So Jumbo turned me in!* . . . *Jumbo saw me!* . . . *Sitting next to me all year!* . . . *Jumbo turned me in! Why, in God's name?*

He looked up at the others. They were all waiting for his answer. He had the most curious feeling of aloofness, of coldness. If he said yes, that he would have turned Jumbo in, it would be a lie, and he knew it. If he answered yes, it would please the headmaster, though. Because it would mean that P.S. still had faith in the school system. If he said no, he wouldn't have turned Jumbo in, it would be as good as admitting that he would not obey the fourth part of the Honor Code—"I will report anyone I see doing so." He waited a moment and then answered, "I don't know. I don't know whether I would have turned Jumbo in or not."

"Thank you very much, P.S.," the headmaster said.

from "So Much Unfairness of Things" by C. D. B. Bryan

In the foregoing passage, the third-person-central narrator is the boy P.S., whose feeling is reported as he feels it, whose actual thoughts (in italics) are rendered as he has them, whose observation of the other characters listening to him is recorded, whose debate with himself is described, and whose actual statement is quoted. What the headmaster responds is also reported as P.S. hears and interprets it.

Below is a diagram demonstrating the third-person-central point of view:

THIRD-PERSON CENTRAL

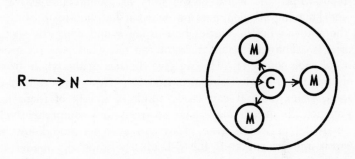

The Reader is led by the Narrator not only into the world of the story but also into the mind of the Central character, whose thoughts, feelings, actions, and observations of what is happening around him— including the actions of Minor characters—and to him and within him are recorded and evaluated.

5. *Third-person omniscient* is the all-knowing, all-seeing narrator, the author himself with full power of authority. It is a point of view possible only in the imaginative world of literature, for no human being in the real world has such power. The author refers to each character as "he" or "she" and may tell what any or all of the characters do, see, or think; the author may also relate events at which none of the characters of the story is present; for example:

Above a century afterwards, when the trackless forest of Richard Digby's day had long been interspersed with settlements, the children of a neighboring farmer were playing at the foot of a hill. . . . Their father, unable to comprehend what had so startled them, took his axe, and, by felling one or two trees, and tearing away the creeping plants, laid the mystery open to the day. He had discovered the entrance of a cave. . . . Friendship, and Love, and Piety, all human and celestial sympathies, should keep aloof from that hidden cave. . . .

from "The Man of Adamant" by Nathaniel Hawthorne

Only an omniscient narrator could tell the story of "The Man of Adamant," since none of the characters in the story could tell what happened before and after the passage of a century. It takes the omniscient narrator, too, to make such an abstract statement as the last sentence of the passage quoted above.

The advantages of omniscient narration are that the author can move freely within the world of the story or around and above it, seeing and knowing all, commenting on what he chooses to observe, telling the reader what he wishes him to know and what the significance of it is. The omniscient narrator can tell what goes on inside the mind of each character. He can give the reader the whole broad scope of human life—here, there, near and far. However, the method has disadvantages too. It can easily result in a lack of focus and emphasis since the author may range so freely and comprehensively. Unlike real life, in which none of us can ever see and know all, third-person omniscience runs the risk of separating the reader too far from the world of the story. The author may be tempted to tell the reader what happened and not permit him the pleasure of figuring out any part of it for himself. The method also risks the reader's passive participation. Nevertheless, this point of view is the oldest method of fictional narration, and in the hands of a skilled author it can transcend its disadvantages. Here is how it works:

THIRD-PERSON OMNISCIENT

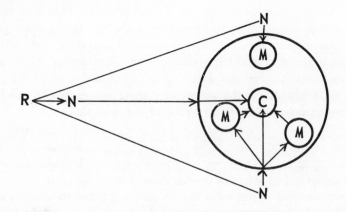

The Reader is led into the world of the story by the third-person Narrator, who knows all and describes the actions and observations of the Central and Minor characters. He also may or may not reveal

*their inner thoughts and feelings. The third-person Narrator may
also reveal information that none of the characters could know.
This method of narration can be objective, external, and dramatic
and/or subjective, internal, and analytic. It is the point of view that
Maupassant chose to tell the story of "The Piece of String."*

As a rule, consistency of point of view is desirable in a work of
short fiction. In a novel the author may use several different points
of view to great advantage, but he has the time and space in which to
do so. The short story, limited in time and space, might lose its unity
if its author were to switch points of view. In "Feuille d'Album,"
two kinds of third-person narration are used: one from the point of
view of a minor character, and the other from the point of view of the
central character. Katherine Mansfield makes the transition skillfully,
however, and the two third-person points of view are appropriate
to her purpose. In Poe's "Metzengerstein" the first two paragraphs
are in the first person, yet they seem to have little bearing on the
rest of the story, which is in third-person omniscient. In Conrad's
"Youth" the novelette starts in first-person minor and switches to first-
person central, but there is a functional reason for the transfer since
the contrasting viewpoints are consistent with the contrast that is the
point of the whole story.

The critical reader can analyze the literary device of point of
view by answering the following questions about a given story:

1. Who is the narrator of the story? Is it the central character? Is
   it a minor character? Is it an unseen narrator outside the world of
   the story?
2. What is the reader's relationship to the characters and action in
   the world of the story? How close is he led to them by the author?
   Does the reader learn what the characters think or only what they
   do and perceive?
3. What is the attitude of the narrator toward the characters, action,
   and theme of the story he tells? Is the attitude of the narrator
   supposed to be the same as the author's? Is the reader's attitude
   supposed to be the same as the narrator's?
4. How reliable is the narrator? Does he seem to tell all he knows?
   Does he seem to misinterpret any significant facts? If so, why?
   Why does he choose to tell what he does tell? If the narrator's
   motives are biased, what is the author's artistic purpose in making
   them so?

5. What has the author accomplished by using the point of view he has used? Is it appropriate to the total effect of the story?

Imagery and Symbolism Image-making words or phrases, which have the power of evoking a sense impression in the reader, are the most vivid means by which an author can create individuality in his narrative style. Besides visual images, there are kinesthetic images that evoke the sixth sense the psychologists have discovered, that of tension and relaxation. Gustatory images evoke taste impressions; olfactory images, smells; auditory images, sounds; and tactile images, sensations of touch.

It is easy to find visual images in any story, since they are the most frequent. But note some of the other kinds of images in "The Piece of String," for instance: "starched blue blouses, shining as though varnished" (tactile and visual); "Some of these fellows dragged a cow or calf at the end of a rope" (kinesthetic); "voices clamorous, sharp, shrill, made a continuous and savage din" (auditory); "It all smelled of the stable, of milk, of hay, and of perspiration, giving off that half-human, half-animal odor which is peculiar to the men of the fields" (olfactory); "Three spits were turning, loaded with chickens, with pigeons, and with joints of mutton: and a delectable odor of roast meat, and of gravy gushing over crisp brown skin, took wing from the hearth, kindled merriment, caused mouths to water" (gustatory, olfactory).

Images and figures of speech—metaphor, simile, personification and the like—contribute concretely to the movement, or *pace*, of the action, the physical and psychological mood of the setting, and the delineation of character. Sometimes a particular image is mentioned so frequently in connection with a character that a pattern of association is created. That kind of pattern is called the character's *signature*. Maître Hauchecorne's rheumatic stoop is a signature. So is the pink handkerchief that the girl in "Feuille d'Album" ties over her hair.

An image or concrete detail in a story, referred to often enough to form a pattern or emphatically enough to draw particular attention to it—its prominent position in a title, for example—becomes a *symbol*. The piece of string Maître Hauchecorne picks up is a symbol of the fateful, insignificant event that ruins his life. The fatted calf in "The Prodigal Son" becomes the symbol of the father's welcoming his son home, which is symbolic of the father's forgiveness: that fatted calf is mentioned three times, conspicuous indeed in a story of only 450 words. A symbol is an image that is conspicuous in a story for some reason other than its factual, literal significance; a symbol is an image that has become metaphorical; that is, it represents something besides itself.

In its broadest sense, a symbol is anything which stands for something else; a word is a symbol, for example. In a literary, critical sense, however, *symbol* is applied only to a word or image that has significant meaning beyond its literal meaning. *Conventional or public symbols,* for instance, convey meanings that are widely known and understood, such as the blindfolded figure of Justice holding her scales, the Cross, the Star of David, the hearth, the American eagle, or the Hammer and Sickle. There are *natural symbols,* too: water as purifier, a rose as beauty, the serpent as evil, light as good, darkness as evil, snow as death, and an egg (a symbol in "Feuille d'Album") as birth, and, by extension, life.

When an image is compared to something else, either explicitly in a simile (an egg is *like* life) or implicitly in a metaphor (an egg *is* life), the concrete image (egg) and the abstract idea (life) are shown to be alike in some ways. When this metaphor is treated in a recurring pattern or in some way so as to make it more significant than a simple metaphor, it is a symbol.

But an image can also become a symbol by representing an emotional association. When an American has been traveling abroad for quite some time, for example, and sees the American flag flying over a United States embassy, the flag symbolizes his country. But the flag also evokes an emotion of homesickness and the traveler also may feel renewed love for his country. Thereafter, whenever he sees the flag, even when he is back home again, through memory and emotional association, the flag symbolizes for him not only his country but also his love of country. The flag may also have become a symbol to him of the emotion of homesickness.

An image may become a symbol by representing an intellectual association. A four-leaf clover is a relatively rare thing in nature. Good luck is also considered by many people to be a rare thing in life. Through metaphor, the concrete object, a four-leafed clover, is compared to good luck, which is an intellectual abstraction. The four-leaf clover, so compared frequently, becomes a symbol of good luck.

Freudian symbols, derived from Sigmund Freud's psychological theory that certain objects have the same meaning for everyone, are used in modern writing. These symbols are usually related in some way to sex. Some interpretations of Kafka's "The Burrow," for example, regard the burrow as a symbol of isolation and as a symbol of the dark, enclosed womb. A close reader should not ignore the possibility of an author's employing Freudian symbolism, but in recent years Freudian symbol-hunting by critics and students has gone to absurd extremes. A true symbol is not an accident, and its author usually has taken care to make an image conspicuous enough that its symbolism is evident. Identification of symbols without sufficient evidence within a story that they are indeed symbols is irresponsible interpretation.

When a story has a moral lesson as its chief purpose, as in a fable or parable, a pattern of symbols and symbolic characters may become apparent; there is a related metaphorical equivalent for each object (including symbolic characters) in a set of objects. This kind of extended symbolism in a pattern of related symbols is called *allegory*. "The Man of Adamant," "Bartleby the Scrivener," and "The Golden Kite, the Silver Wind" illustrate varying degrees of allegory, as does "The Burrow." Jesus tells "The Prodigal Son" allegorically, interpreting the father in the parable as God, the killing of the fatted calf as God's forgiveness of man, the younger son as the sinner, and the elder son as the uncomprehending unbeliever.

Irony   Irony is a literary device that an author uses to heighten suspense, add humor or pathos, give dimension to character, or imply theme. Irony is present in almost every good modern story. Irony results from the discovery that appearance is not reality, that something is the opposite of what we have been led to expect.

Two kinds of irony in literature are dramatic irony and verbal irony. *Dramatic irony*, or irony of situation, is the contrast between the expected outcome and its actual outcome. *Verbal irony* is the contrast between what a speaker says and what he really means, though usually his tone of voice says what he really means in contrast to what the words he uses make him *appear* to be saying. The irony of situation in "The Piece of String" is the discrepancy between what actually happened to Maître Hauchecorne and what Malandain and the other neighbors thought had happened. This irony is intensified: Maître Hauchecorne reacts as though what had happened to him was what the others believed had happened despite his knowing what really happened.

Another way in which the author of a story can employ the literary device of irony effectively is to use a style of language that contrasts with the fantastic nature of the action being described. The formal, scholarly language of "Metzengerstein" is an ironic contrast to the fantastic, supernatural ghost story the language tells. The almost Biblical language of "The Man of Adamant" is also an ironic vehicle for a story whose main character makes a mockery of the teachings of the Bible.

The whole humorous point of "Charles" is based on irony of situation; "So Much Unfairness of Things" illustrates still another interesting use of irony: the boy's fear of displeasing his father causes the boy to cheat. When the boy must pay the consequences by being expelled from school, far from losing his father's love as he expects, he actually gains his father's love, actually feeling and being assured of it for the first time.

Still another way in which an author uses irony is through the tone he gives his story. The *tone* of a story is not the same as its emotional atmosphere (see p. 29). The tone is the author's attitude toward the characters in his story and their action. It may also imply an attitude toward the reader and toward the author himself. His attitude may be approving, disapproving, humorous, loving, scornful, sarcastic, or ironic. An ironic tone arises from the language the author uses—verbal irony, images, metaphors, symbols—or the ironic situation he describes. An ironic tone is the over-all effect of these other literary devices. "What Mistake?" and "The Burrow" both have ironic tone.

Many devices other than those mentioned in this chapter are used by authors; but the major ones, all necessary to an understanding of the form of short fiction, have been explained to assist the reader in responsible reading, interpreting, and evaluating the stories in this book. Whatever the literary devices an author uses, if his story is an organic work of the art of short fiction, every detail of the material on which he imposes form will be relevant to the content. Keeping this principle in mind, the reader should be able to analyze and interpret a story by using as a guide the questions that appear on pages 30 and 39 and the ones below:

General Questions for Story Analysis and Interpretation

1. What does the title contribute to the understanding you have of the meaning of the story? Are the first and last sentences of the story (considering the prominence of such positions) significant clues to the meaning?
2. What kind of people are the characters? How do you know?
3. What is their motivation? How do you know?
4. Are they believable in the context of the story's world? Why?

5. How are the episodes of the action related to one another? What is the conflict or problem? What are the opposing forces creating the tension? What change takes place in the story? Are there both external and internal changes? Exactly at what point does the climax occur?
6. What is the theme? How does it emerge? Is it stated or implied?
7. From whose point of view is the story narrated? What does point of view have to do with character, action, and theme?
8. How do imagery, symbolism, and irony contribute to the whole effect of the story?
9. Are material, content, and form harmoniously interrelated?
10. Is the story a work of art—a harmonious expression of man's thought and feeling for the purpose of giving pleasure, a communication that imitates and interprets what man has observed, imagined, and reacted to emotionally?

Stories by Artists
of
Short Fiction

Love and Hate

Introduction

Man's humanity to man—love—and its negation, man's inhumanity to man—hate—are universal themes in the art of short fiction. Man's search for individuality is coupled with his quest for identification with society and with mankind in general. When he loves and is loved by other human beings, he fulfills his social needs and responsibilities, and he also satisfies his emotional outreach and altruistic drive. But when his quest for identification fails, either because he feels unloved or is unable to love, the void that results often makes him hostile, hateful, hated—in conflict with life, with others around him, with himself.

Why does man love or hate? How does he love or hate? How many kinds and degrees of love are there? These are among the questions the humanities seek to answer. The love of a father for his sons is one of the fundamental kinds of human love that is illuminated by "The Prodigal Son." Absence of love in his life is one of the intolerable facts of Maître Hauchecorne's pathetic existence in "The Piece of String."

Romantic love is another of the kinds of love that artists frequently probe in literature. The sweetness and sometimes heady nature of young love is explored in Katherine Mansfield's story "Feuille d'Album," the first story in this section. But the precarious uncertainty of flirtation and infatuation and the pain and scorn caused by the fickle-hearted are the subject of Dylan Thomas's story "Patricia, Edith and Arnold."

Another kind of love is based on co-operation, which inspires and is inspired by human understanding and a desire among men to help one another. That co-operation is superior to selfish competition among men, a competition that often causes hate, is the subject of Ray Bradbury's parable "The Golden Kite, the Silver Wind." Love in a marriage based on a mutual respect and co-operation rather than competition underlies "Benediction" by Patricia Collinge, a story in a later section of this book. On the other hand, Chekhov's "The Lottery Ticket," in this section, illustrates that when love and co-operation between a man and wife cease to exist, a particularly vitiating form of competitiveness that leads to hate may be the consequence.

When hatred between groups of men erupts into armed conflict, we find war, which epitomizes man's inhumanity to man. "The Upturned Face" by Stephen Crane is an ironic incident of war, in which man's basic decency and respect for his fellow man are poignantly contrasted with his helpless victimization by forces beyond his individual control.

Love and hate in varying degrees will probably never be exhausted as subjects of fiction. Of the thousands of stories that have explored this universal polarity, the five which follow probe a few of its fascinating aspects.

Feuille d'Album

Katherine Mansfield

He really was an impossible person. Too shy altogether. With absolutely nothing to say for himself. And such a weight. Once he was in your studio he never knew when to go, but would sit on and on until you nearly screamed, and burned to throw something enormous after him when he did finally blush his way out—something like the tortoise stove. The strange thing was that at first sight he looked most interesting. Everybody agreed about that. You would drift into the café one evening and there you would see, sitting in a corner, with a glass of coffee in front of him, a thin, dark boy, wearing a blue jersey with a little grey flannel jacket buttoned over it. And somehow that blue jersey and the grey jacket with the sleeves that were too short gave him the air of a boy that has made up his mind to run away to sea. Who has run away, in fact, and will get up in a moment and sling a knotted handkerchief containing his nightshirt and his mother's picture on the end of a stick, and walk out into the night and be drowned. . . . Stumble over the wharf edge on his way to the ship, even. . . . He had black close-cropped hair, grey eyes with long lashes, white cheeks and a mouth pouting as though he were determined not to cry. . . . How could one resist him? Oh, one's heart was wrung at sight. And, as if that were not enough, there was his trick of blushing. . . . Whenever the waiter came near him he turned crimson—he might have been just out of prison and the waiter in the know. . . .

"Who is he, my dear? Do you know?"

"Yes. His name is Ian French. Painter. Awfully clever, they say. Someone started by giving him a mother's tender care. She asked him how often he heard from home, whether he had enough blankets on his bed, how much milk he drank a day. But when she went round to his studio to give an eye to his socks, she rang and rang, and though she could have sworn she heard someone breathing inside, the door was not answered. . . . Hopeless!"

Someone else decided that he ought to fall in love. She summoned him to her side, called him "boy," leaned over him so that he might smell the enchanting perfume of her hair, took his arm, told him how marvellous life could be if one only had the courage, and went round to his studio one evening and rang and rang. . . . Hopeless.

"What the poor boy really wants is thoroughly rousing," said a third. So off they went to cafés and cabarets, little dances, places where you drank something that tasted like tinned apricot juice, but cost twenty-seven shillings a bottle and was called champagne, other places, too thrilling for words, where you sat in the most awful gloom, and where some one had always been shot the night before. But he did not turn a hair. Only once he got very drunk, but instead of blossoming forth, there he sat, stony, with two spots of red on his cheeks, like, my dear, yes, the dead image of that ragtime thing they were playing, like a "Broken Doll." But when she took him back to his studio he had quite recovered, and said "good night" to her in the street below, as though they had walked home from church together. . . . Hopeless.

After heaven knows how many more attempts—for the spirit of kindness dies very hard in women—they gave him up. Of course, they were still perfectly charming, and asked him to their shows, and spoke to him in the café, but that was all. When one is an artist one has no time simply for people who won't respond. Has one?

"And besides I really think there must be something rather fishy somewhere . . . don't you? It can't all be as innocent as it looks! Why come to Paris if you want to be a daisy in the field? No, I'm not suspicious. But——"

He lived at the top of a tall mournful building overlooking the river. One of those buildings that look so romantic on rainy nights and moon-light nights, when the shutters are shut, and the heavy door, and the sign advertising "a little apartment to let immediately" gleams forlorn beyond words. One of those buildings that smell so unromantic all the year round, and where the concierge lives in a glass cage on the ground floor, wrapped up in a filthy shawl, stirring something in a saucepan and ladling out tit-bits to the swollen old dog lolling on a bead cushion. . . . Perched up in the air the studio had a wonderful view. The two big windows faced the water; he could see the boats and the barges swing-ing up and down, and the fringe of an island planted with trees, like a round bouquet. The side window looked across to another house, shabbier still and smaller, and down below there was a flower market. You could see the tops of huge umbrellas, with frills of bright flowers escaping from them, booths covered with striped awning where they sold plants in boxes and clumps of wet gleaming palms in terra-cotta jars. Among the flowers the old women scuttled from side to side, like crabs. Really there was no need for him to go out. If he sat at the window until his white beard fell over the sill he still would have found something to draw. . . .

How surprised those tender women would have been if they had managed to force the door. For he kept his studio as neat as a pin. Everything was arranged to form a pattern, a little "still life" as it were —the saucepans with their lids on the wall behind the gas stove, the bowl of eggs, milk jug and teapot on the shelf, the books and the lamp with the crinkly paper shade on the table. An Indian curtain that had a fringe of red leopards marching round it covered his bed by day, and on the wall beside the bed on a level with your eyes when you were lying down there was a small neatly printed notice: GET UP AT ONCE.

Every day was much the same. While the light was good he slaved at his painting, then cooked his meals and tidied up the place. And in the evenings he went off to the café, or sat at home reading or making out the most complicated list of expenses headed: "What I ought to be able to do it on," and ending with a sworn statement . . . "I swear not to exceed this amount for next month. Signed, Ian French."

Nothing very fishy about this; but those far-seeing women were quite right. It wasn't all.

One evening he was sitting at the side window eating some prunes and throwing the stones on to the tops of the huge umbrellas in the deserted flower market. It had been raining—the first real spring rain of the year had fallen—a bright spangle hung on everything, and the air smelled of buds and moist earth. Many voices sounding languid and content rang out in the dusky air, and the people who had come to close their windows and fasten the shutters leaned out instead. Down below in the market the trees were peppered with new green. What kind of trees were they? he wondered. And now came the lamplighter. He stared at the house across the way, the small, shabby house, and suddenly, as if in answer to his gaze, two wings of windows opened and a girl came out on to the tiny balcony carrying a pot of daffodils. She was a strangely thin girl in a dark pinafore, with a pink handkerchief tied over her hair. Her sleeves were rolled up almost to her shoulders and her slender arms shone against the dark stuff.

"Yes, it is quite warm enough. It will do them good," she said, putting down the pot and turning to some one in the room inside. As she turned she put her hands up to the handkerchief and tucked away some wisps of hair. She looked down at the deserted market and up at the sky, but where he sat there might have been a hollow in the air. She simply did not see the house opposite. And then she disappeared.

His heart fell out of the side window of his studio, and down to the balcony of the house opposite—buried itself in the pot of daffodils under the half-opened buds and spears of green. . . . That room with the balcony was the sitting-room, and the one next door to it was the kitchen. He heard the clatter of the dishes as she washed up after supper, and then she came to the window, knocked a little mop against the ledge, and hung it on a·nail to dry. She never sang or unbraided her hair, or held out her arms to the moon as young girls are supposed to do. And she always wore the same dark pinafore and the pink hand-kerchief over her hair. . . . Whom did she live with? Nobody else came to those two windows, and yet she was always talking to some one in the room. Her mother, he decided, was an invalid. They took in sew-ing. The father was dead. . . . He had been a journalist—very pale, with long moustaches, and a piece of black hair falling over his fore-head.

By working all day they just made enough money to live on, but they never went out and they had no friends. Now when he sat down at his table he had to make an entirely new set of sworn statements. . . . Not to go to the side window before a certain hour: signed, Ian French. Not to think about her until he had put away his painting things for the day: signed, Ian French.

It was quite simple. She was the only person he really wanted to know, because she was, he decided, the only other person alive who was just his age. He couldn't stand giggling girls, and he had no use for grown-up women. . . . She was his age, she was—well, just like him. He sat in his dusky studio, tired,·with one arm hanging over the back of his chair, staring in at her window and seeing himself in there with her. She had a violent temper; they quarrelled terribly at times, he and she. She had a way of stamping her foot and twisting her hands in her pinafore . . . furious. And she very rarely laughed. Only when she told him about an absurd little kitten she once had who used to roar and pretend to be a lion when it was given meat to eat. Things like that made her laugh. . . . But as a rule they sat together very quietly; he, just as he was sitting now, and she with her hands folded in her lap and her feet tucked under, talking in low tones, or silent and tired after the day's work. Of course, she never asked him about his pictures, and of course he made the most wonderful drawings of her which she hated, because he made her so thin and so dark. . . . But how could he get to know her? This might go on for years. . . .

Then he discovered that once a week, in the evenings, she went out shopping. On two successive Thursdays she came to the window wearing an old-fashioned cape over the pinafore, and carrying a basket. From where he sat he could not see the door of her house, but on the next Thursday evening at the same time he snatched up his cap and ran down the stairs. There was a lovely pink light over everything. He saw it glowing in the river, and the people walking towards him had pink faces and pink hands.

He leaned against the side of his house waiting for her and he had no idea of what he was going to do or say. "Here she comes," said a voice in his head. She walked very quickly, with small, light steps; with one hand she carried the basket, with the other she kept the cape together. . . . What could he do? He could only follow. . . . First she went into the grocer's and spent a long time in there, and then she went into the butcher's where she had to wait her turn. Then she was an age at the draper's matching something, and then she went to the fruit shop and bought a lemon. As he watched her he knew more surely than ever he must get to know her, now. Her composure, her seriousness and her loneliness, the very way she walked as though she was eager to be done with this world of grown-ups all was so natural to him and so inevitable.

"Yes, she is always like that," he thought proudly. "We have nothing to do with these people."

But now she was on her way home and he was as far off as ever. . . . She suddenly turned into the dairy and he saw her through the window buying an egg. She picked it out of the basket with such care—a brown one, a beautifully shaped one, the one he would have chosen. And when she came out of the dairy he went in after her. In a moment he was out again, and following her past his house across the flower market, dodging among the huge umbrellas and treading on the fallen flowers and the round marks where the pots had stood. . . . Through her door he crept, and up the stairs after, taking care to tread in time with her so that she should not notice. Finally, she stopped on the landing, and took the key out of her purse. As she put it into the door he ran up and faced her.

Blushing more crimson than ever, but looking at her severely he said, almost angrily: "Excuse me, Mademoiselle, you dropped this."

And he handed her an egg.

Commentary

A shy young painter sees a girl, daydreams about her, decides to meet
her, and arranges a situation in which he can. That is all the action
in what appears to be a simple little love story. The theme is slightly
more complex; it is a frequent theme in literature, that of appearance
versus reality. Things with the boy are not as they seem. "Feuille
d'Album" is a character vignette, a "leaf from an album," a figurative
page from the book that is Ian French's life. That is all. The reader
figuratively turns the page to find out what happened to Ian. The
page is blank.

The story's charm lies in its capacity to tantalize. What happened
next? the reader wants to know, having become involved with the
character of the hero and his romance. Wait and see, is the author's
implied reply, but even if you were to see, would you really know?
It is enough to know this much: Ian does break out of his isolation
long enough to meet the girl. His shy offering of friendship is as fragile
as the egg he gives her, as promising of life as the elemental symbol of
the egg, as capable of being broken as an egg would be if it were
dropped.

But to give a girl an egg she has *not* dropped is ridiculous! To give
a girl an egg she *has* dropped is impossible, for if she had dropped it,
he could not very well give it to her! The narrator who starts the story
was right: Ian "really was an impossible person." But the narrator
was not completely right: "Too shy altogether. With absolutely nothing to say for himself." These comments state the appearance, not the
reality. When Ian *does* have something to say for himself, he overcomes his shyness enough to say it: "Excuse me, Mademoiselle, you
dropped this." The egg he proffers is not the egg she did not drop—
"a brown one, a beautifully shaped one, the one he would have chosen."
This egg that he gives her is another egg. But if she *had* dropped the
first egg, if her life *were* the lonely, broken thing he imagines it to be—
because she was "just like him"—then perhaps a new egg, a new
promise of life, will be a welcome gift and elicit a receptive response
from her.

To go back to the first narrator: he (or she) would seem to be a
fellow artist in Paris. We learn a good deal about Ian through this
third person point of view (see p. 34). But the third person point of
view changes several times during the story. It is the transitions from
one point of view to another that are difficult, that contribute to the

enigma of the story and its art, that heighten the theme of appearance versus reality.

From the first narrator we receive a not wholly flattering picture of Ian French: Ian is a blushing bore. He wears a blue jersey and grey jacket, whose sleeves are too short. He has the air of one who has made up his mind to run away to sea—to be drowned. Yet he touches readers' hearts, this boy who blushes even when a waiter in the café comes near him.

Suddenly, the third-person narrator is carrying on a conversation with someone; his tone is gossipy and not altogether reliable. We learn more about Ian through this conversation, a secondhand account of three women's experiences with him. Each sought to be the one to save him from himself, his apparent loneliness. Each found he did not need her. Each found and dismissed Ian as "Hopeless."

Following these three accounts, the story returns to the narrator of the conversation: "When one is an artist one has no time simply for people who won't respond." "It can't be all as innocent as it looks!" the narrator's companion says, partially right. "It" is not as it looks, all right, but the reality, we soon learn, is quite innocent.

Next comes the complete shift of point of view. It is still third person, but a different third person is telling the story now, an unseen narrator. Like the zoomar lens of a television camera (see p. 34), the new narrator closes in on the real world of Ian French. Through this lens we see the "mournful" building Ian lives in. The descriptive details become sharper—as they would to a painter: "the concierge lives in a glass cage on the ground floor, wrapped up in a filthy shawl, stirring something in a saucepan and ladling out tit-bits to the swollen old dog lolling on a bead cushion." As the lens focuses still more closely, we see more as the artist does: "the fringe of an island planted with trees, like a round bouquet." And now the third-person narrator comes in for a close-up of the artist himself. He is at his window. Now we see inside his neat studio where "Everything was arranged to form a pattern, a little 'still life.' "

But the camera moves even more closely to its subject of focus, this time with an x-ray lens. Not only do we see and hear what Ian sees and hears, we also imagine what he imagines. We are inside his mind and heart. It is spring: "the trees were peppered with green." And then, as though curtains on a stage had been opened: "two wings of windows opened and a girl came out on to the tiny balcony carrying a pot of daffodils."

"His heart fell out of the side window of his studio, and down to the balcony of the house opposite—buried itself in the pot of daffodils under the half-opened buds and spears of green." What a touching metaphor for falling in love at first sight!

But is this after all a sentimental love story? No. The girl does not sing or unbraid her hair or hold out "her arms to the moon as young girls are supposed to do." Ian's report of his observations of her shows them to be not romantic, subjective ones. They are objective. He is curious about *her*.

But then, he begins to speculate, using his imagination in addition to his sense impressions (as painters do), on what the girl's life is like, on what their life together would be like. Yet he is not content simply to daydream about her. He makes the effort to get out of his lonely existence: "But how could he get to know her?" And he finds the way.

Just as he meets her, though, the narrator's camera lens quickly turns away. Fade-out. We have been enabled to penetrate appearance, but we have also been given a glimpse of reality. Through the camera lens and the sharp detailed perceptions of Ian's lens—his senses, as the author describes them—we have viewed a work of art. The author, by the way she uses two important literary devices, point of view and imagery, has piqued our curiosity and fired our imagination. Like a painter, we must, in order to see the total picture, make our imagination work on the sense impressions we have received.

Questions

1. We never get to know the girl, her name and whether what Ian has imagined about her is true. To what extent is his artist's eye perceptive enough that his observations justify what he imagines the girl's life to be? Why or why not?
2. Why are so many objects in the story *pink*?
3. Why does Ian need reminders like the sign near his bed: "GET UP AT ONCE"? Why does he need his sworn statements: "I swear not to exceed this amount for next month" and "Not to think about her until he had put away his painting things for the day"?
4. Why are we told so frequently that Ian blushes?
5. How do we learn what the setting of the story is? How is the setting important to the development of character, action, and theme?
6. To emphasize the painter's keen perceptions, what visual, kinesthetic, olfactory, gustatory, auditory, and tactile images does the author employ in the story? (See p. 40.)

7. Why does Miss Mansfield not tell us what happens after Ian offers
   the girl the egg? Why is that incident the end of the story, though
   obviously not the end of what happens to Ian in his relationship
   with the girl? How does the ending of the story convey the theme
   as suggested by the title?

The Upturned Face

Stephen Crane

What will we do now?" said the adjutant, troubled and excited.

"Bury him," said Timothy Lean.

The two officers looked down close to their toes where lay the body of their comrade. The face was chalk-blue; gleaming eyes stared at the sky. Over the two upright figures was a windy sound of bullets, and on the top of the hill Lean's prostrate company of Spitzbergen infantry was firing measured volleys.

"Don't you think it would be better—" began the adjutant. "We might leave him until to-morrow."

"No," said Lean. "I can't hold that post an hour longer. I've got to fall back, and we've got to bury old Bill."

"Of course," said the adjutant, at once. "Your men got entrenching tools?"

Lean shouted back to his little line, and two men came slowly, one with a pick, one with a shovel. They started in the direction of the Rostina sharpshooters. Bullets cracked near their ears. "Dig here," said Lean gruffly. The men, thus caused to lower their glances to the turf, became hurried and frightened, merely because they could not look to see whence the bullets came. The dull beat of the pick striking the earth sounded amid the swift snap of close bullets. Presently the other private began to shovel.

"I suppose," said the adjutant, slowly, "we'd better search his clothes for—things."

Lean nodded. Together in curious abstraction they looked at the body. Then Lean stirred his shoulders suddenly, arousing himself.

"Yes," he said, "we'd better see what he's got." He dropped to his knees, and his hands approached the body of the dead officer. But his hands wavered over the buttons of the tunic. The first button was brick-red with drying blood, and he did not seem to dare touch it.

"Go on," said the adjutant, hoarsely.

Lean stretched his wooden hand, and his fingers fumbled the blood-stained buttons. At last he rose with ghastly face. He had gathered a watch, a whistle, a pipe, a tobacco-pouch, a handkerchief, a little case of cards and papers. He looked at the adjutant. There was a silence. The adjutant was feeling that he had been a coward to make Lean do all the grisly business.

"Well," said Lean, "that's all, I think. You have his sword and revolver?"

"Yes," said the adjutant, his face working, and then he burst out in a sudden strange fury at the two privates. "Why don't you hurry up with that grave? What are you doing, anyhow? Hurry, do you hear? I never saw such stupid—"

Even as he cried out in his passion the two men were labouring for their lives. Ever overhead the bullets were spitting.

The grave was finished. It was not a masterpiece—a poor little shallow thing. Lean and the adjutant again looked at each other in a curious silent communication.

Suddenly the adjutant croaked out a weird laugh. It was a terrible laugh, which had its origin in that part of the mind which is first moved by the singing of the nerves. "Well," he said humorously to Lean, "I suppose we had best tumble him in."

"Yes," said Lean. The two privates stood waiting, bent over their implements. "I suppose," said Lean, "it would be better if we laid him in ourselves."

"Yes," said the adjutant. Then, apparently remembering that he had made Lean search the body, he stooped with great fortitude and took hold of the dead officer's clothing. Lean joined him. Both were particular that their fingers should not feel the corpse. They tugged away; the corpse lifted, heaved, toppled, flopped into the grave, and the two officers, straightening, looked again at each other—they were always looking at each other. They sighed with relief.

The adjutant said, "I suppose we should—we should say something. Do you know the service, Tim?"

"They don't read the service until the grave is filled in," said Lean, pressing his lips to an academic expression.

"Don't they?" said the adjutant, shocked that he had made the mistake. "Oh, well," he cried, suddenly, "let us—let us say something—while he can hear us."

"All right," said Lean. "Do you know the service?"

"I can't remember a line of it," said the adjutant.

Lean was extremely dubious. "I can repeat two lines, but—"

"Well, do it," said the adjutant. "Go as far as you can. That's better than nothing. And the beasts have got our range exactly."

Lean looked at his two men. "Attention," he barked. The privates came to attention with a click, looking much aggrieved. The adjutant lowered his helmet to his knee. Lean, bareheaded, stood over the grave. The Rostina sharpshooters fired briskly.

"O Father, our friend has sunk in the deep waters of death, but his spirit has leaped toward Thee as the bubble arises from the lips of the drowning. Perceive, we beseech, O Father, the little flying bubble, and—"

Lean, although husky and ashamed, had suffered no hesitation up to this point, but he stopped with a hopeless feeling and looked at the corpse.

The adjutant moved uneasily. "And from Thy superb heights—" he began, and then he too came to an end.

"And from Thy superb heights," said Lean.

The adjutant suddenly remembered a phrase in the back of the Spitzbergen burial service, and he exploited it with the triumphant manner of a man who has recalled everything, and can go on.

"O God, have mercy—"

"O God, have mercy—" said Lean.

"Mercy," repeated the adjutant, in quick failure.

"Mercy," said Lean. And then he was moved by some violence of feeling, for he turned upon his two men and tigerishly said, "Throw the dirt in."

The fire of the Rostina sharpshooters was accurate and continuous.

One of the aggrieved privates came forward with his shovel. He lifted his first shovel-load of earth, and for a moment of inexplicable hesitation it was held poised above this corpse, which from its chalk-blue face looked keenly out from the grave. Then the soldier emptied his shovel on—on the feet.

Timothy Lean felt as if tons had been swiftly lifted from off his forehead. He had felt that perhaps the private might empty the shovel on—on the face. It had been emptied on the feet. There was a great point gained there—ha, ha!—the first shovelful had been emptied on the feet. How satisfactory!

The adjutant began to babble. "Well, of course—a man we've messed with all these years—impossible—you can't, you know, leave your intimate friends rotting on the field. Go on, for God's sake, and shovel, you."

The man with the shovel suddenly ducked, grabbed his left arm with his right hand, and looked at his officer for orders. Lean picked the shovel from the ground. "Go to the rear," he said to the wounded man. He also addressed the other private. "You get under cover, too; I'll finish this business."

The wounded man scrambled hard still for the top of the ridge without devoting any glances to the direction from whence the bullets came, and the other man followed at an equal pace; but he was different, in that he looked back anxiously three times.

This is merely the way—often—of the hit and unhit.

Timothy Lean filled the shovel, hesitated, and then, in a movement which was like a gesture of abhorrence, he flung the dirt into the grave, and as it landed it made a sound—plop. Lean suddenly stopped and mopped his brow—a tired labourer.

"Perhaps we have been wrong," said the adjutant. His glance wavered stupidly. "It might have been better if we hadn't buried him just at this time. Of course, if we advance to-morrow the body would have been—"

"Damn you," said Lean, "shut your mouth." He was not the senior officer.

He again filled the shovel and flung the earth. Always the earth made that sound—plop. For a space Lean worked frantically, like a man digging himself out of danger.

Soon there was nothing to be seen but the chalk-blue face. Lean filled the shovel. "Good God," he cried to the adjutant. "Why didn't you turn him somehow when you put him in? This—" Then Lean began to stutter.

The adjutant understood. He was pale to the lips. "Go on, man," he cried, beseechingly, almost in a shout.

Lean swung back the shovel. It went forward in a pendulum curve. When the earth landed it made a sound—plop.

Commentary

That war is the ultimate in illustrating man's inhumanity to man—man's capacity to hate—is an old theme of literature. In this short-short war story by Stephen Crane, fear of death and revulsion from the fact of death are starkly placed side by side in realistic terms. Throughout the action of this brief, single episode, the men who are burying their comrade are aware of their own danger from "the swift snap of close bullets": "Ever overhead the bullets were spitting"; "The Rostina sharpshooters fired briskly"; their fire "was accurate and continuous."

But the adjutant and Timothy Lean recognize the humane code that requires them to bury their comrade as a token of respect. Yet, threatened by man's inhumanity to man, their hearts are not in their grisly act of homage to a man. "This is merely the way—often—of the hit and unhit," dryly comments the otherwise unobtrusive, detached third-person narrator (see p. 35).

Twice the adjutant suggests putting off the task of decent burial of a fellow man. He and Lean both shudder at having to touch the ghastly corpse. Although they cannot perform the act of burial with love, however, their sense of duty forces them to pursue their task. They summon the fortitude to put the corpse in the shallow grave. Between them, they haltingly manage to "say something" appropriate. And finally, Lean, completely unnerved, is able to fling a last shovelful of dirt upon the upturned face.

The emotional impact of the story is like a slap in the face. One of the characteristics of the short-short story (500-2500 words) is that it has this shock value for the reader. It tells a story swiftly, limiting the action to a single incident, and the characterization to a small number of characters and to only one phase of character development. In this particular story, the impact is achieved through such literary devices as the repetition of the word *plop*. The flat finality of the sound is made even more oppressive to the nerves of the characters and reader alike by the contrasting repetition of the sound of the rifle fire.

Questions

1. What is the relationship between Lean and the adjutant? Does the unpleasant experience they share bring them together or isolate each?
2. What is the effect of such hesitations as in "we'd better search his clothes for—things," "I suppose we should—we should say something," "let us—let us say something," and "He had felt that perhaps the private might empty the shovel on—on the face"? Find other suggestions of hesitation, halting speech and delayed action in the story.
3. Why does the adjutant say to Lean, "I suppose we had best *tumble* him in"? Why is the use of *tumble* so shocking?
4. How does the presence of the two privates affect the two officers?
5. What is the effect of the dead man's upturned face? Why does it merit so much importance as to figure prominently as the title of the story?

The Golden Kite,
The Silver Wind

Ray Bradbury

In the shape of a *pig*?" cried the Mandarin.

"In the shape of a pig," said the messenger, and departed.

"Oh, what an evil day in an evil year," cried the Mandarin. "The town of Kwan-Si, beyond the hill, was very small in my childhood. Now it has grown so large that at last they are building a wall."

"But why should a wall two miles away make my good father sad and angry all within the hour?" asked his daughter quietly.

"They build their wall," said the Mandarin, "in the shape of a pig! Do you see? Our own city wall is built in the shape of an orange. That pig will devour us, greedily!"

"Ah."

They both sat thinking.

Life was full of symbols and omens. Demons lurked everywhere, Death swam in the wetness of an eye, the turn of a gull's wing meant rain, a fan held *so*, the tilt of a roof, and, yes, even a city wall was of immense importance. Travelers and tourists, caravans, musicians, artists, coming upon these two towns, equally judging the portents, would say, "The city shaped like an orange? No! I will enter the city shaped like a pig and prosper, eating all, growing fat with good luck and prosperity!"

The Mandarin wept. "All is lost! These symbols and signs terrify. Our city will come on evil days."

"Then," said the daughter, "call in your stonemasons and temple builders. I will whisper from behind the silken screen and you will know the words."

The old man clapped his hands despairingly. "Ho, stonemasons! Ho, builders of towns and palaces!"

The men who knew marble and granite and onyx and quartz came quickly. The Mandarin faced them most uneasily, himself waiting for a whisper from the silken screen behind his throne. At last the whisper came.

"I have called you here," said the whisper.

"I have called you here," said the Mandarin aloud, "because our city is shaped like an orange, and the vile city of Kwan-Si has this day shaped theirs like a ravenous pig——"

Here the stonemasons groaned and wept. Death rattled his cane in the outer courtyard. Poverty made a sound like a wet cough in the shadows of the room.

"And so," said the whisper, said the Mandarin, "you raisers of walls must go bearing trowels and rocks and change the shape of *our* city!"

The architects and masons gasped. The Mandarin himself gasped at what he had said. The whisper whispered. The Mandarin went on: "And you will change our walls into a club which may beat the pig and drive it off!"

The stonemasons rose up, shouting. Even the Mandarin, delighted at the words from his mouth, applauded, stood down from his throne. "Quick!" he cried. "To work!"

When his men had gone, smiling and bustling, the Mandarin turned with great love to the silken screen. "Daughter," he whispered, "I will embrace you." There was no reply. He stepped around the screen, and she was gone.

Such modesty, he thought. She has slipped away and left me with a triumph, as if it were mine.

The news spread through the city; the Mandarin was acclaimed. Everyone carried stone to the walls. Fireworks were set off and the demons of death and poverty did not linger, as all worked together. At the end of the month the wall had been changed. It was now a mighty bludgeon with which to drive pigs, boars, even lions, far away. The Mandarin slept like a happy fox every night.

"I would like to see the Mandarin of Kwan-Si when the news is learned. Such pandemonium and hysteria; he will likely throw himself from a mountain! A little more of that wine, oh Daughter-who-thinks-like-a-son."

But the pleasure was like a winter flower; it died swiftly. That very afternoon the messenger rushed into the courtroom. "Oh, Mandarin, disease, early sorrow, avalanches, grasshopper plagues, and poisoned well water!"

The Mandarin trembled.

"The town of Kwan-Si," said the messenger, "which was built like a pig and which animal we drove away by changing our walls to a mighty stick, has now turned triumph to winter ashes. They have built their city's walls like a great bonfire to burn our stick!"

The Mandarin's heart sickened within him, like an autumn fruit upon an ancient tree. "Oh, gods! Travelers will spurn us. Tradesmen, reading the symbols, will turn from the stick, so easily destroyed, to the fire, which conquers all!"

"No," said a whisper like a snowflake from behind the silken screen.

"No," said the startled Mandarin.

"Tell my stonemasons," said the whisper that was a falling drop of rain, "to build our walls in the shape of a shining lake."

The Mandarin said this aloud, his heart warmed.

"And with this lake of water," said the whisper and the old man, "we will quench the fire and put it out forever!"

The city turned out in joy to learn that once again they had been saved by the magnificent Emperor of ideas. They ran to the walls and built them nearer to this new vision, singing, not as loudly as before, of course, for they were tired, and not as quickly, for since it had taken a month to rebuild the wall the first time, they had had to neglect business and crops and therefore were somewhat weaker and poorer.

There then followed a succession of horrible and wonderful days, one in another like a nest of frightening boxes.

"Oh, Emperor," cried the messenger, "Kwan-Si has rebuilt their walls to resemble a mouth with which to drink all our lake!"

"Then," said the Emperor, standing very close to his silken screen, "build our walls like a needle to sew up that mouth!"

"Emperor!" screamed the messenger. "They make their walls like a sword to break your needle!"

The Emperor held, trembling, to the silken screen. "Then shift the stones to form a scabbard to sheathe that sword!"

"Mercy," wept the messenger the following morn, "they have worked all night and shaped their walls like lightning which will explode and destroy that sheath!"

Sickness spread in the city like a pack of evil dogs. Shops closed. The population, working now steadily for endless months upon the changing of the walls, resembled Death himself, clattering his white bones like musical instruments in the wind. Funerals began to appear in the streets, though it was the middle of summer, a time when all should be tending and harvesting. The Mandarin fell so ill that he had

his bed drawn up by the silken screen and there he lay, miserably giving his architectural orders. The voice behind the screen was weak
now, too, and faint, like the wind in the eaves.

"Kwan-Si is an eagle. Then our walls must be a net for that eagle.
They are a sun to burn our net. Then we build a moon to eclipse their
sun!"

Like a rusted machine, the city ground to a halt.

At last the whisper behind the screen cried out:

"In the name of the gods, send for Kwan-Si!"

Upon the last day of summer the Mandarin Kwan-Si, very ill and
withered away, was carried into our Mandarin's courtroom by four
starving footmen. The two mandarins were propped up, facing each
other. Their breaths fluttered like winter winds in their mouths. A
voice said:

"Let us put an end to this."

The old men nodded.

"This cannot go on," said the faint voice. "Our people do nothing but
rebuild our cities to a different shape every day, every hour. They have
no time to hunt, to fish, to love, to be good to their ancestors and their
ancestors' children."

"This I admit," said the mandarins of the towns of the Cage, the
Moon, the Spear, the Fire, the Sword and this, that, and other things.

"Carry us into the sunlight," said the voice.

The old men were borne out under the sun and up a little hill. In
the late summer breeze a few very thin children were flying dragon
kites in all the colors of the sun, and frogs and grass, the color of the
sea and the color of coins and wheat.

The first Mandarin's daughter stood by his bed.

"See," she said.

"Those are nothing but kites," said the two old men.

"But what is a kite on the ground?" she said. "It is nothing. What
does it need to sustain it and make it beautiful and truly spiritual?"

"The wind, of course!" said the others.

"And what do the sky and the wind need to make *them* beautiful?"

"A kite, of course—many kites, to break the monotony, the sameness
of the sky. Colored kites, flying!"

"So," said the Mandarin's daughter. "You, Kwan-Si, will make a last
rebuilding of your town to resemble nothing more nor less than the
wind. And we shall build like a golden kite. The wind will beautify
the kite and carry it to wondrous heights. And the kite will break the
sameness of the wind's existence and give it purpose and meaning.

One without the other is nothing. Together, all will be beauty and co-operation and a long and enduring life."

Whereupon the two mandarins were so overjoyed that they took their first nourishment in days, momentarily were given strength, embraced, and lavished praise upon each other, called the Mandarin's daughter a boy, a man, a stone pillar, a warrior, and a true and unforgettable son. Almost immediately they parted and hurried to their towns, calling out and singing, weakly but happily.

And so, in time, the towns became the Town of the Golden Kite and the Town of the Silver Wind. And harvestings were harvested and business tended again, and the flesh returned, and disease ran off like a frightened jackal. And on every night of the year the inhabitants in the Town of the Kite could hear the good clear wind sustaining them. And those in the Town of the Wind could hear the kite singing, whispering, rising, and beautifying them.

"So be it," said the Mandarin in front of his silken screen.

Questions

1. Why is "The Golden Kite, the Silver Wind" a more appropriate title than "The Pig and the Orange" would be?
2. A parable (see p. 17), this story clearly intends a moral lesson. What is it?
3. The story is allegorical (see p. 42). Interpret the story by selecting from it a set of objects (including characters) and giving each object a metaphorical equivalent. For example, in modern American industrial society what would be the metaphorical equivalents to the two Mandarins, the walls, the two towns, the Mandarin's daughter, etc.? Can you also make point-to-point equations between a set of objects in the story and corresponding objects in the present world-power struggle?
4. Why does the Mandarin's daughter whisper to him from behind the silken screen? Why do the joyful Mandarins toward the end of the story call her "a boy, a man, a stone pillar, a warrior, and a true and unforgettable son"?
5. Are the relative merits of competition and co-operation an appropriate subject of art? of the humanities in general? Why or why not?

Patricia, Edith and Arnold

Dylan Thomas

The small boy in his invisible engine, the Cwmdonkin Special, its wheels, polished to dazzle, crunching on the small back garden scattered with breadcrumbs for the birds and white with yesterday's snow, its smoke rising thin and pale as breath in the cold afternoon, hooted under the washline, kicked the dog's plate at the washhouse stop, and puffed and pistoned slower and slower while the servant girl lowered the pole, unpegged the swinging vests, showed the brown stains under her arms, and called over the wall: 'Edith, Edith, come here, I want you.'

Edith climbed on two tubs on the other side of the wall and called back: 'I'm here, Patricia.' Her head bobbed up above the broken glass.

He backed the Flying Welshman from the washhouse to the open door of the coal-hole and pulled hard on the brake that was a hammer in his pocket; assistants in uniform ran out with fuel; he spoke to a saluting fireman, and the engine shuffled off, round the barbed walls of China that kept the cats away, by the frozen rivers in the sink, in and out of the coal-hole tunnel. But he was listening carefully all the time, through the squeals and whistles, to Patricia and the next-door servant, who belonged to Mrs Lewis, talking when they should have been working, calling his mother Mrs T., being rude about Mrs L.

He heard Patricia say: 'Mrs T. won't be back till six.'

And Edith next door replied: 'Old Mrs L. has gone to Neath to look for Mr Robert.'

'He's on the randy again,' Patricia whispered.

'Randy, sandy, bandy!' cried the boy out of the coal-hole.

'You get your face dirty, I'll kill you,' Patricia said absent-mindedly.

She did not try to stop him when he climbed up the coal-heap. He stood quietly on the top, King of the Coal Castle, his head touching the roof, and listened to the worried voices of the girls. Patricia was almost

in tears, Edith was sobbing and rocking on the unsteady tubs. 'I'm
standing on the top of the coal,' he said, and waited for Patricia's anger.

She said: 'I don't want to see him, you go alone.'

'We must, we must go together,' said Edith. 'I've got to know.'

'I don't want to know.'

'I can't stand it, Patricia, you must go with me.'

'You go alone, he's waiting for you.'

'Please, Patricia!'

'I'm lying on my face in the coal,' said the boy.

'No, it's your day with him. I don't want to know. I just want to
think he loves me.'

'Oh, talk sense, Patricia, please! Will you come or no? I've got to
hear what he says.'

'All right then, in half an hour. I'll shout over the wall.'

'You'd better come soon,' the boy said, 'I'm dirty as Christ knows
what.'

Patricia ran to the coal-hole. 'The language! Come out of there at
once!' she said.

The tubs began to slide and Edith vanished.

'Don't you dare use language like that again. Oh! your suit!' Patricia took him indoors.

She made him change his suit in front of her. 'Otherwise there's no
telling.' He took off his trousers and danced around her, crying: 'Look
at me, Patricia!'

'You be decent,' she said, 'or I won't take you to the park.'

'Am I going to the park, then?'

'Yes, we're all going to the park; you and me and Edith next door.'

He dressed himself neatly, not to annoy her, and spat on his hands
before parting his hair. She appeared not to notice his silence and neat-
ness. Her large hands were clasped together; she stared down at the
white brooch on her chest. She was a tall, thick girl with awkward
hands, her fingers were like toes, her shoulders were wide as a man's.

'Am I satisfactory?' he asked.

'There's a long word,' she said, and looked at him lovingly. She
lifted him up and seated him on the top of the chest of drawers. 'Now
you're as tall as I am.'

'But I'm not so old,' he said.

He knew that this was an afternoon on which anything might happen; it might snow enough for sliding on a tray; uncles from America,
where he had no uncles, might arrive with revolvers and St. Bernards;
Ferguson's shop might catch on fire and all the piece-packets fall on the

pavements; and he was not surprised when she put her black, straight-haired, heavy head on his shoulder and whispered into his collar: 'Arnold, Arnold Matthews.'

'There, there,' he said, and rubbed her parting with his finger and winked at himself in the mirror behind her and looked down her dress at the back.

'Are you crying?'

'No.'

'Yes you are, I can feel the wet.'

She dried her eyes on her sleeve. 'Don't you let on that I was crying.'

'I 'll tell everybody, I 'll tell Mrs T. and Mrs L., I 'll tell the policeman and Edith and my dad and Mr Chapman, Patricia was crying on my shoulder like a nanny-goat, she cried for two hours; she cried enough to fill a kettle. I won't really,' he said.

As soon as he and Patricia and Edith set off for the park, it began to snow. Big flakes unexpectedly fell on the rocky hill, and the sky grew dark as dust though it was only three in the afternoon. Another boy, somewhere in the allotments behind the houses, shouted as the first flakes fell. Mrs Ocky Evans opened the top bay-window of Spring-mead and thrust her head and hands out, as though to catch the snow. He waited, without revolt, for Patricia to say, 'Quick! hurry back, it's snowing!' and to pack him in out of the day before his feet were wet. Patricia can't have seen the snow, he thought at the top of the hill, though it was falling heavily, sweeping against her face, covering her black hat. He dared not speak, for fear of waking her, as they turned the corner into the road that led down to the park. He lagged behind to take his cap off and catch the snow in his mouth.

'Put on your cap,' said Patricia, turning. 'Do you want to catch your death of cold?'

She tucked his muffler inside his coat, and said to Edith: 'Will he be there in the snow, do you think? He's bound to be there, isn't he? He was always there on my Wednesdays, wet or fine.' The tip of her nose was red, her cheeks glowed like coals, she looked handsomer in the snow than in the summer, when her hair would lie limp on her wet fore-head and a warm patch spread on her back.

'He 'll be there,' Edith said. 'One Friday it was pelting down and he was there. He hasn't got anywhere else to go, he 's always there. Poor Arnold!' She looked white and tidy in a coat with a fur piece, and twice as small as Patricia; she stepped through the thick snow as though she were going shopping.

'Wonders will never cease,' he said aloud to himself. This was Patricia letting him walk in the snow, this was striding along in a storm with two big girls. He sat down in the road. 'I'm on a sledge,' he said, 'pull me, Patricia, pull me like an Eskimo.'

'Up you get, you moochin, or I'll take you home.'

He saw that she did not mean it. 'Lovely Patricia, beautiful Patricia,' he said, 'pull me along on my bottom.'

'Any more dirty words, and you know who I'll tell.'

'Arnold Matthews,' he said.

Patricia and Edith drew closer together.

'He notices everything,' Patricia whispered.

Edith said: 'I'm glad I haven't got your job.'

'Oh,' said Patricia, catching him by the hand and pressing it on her arm, 'I wouldn't change him for the world!'

He ran down the gravel path on to the upper walk of the park. 'I'm spoilt!' he shouted, 'I'm spoilt! Patricia spoils me!'

Soon the park would be white all over; already the trees were blurred round the reservoir and fountain, and the training college on the gorse hill was hidden in a cloud.

Patricia and Edith took the steep path down to the shelter. Following on the forbidden grass, he slid past them straight into a bare bush, but the bump and the pricks left him shouting and unhurt. The girls gossiped sadly now. They shook their coats in the deserted shelter, scattering snow on the seats, and sat down, close together still, outside the bowling-club window.

'We're only just on time,' said Edith. 'It's hard to be punctual in the snow.'

'Can I play by here?'

Patricia nodded. 'Play quietly then; don't be rough with the snow.'

'Snow! snow! snow!' he said, and scooped it out of the gutter and made a small ball.

'Perhap's he's found a job,' Patricia said.

'Not Arnold.'

'What if he doesn't come at all?'

'He's bound to come, Patricia; don't say things like that.'

'Have you brought your letters?'

'They're in my bag. How many have you got?'

'No, how many have you got, Edith?'

'I haven't counted.'

'Show me one of yours,' Patricia said.

He was used to their talk by this time; they were old and cuckoo, sitting in the empty shelter sobbing over nothing. Patricia was reading a letter and moving her lips.

'He told me that, too,' she said, 'that I was his star.'

'Did he begin: "Dear Heart"?'

'Always: "Dear Heart." '

Edith broke into real, loud tears. With a snowball in his hand, he watched her sway on the seat and hide her face in Patricia's snowy coat.

Patricia said, patting and calming Edith, rocking her head: 'I'll give him a piece of my mind when he comes!'

When who comes? He threw the snowball high into the silently driving fall. Edith's crying in the deadened park was clear and thin as a whistle, and, disowning the soft girls and standing away from them in case a stranger passed, a man with boots to his thighs, or a sneering, bigger boy from the Uplands, he piled the snow against the wire of the tennis court and thrust his hands into the snow like a baker making bread. As he delved and moulded the snow into loaves, saying under his breath, 'This is the way it is done, ladies and gentlemen,' Edith raised her head and said: 'Patricia, promise me, don't be cross with him. Let's all be quiet and friendly.'

'Writing, "Dear Heart" to us both,' said Patricia angrily. 'Did he ever take off your shoes and pull your toes and——'

'No, no, you mustn't, don't go on, you mustn't speak like that!' Edith put her fingers to her cheeks. 'Yes, he did,' she said.

'Somebody has been pulling Edith's toes,' he said to himself, and ran round the other side of the shelter, chuckling. 'Edith went to market,' he laughed aloud, and stopped at the sight of a young man without an overcoat sitting in a corner seat and cupping his hands and blowing into them. The young man wore a white muffler and a check cap. When he saw the boy, he pulled his cap down over his eyes. His hands were pale blue and the ends of his fingers yellow.

The boy ran back to Patricia. 'Patricia, there's a man!' he cried.

'Where's a man?'

'On the other side of the shelter; he hasn't got an overcoat and he's blowing in his hands like this.'

Edith jumped up. 'It's Arnold!'

'Arnold Matthews, Arnold Matthews, we know you're there!' Patricia called round the shelter, and, after a long minute, the young man, raising his cap and smiling, appeared at the corner and leant against a wooden pillar.

The trousers of his sleek blue suit were wide at the bottoms; the shoulders were high and hard, and sharp at the ends; his pointed patent shoes were shining; a red handkerchief stuck from his breast pocket; he had not been out in the snow.

'Fancy you two knowing each other,' he said loudly, facing the red-eyed girls and the motionless, open-mouthed boy who stood at Patricia's side with his pockets full of snowballs.

Patricia tossed her head and her hat fell over one eye. As she straightened her hat, 'You come and sit down here, Arnold Matthews, you've got some questions to answer!' she said in her washing-day voice.

Edith clutched at her arm: 'Oh! Patricia, you promised.' She picked at the edge of her handkerchief. A tear rolled down her cheek.

Arnold said softly then: 'Tell the little boy to run away and play.'

The boy ran round the shelter once and returned to hear Edith saying, 'There's a hole in your elbow, Arnold,' and to see the young man kicking the snow at his feet and staring at the names and hearts cut on the wall behind the girls' heads.

'Who did you walk out with on Wednesdays?' Patricia asked. Her clumsy hands held Edith's letter close to the sprinkled folds of her chest.

'You, Patricia.'

'Who did you walk out with on Fridays?'

'With Edith, Patricia.'

He said to the boy: 'Here, son, can you roll a snowball as big as a football?'

'Yes, as big as two footballs.'

Arnold turned back to Edith, and said: 'How did you come to know Patricia Davies? You work in Brynmill.'

'I just started working in Cwmdonkin,' she said. 'I haven't seen you since, to tell you. I was going to tell you to-day, but I found out. How could you, Arnold? Me on my afternoon off, and Patricia on Wednesdays.'

The snowball had turned into a short snowman with a lopsided, dirty head and a face full of twigs, wearing a boy's cap and smoking a pencil.

'I didn't mean any harm,' said Arnold. 'I love you both.'

Edith screamed. The boy jumped forward, and the snowman with a broken back collapsed.

'Don't tell your lies, how can you love two of us?' Edith cried, shaking her handbag at Arnold. The bag snapped open, and a bundle of letters fell on the snow.

'Don't you dare pick up those letters,' Patricia said.

Arnold had not moved.   The boy was searching for his pencil in the snowman's ruins.

'You make your choice, Arnold Matthews, here and now.'

'Her or me,' said Edith.

Patricia turned her back to him.   Edith, with her bag in her hand hanging open, stood still.   The sweeping snow turned up the top page of a letter.

'You two,' he said, 'you go off the handle.   Sit down and talk.   Don't cry like that, Edith.   Hundreds of men love more than one woman, you're always reading about it.   Give us a chance, Edith, there's a girl.'

Patricia looked at the hearts and arrows and old names.   Edith saw the letters curl.

'It's you, Patricia,' said Arnold.

Still Patricia stood turned away from him.   Edith opened her mouth to cry, and he put a finger to his lips.   He made the shape of a whisper, too soft for Patricia to hear.   The boy watched him soothing and promising Edith, but she screamed again and ran out of the shelter and down the path, her handbag beating against her side.

'Patricia,' he said, 'turn round to me.   I had to say it.   It's you, Patricia.'

The boy bent down over the snowman and found his pencil driven through its head.   When he stood up he saw Patricia and Arnold arm in arm.

Snow dripped through his pockets, snow melted in his shoes, snow trickled down his collar into his vest.   'Look at you now,' said Patricia, rushing to him and holding him by the hands, 'you're wringing wet.'

'Only a bit of snow,' said Arnold, suddenly alone in the shelter.

'A bit of snow indeed, he's cold as ice and his feet are like sponges.   Come on home at once!'

The three of them climbed the path to the upper walk, and Patricia's footprints were large as a horse's in the thickening snow.

'Look, you can see our house, it's got a white roof!'

'We'll be there, ducky, soon.'

'I'd rather stay out and make a snow man like Arnold Matthews.'

'Hush! hush! your mother'll be waiting.   You must come home.'

'No she won't.   She's gone on a randy with Mr Robert.   Randy, sandy, bandy!'

'You know very well she's shopping with Mrs Partridge, you mustn't tell wicked lies.'

'Well Arnold Matthews told lies. He said he loved you better than Edith, and he whispered behind your back to her.'

'I swear I didn't, Patricia, I don't love Edith at all!'

Patricia stopped walking. 'You don't love Edith?'

'No, I've told you, it's you. I don't love her at all,' he said. 'Oh! my God, what a day! Don't you believe me? It's you, Patricia. Edith isn't anything. I just used to meet her; I'm always in the park.'

'But you told her you loved her.'

The boy stood bewildered between them. Why was Patricia so angry and serious? Her face was flushed and her eyes shone. Her chest moved up and down. He saw the long black hairs on her leg through a tear in her stocking. Her leg is as big as my middle, he thought. I'm cold; I want tea; I've got snow in my fly.

Arnold backed slowly down the path. 'I had to tell her that or she wouldn't have gone away I had to, Patricia. You saw what she was like. I hate her. Cross my heart!'

'Bang! bang!' cried the boy.

Patricia was smacking Arnold, tugging at his muffler, knocking him with her elbows. She pummelled him down the path, and shouted at the top of her voice: 'I'll teach you to lie to Edith! You pig! you black! I'll teach you to break her heart!'

He shielded his face from her blows as he staggered back. 'Patricia, Patricia, don't hit me! There's people!'

As Arnold fell, two women with umbrellas up peered through the whirling snow from behind a bush.

Patricia stood over him. 'You lied to her and you'd lie to me,' she said. 'Get up, Arnold Matthews!'

He rose and set his muffler straight and wiped his eyes with the red handkerchief, and raised his cap and walked towards the shelter.

'And as for you,' Patricia said, turning to the watching women, 'you should be ashamed of yourselves! Two old woman playing about in the snow.'

They dodged behind the bush.

Patricia and the boy climbed, hand in hand, back to the upper walk.

'I've left my cap by the snowman,' he remembered. 'It's my cap with the Tottenham colours.'

'Run back quickly,' she said, 'you can't get any wetter than you are.'

He found his cap half hidden under snow. In a corner of the shelter, Arnold sat reading the letters that Edith had dropped, turning the wet pages slowly. He did not see the boy, and the boy, behind a pillar, did not interrupt him. Arnold read every letter carefully.

'You've been a long time finding your cap,' Patricia said. 'Did you see the young man?'

'No,' he said, 'he was gone.'

At home, in the warm living-room, Patricia made him change his clothes again. He held his hands in front of the fire, and soon they began to hurt.

'My hands are on fire,' he told her, 'and my toes, and my face.'

After she had comforted him, she said: 'There, that's better. The hurting's gone. You won't call the king your uncle in a minute.' She was bustling about the room. 'Now we've all had a good cry to-day.'

Commentary

The action in "Patricia, Edith and Arnold" is fairly simple. A young man has been courting two girls, using the same techniques—letters in which he addresses each as "Dear Heart"; meetings in the park, with Patricia on Wednesdays, with Edith on Fridays; taking off the shoes of each and tickling her toes. The girls meet, compare notes, and determine to have a showdown with the two-timing Arnold Matthews. He seems to make his choice—Patricia, who, instead of triumphing in her victory, sends Arnold packing because "You lied to her. You'd lie to me."

What makes this story more complex than its simple action would suggest, however, is that it is told from the third-person limited point of view of a nameless little boy, the charge of Patricia, presumably his mother's maid. Not a member of the romantic love triangle of the action, the little boy nevertheless becomes quite the most important character in the story.

As readers we see only what he can see, hear only what he hears. We get the story of Patricia, Edith, and Arnold only as a parallel to what the boy is doing in reality and imagining in his world of games of pretend. His observations of the real world of the three adults come as intrusions upon his own world of play. The situation is a humorous one, devoid of adult sophistication and full of the disarming candor of the boy. He does not interpret his blunt, clear-eyed observations for us, but he registers them, and it is up to us to interpret them.

Besides the complexity of point of view, which gives the reader the pleasure of drawing inferences and piecing together the puzzle of the characters in action, the story has another outstanding literary device. It is vivid with detail, supplied by the concrete images of the boy's imagination as well as those of the clarity of his perceptions. Through the specific details of his imaginative play, we get a clear picture of the boy himself, so that he emerges as not merely a casual observer. He plies his "invisible engine, the Cwmdonkin Special" through the reality of "the small back garden scattered with breadcrumbs for the birds and white with yesterday's snow." He pulls hard on the brake of his Flying Welshman, "assistants in uniform run out with fuel," and the engine shuffles off "round the barbed walls of China that kept the cats away." He knows that the snowy afternoon is one in which anything can happen: "uncles from America, where he had no uncles, might arrive with revolvers and St. Bernards."

But his sense impressions of what is really happening around him, as parallels to those of his imaginary world, reveal the other characters in the story, particularly Patricia and Arnold. Edith does not emerge so clearly. But through the boy's experience, we learn that Patricia is "a tall, thick girl with awkward hands, her fingers were like toes, her shoulders were wide as a man's." We learn that she is affectionate though disciplinary toward her young charge, tolerant of his teasing. We also learn that Arnold wears a white muffler and a check cap, that "his hands were pale blue and the ends of his fingers yellow." He has a hole in his elbow. The visual details are sharp: the young man is something of a bum. We wonder, too, what kind of young man can be so free of responsibility as to be able to spend so much of his time in the park.

Questions

1. Why do we never learn the little narrator's name? Patricia could have addressed him directly some time during the story, but she does not, nor is his name included in the title. Note that the first mention of "him," who we shall later learn is Arnold, is an ambiguous pronoun reference: "She said, 'I don't want to see *him*, you go alone.' " And later, Patricia says, "I'll give *him* a piece of my mind when he comes." We share the little boy's bewilderment as he remarks to himself, "When *who* comes?"

2. Why does the boy not tell Patricia that when he went back to the park for his cap with the Tottenham colors he found Arnold reading the letters Edith had dropped? What is the significance of Arnold's reading those letters so carefully?

3. Which passages indicate Patricia's feeling for the little boy?

4. When an image recurs frequently in a story (see p. 40), we may assume that the author's emphasis is intentional and that the image has

symbolic value. Why is snow, for example, mentioned so often in "Patricia, Edith and Arnold"? What is the symbolism of the snowman?

5. How does this story illuminate different kinds of love? Discuss whether it also illuminates hate, the negation of love.

The Lottery Ticket

Anton Chekhov

Ivan Dmitritch, a middle-class man who lived with his family on an income of twelve hundred a year and was very well satisfied with his lot, sat down on the sofa after supper and began reading the newspaper.

"I forgot to look at the newspaper today," his wife said to him as she cleared the table. "Look and see whether the list of drawings is there."

"Yes, it is," said Ivan Dmitritch; "but hasn't your ticket lapsed?"

"No; I took the interest on Tuesday."

"What is the number?"

"Series 9,499, number 26."

"All right . . . we will look . . . 9,499 and 26."

Ivan Dmitritch had no faith in lottery luck, and would not, as a rule, have consented to look at the lists of winning numbers, but now, as he had nothing else to do and as the newspaper was before his eyes, he passed his finger downwards along the column of numbers. And immediately, as though in mockery of his scepticism, no further than the second line from the top, his eye was caught by the figure 9,499! Unable to believe his eyes, he hurriedly dropped the paper on his knees without looking to see the number of the ticket, and, just as though some one had given him a douche of cold water, he felt an agreeable chill in the pit of the stomach; tingling and terrible and sweet!

"Masha, 9,499 is there!" he said in a hollow voice.

His wife looked at his astonished and panic-stricken face, and realized that he was not joking.

"9,499?" she asked, turning pale and dropping the folded tablecloth on the table.

"Yes, yes . . . it really is there!"

"And the number of the ticket?"

"Oh, yes! There's the number of the ticket too. But stay . . . wait! No, I say! Anyway, the number of our series is there! Anyway, you understand. . . ."

Looking at his wife, Ivan Dmitritch gave a broad, senseless smile, like a baby when a bright object is shown it. His wife smiled too; it was as pleasant to her as to him that he only mentioned the series, and did not try to find out the number of the winning ticket. To torment and tantalize oneself with hopes of possible fortune is so sweet, so thrilling!

"It is our series," said Ivan Dmitritch, after a long silence. "So there is a probability that we have won. It's only a probability, but there it is!"

"Well, now look!"

"Wait a little. We have plenty of time to be disappointed. It's on the second line from the top, so the prize is seventy-five thousand. That's not money, but power, capital! And in a minute I shall look at the list, and there—26! Eh? I say, what if we really have won?"

The husband and wife began laughing and staring at one another in silence. The possibility of winning bewildered them; they could not have said, could not have dreamed, what they both needed that seventy-five thousand for, what they would buy, where they would go. They thought only of the figures 9,499 and 75,000 and pictured them in their imagination, while somehow they could not think of the happiness itself which was so possible.

Ivan Dmitritch, holding the paper in his hand, walked several times from corner to corner, and only when he had recovered from the first impression began dreaming a little.

"And if we have won," he said—"why, it will be a new life, it will be a transformation! The ticket is yours, but if it were mine I should, first of all, of course, spend twenty-five thousand on real property in the shape of an estate; ten thousand on immediate expenses, new furnishing . . . travelling . . . paying debts, and so on. . . . The other forty thousand I would put in the bank and get interest on it."

"Yes, an estate, that would be nice," said his wife, sitting down and dropping her hands in her lap.

"Somewhere in the Tula or Oryol provinces. . . . In the first place we shouldn't need a summer villa, and besides, it would always bring in an income."

And pictures came crowding on his imagination, each more gracious and poetical than the last. And in all these pictures he saw himself well-fed, serene, healthy, felt warm, even hot! Here, after eating a summer soup, cold as ice, he lay on his back on the burning sand close to a stream or in the garden under a lime-tree. . . . It is hot. . . . His little boy and girl are crawling about near him, digging in the sand

or catching ladybirds in the grass. He dozes sweetly, thinking of nothing, and feeling all over that he need not go to the office today, tomorrow, or the day after. Or, tired of lying still, he goes to the hayfield, or to the forest for mushrooms, or watches the peasants catching fish with a net. When the sun sets he takes a towel and soap and saunters to the bathing-shed, where he undresses at his leisure, slowly rubs his bare chest with his hands, and goes into the water. And in the water, near the opaque soapy circles, little fish flit to and fro and green water-weeds nod their heads. After bathing there is tea with cream and milk rolls.
. . . In the evening a walk or *vint* with the neighbours.

"Yes, it would be nice to buy an estate," said his wife, also dreaming, and from her face it was evident that she was enchanted by her thoughts.

Ivan Dmitritch pictured to himself autumn with its rains, its cold evenings, and its St. Martin's summer. At that season he would have to take longer walks about the garden and beside the river, so as to get thoroughly chilled, and then drink a big glass of vodka and eat a salted mushroom or a soused cucumber, and then—drink another. . . . The children would come running from the kitchen-garden, bringing a carrot and a radish smelling of fresh earth. . . . And then, he would lie stretched full length on the sofa, and in leisurely fashion turn over the pages of some illustrated magazine, or, covering his face with it and unbuttoning his waistcoat, give himself up to slumber.

The St. Martin's summer is followed by cloudy, gloomy weather. It rains day and night, the bare trees weep, the wind is damp and cold. The dogs, the horses, the fowls—all are wet, depressed, downcast. There is nowhere to walk; one can't go out for days together; one has to pace up and down the room, looking despondently at the grey window. It is dreary!

Ivan Dmitritch stopped and looked at his wife.

"I should go abroad, you know, Masha," he said.

And he began thinking how nice it would be in late autumn to go abroad somewhere to the South of France . . . to Italy . . . . to India!

"I should certainly go abroad too," his wife said. "But look at the number of the ticket!"

"Wait, wait! . . ."

He walked about the room and went on thinking. It occurred to him: what if his wife really did go abroad? It is pleasant to travel alone, or in the society of light, careless women who live in the present, and not such as think and talk all the journey about nothing but their children, sigh, and tremble with dismay over every farthing. Ivan

Dmitritch imagined his wife in the train with a multitude of parcels, baskets, and bags; she would be sighing over something, complaining that the train made her head ache, that she had spent so much money. . . . At the stations he would continually be having to run for boiling water, bread and butter. . . . She wouldn't have dinner because of its being too dear. . . .

"She would begrudge me every farthing," he thought, with a glance at his wife. "The lottery ticket is hers, not mine! Besides, what is the use of her going abroad? What does she want there? She would shut herself up in the hotel, and not let me out of her sight. . . . I know!"

And for the first time in his life his mind dwelt on the fact that his wife had grown elderly and plain, and that she was saturated through and through with the smell of cooking, while he was still young, fresh, and healthy, and might well have got married again.

"Of course, all that is silly nonsense," he thought; "but . . . why should she go abroad? What would she make of it? And yet she would go, of course. . . . I can fancy . . . In reality it is all one to her, whether it is Naples or Klin. She would only be in my way. I should be dependent upon her. I can fancy how, like a regular woman, she will lock the money up as soon as she gets it. . . . She will hide it from me. . . . She will look after her relations and grudge me every farthing."

Ivan Dmitritch thought of her relations. All those wretched brothers and sisters and aunts and uncles would come crawling about as soon as they heard of the winning ticket, would begin whining like beggars, and fawning upon them with oily, hypocritical smiles. Wretched, detestable people! If they were given anything, they would ask for more; while if they were refused, they would swear at them, slander them, and wish them every kind of misfortune.

Ivan Dmitritch remembered his own relations, and their faces, at which he had looked impartially in the past, struck him now as repulsive and hateful.

"They are such reptiles!" he thought.

And his wife's face, too, struck him as repulsive and hateful. Anger surged up in his heart against her, and he thought malignantly:

"She knows nothing about money, and so she is stingy. If she won it she would give me a hundred roubles, and put the rest away under lock and key."

And he looked at his wife, not with a smile now, but with hatred. She glanced at him too, and also with hatred and anger. She had her own daydreams, her own plans, her own reflections; she understood perfectly well what her husband's dreams were. She knew who would be the first to try and grab her winnings.

"It's very nice making daydreams at other people's expense!" is what her eyes expressed. "No, don't you dare!"

Her husband understood her look; hatred began stirring again in his breast, and in order to annoy his wife he glanced quickly, to spite her at the fourth page on the newspaper and read out triumphantly:

"Series 9,499, number 46! Not 26!"

Hatred and hope both disappeared at once, and it began immediately to seem to Ivan Dmitritch and his wife that their rooms were dark and small and low-pitched, that the supper they had been eating was not doing them good, but lying heavy on their stomachs, that the evenings were long and wearisome. . . .

"What the devil's the meaning of it?" said Ivan Dmitritch, beginning to be ill-humoured. "Wherever one steps there are bits of paper under one's feet, crumbs, husks. The rooms are never swept! One is simply forced to go out. Damnation take my soul entirely! I shall go and hang myself on the first aspen-tree!"

Questions

1. How many words does the author (as translated) use to give the background for this story? Why is this length of exposition (see p. 26) particularly important to the total effect of "The Lottery Ticket"?
2. Unlike most other stories, the opposing forces of the conflict in this story are not established till we are halfway through. When do these opposing forces (see p. 25) become apparent? What are they? How does the climax resolve the tension?
3. Why does Ivan delay so long in looking for the number 26 in the lottery series 9,499? Why would anyone deliberately so inhibit his curiosity? Could it be said that the author intended to heighten the suspense of the story? He does heighten it, but is that the chief purpose of having Ivan delay in looking for number 26?
4. Will this very brief event, this "moment of truth"—which is all that the story really is—make any difference in Masha's and Ivan's future life together? Why or why not?
5. How does Chekhov make the story not simply a conflict between husband and wife but also, and more importantly, a study of their shabby, materialistic ideas and their shabby way of living?
6. Why are the innermost thoughts and feelings of Ivan so thoroughly

rendered while Masha's are only summarized briefly by the following passage?

. . . She glanced at him too, and also with hatred and anger. She had her own daydreams, her own plans, her own reflections; she understood perfectly well what her husband's dreams were. She knew who would be the first to try and grab her winnings.

Love and Hate: General Questions

1. Compare and contrast the use of point of view in "The Upturned Face" and "The Lottery Ticket." How does the particular point of view chosen by each of the two authors serve to give meaning to his story? (See p. 31.) What is the tone of each story (see p. 43), and in what ways do irony (see p. 42) and point of view contribute to the tone? On the basis of these two stories, what conclusions might be drawn as to the respective attitudes of Crane and Chekhov concerning man's inhumanity to man?
2. "Feuille d'Album" and "The Golden Kite, the Silver Wind" have foreign countries as their settings. In each case, how necessary to the meaning of the story is the setting, and why? How does the setting affect the universality of each story? How does the setting affect the individuality of each story? (See p. 11.)
3. "Patricia, Edith and Arnold" and "Feuille d'Album" deal with the subject of romantic young love. Compare and contrast the attitudes toward love of the observers in "Feuille d'Album" and of the boy in "Patricia, Edith and Arnold." Discuss, also, the respective attitudes toward love of Ian French and Arnold, on the one hand, and of the girl in "Feuille d'Album" and Patricia and Edith, on the other hand. As a result of these observations of the characters' attitudes, what conclusions may be drawn in respect to the irony of falling in love?
4. How does "The Lottery Ticket" negate or affirm the conclusions about romantic love to which "Feuille d'Album" and "Patricia, Edith and Arnold" lead?
5. Select a symbol from each of the five stories in this section and trace the pattern or other device used to make the image significant enough to qualify as a symbol (see p. 40). In each case, what is the relationship between the symbol and the story's generalization about love and/or hate?
6. Drawing upon the five stories of love and hate, define love, by showing it as it operates in the stories; define hate, by showing it as it operates in the stories.

84

Youth and Age

Introduction

Childhood, adolescence, maturity, and old age are phases of living that all men who have a normal span of existence have in common. Each of the ages of man has its own joy and sorrow, humor and seriousness, wonder and terror. The relationship among people of different ages also presents contrasts of various kinds that all men have experienced. Because the comforts and problems of youth and age are most marked in the social unit of the family, artists have always been intrigued by family interrelationships. Mother and child, the most elemental of human ties, is the serious and beautiful subject of Michelangelo's *Pieta,* but in an entirely different way it is also the amusing idea behind Shirley Jackson's short-short story "Charles." Another story of family life, as it is experienced by a precocious, observant boy, is John Updike's "Pigeon Feathers," which presents the contrasting effects that people of three different generations have upon each other while living under the same farmhouse roof.

Another family story is Nobel prize winner Björnstjerne Björnson's short-short story "The Father." Like "The Prodigal Son," "The Father" is about the love of a father for his son, but unlike the Biblical parable, which points out a lesson that youth can learn from age, "The Father" is concerned with the loss of a son and the lesson that age learns from such sorrow.

Joseph Conrad's "Youth" shows still another kind of contrast between youth and age—through an elderly man's reminiscences of himself as a very young man, whom, in retrospect, he both admires and scorns.

One of the stories written by a student in a later section of this book illustrates friendship between generations, another side of the universal theme of youth and age. The story is "Checking-Out," which tenderly tells of a brief friendship between an elderly woman and a boy.

Other stories in this book, though predominately illustrative of other themes, also deal in part with the theme of youth and age: "Patricia, Edith and Arnold"; "So Much Unfairness of Things"; "The Affair at 7, Rue de M——"; "The Sisters"; "Holiday"; and "Leon."

Charles

Shirley Jackson

The day my son Laurie started kindergarten he renounced corduroy overalls with bibs and began wearing blue jeans with a belt; I watched him go off the first morning with the older girl next door, seeing clearly that an era of my life was ended, my sweet-voiced nursery-school tot replaced by a long-trousered, swaggering character who forgot to stop at the corner and wave good-bye to me.

He came home the same way, the front door slamming open, his cap on the floor, and the voice suddenly become raucous shouting, "Isn't anybody *here?*"

At lunch he spoke insolently to his father, spilled his baby sister's milk, and remarked that his teacher said we were not to take the name of the Lord in vain.

"How *was* school today?" I asked, elaborately casual.

"All right," he said.

"Did you learn anything?" his father asked.

Laurie regarded his father coldly. "I didn't learn nothing," he said.

"Anything," I said. "Didn't learn anything."

"The teacher spanked a boy, though," Laurie said, addressing his bread and butter. "For being fresh," he added, with his mouth full.

"What did he do?" I asked. "Who was it?"

Laurie thought. "It was Charles," he said. "He was fresh. The teacher spanked him and made him stand in a corner. He was awfully fresh."

"What did he do?" I asked again, but Laurie slid off his chair, took a cookie, and left, while his father was still saying, "See here, young man."

The next day Laurie remarked at lunch, as soon as he sat down, "Well, Charles was bad again today." He grinned enormously and said, "Today Charles hit the teacher."

"Good heavens," I said, mindful of the Lord's name, "I suppose he got spanked again?"

"He sure did," Laurie said. "Look up," he said to his father.

"What?" his father said, looking up.

"Look down," Laurie said. "Look at my thumb. Gee, you're dumb." He began to laugh insanely.

"Why did Charles hit the teacher?" I asked quickly.

"Because she tried to make him color with red crayons," Laurie said. "Charles wanted to color with green crayons so he hit the teacher and she spanked him and said nobody play with Charles but everybody did."

The third day—it was Wednesday of the first week—Charles bounced a see-saw on to the head of a little girl and made her bleed, and the teacher made him stay inside all during recess. Thursday Charles had to stand in a corner during story-time because he kept pounding his feet on the floor. Friday Charles was deprived of blackboard privileges because he threw chalk.

On Saturday I remarked to my husband, "Do you think kindergarten is too unsettling for Laurie? All this toughness, and bad grammar, and this Charles boy sounds like such a bad influence."

"It'll be all right," my husband said reassuringly. "Bound to be people like Charles in the world. Might as well meet them now as later."

On Monday Laurie came home late, full of news. "Charles," he shouted as he came up the hill; I was waiting anxiously on the front steps. "Charles," Laurie yelled all the way up the hill, "Charles was bad again."

"Come right in," I said, as soon as he came close enough. "Lunch is waiting."

"You know what Charles did?" he demanded, following me through the door. "Charles yelled so in school they sent a boy in from first grade to tell the teacher she had to make Charles keep quiet, and so Charles had to stay after school. And so all the children stayed to watch him."

"What did he do?" I asked.

"He just sat there," Laurie said, climbing into his chair at the table. "Hi, Pop, y'old dust mop."

"Charles had to stay after school today," I told my husband. "Everyone stayed with him."

"What does this Charles look like?" my husband asked Laurie. "What's his other name?"

"He's bigger than me," Laurie said. "And he doesn't have any rubbers and he doesn't ever wear a jacket."

Monday night was the first Parent-Teachers meeting, and only the fact that the baby had a cold kept me from going; I wanted passionately to meet Charles's mother. On Tuesday Laurie remarked suddenly, "Our teacher had a friend come to see her in school today."

"Charles's mother?" my husband and I asked simultaneously.

"Naaah," Laurie said scornfully. "It was a man who came and made us do exercises, we had to touch our toes. Look." He climbed down from his chair and squatted down and touched his toes. "Like this," he said. He got solemnly back into his chair and said, picking up his fork, "Charles didn't even *do* exercises."

"That's fine," I said heartily. "Didn't Charles want to do exercises?"

"Naaah," Laurie said. "Charles was so fresh to the teacher's friend he wasn't *let* do exercises."

"Fresh again?" I said.

"He kicked the teacher's friend," Laurie said. "The teacher's friend told Charles to touch his toes like I just did and Charles kicked him."

"What are they going to do about Charles, do you suppose?" Laurie's father asked him.

Laurie shrugged elaborately. "Throw him out of school, I guess," he said.

Wednesday and Thusday were routine; Charles yelled during story hour and hit a boy in the stomach and made him cry. On Friday Charles stayed after school again and so did all the other children.

With the third week of kindergarten Charles was an institution in our family; the baby was being a Charles when she cried all afternoon; Laurie did a Charles when he filled his wagon full of mud and pulled it through the kitchen; even my husband, when he caught his elbow in the telephone cord and pulled telephone, ashtray, and a bowl of flowers off the table, said, after the first minute, "Looks like Charles."

During the third and fourth weeks it looked like a reformation in Charles; Laurie reported grimly at lunch on Thursday of the third week, "Charles was so good today the teacher gave him an apple."

"What?" I said, and my husband added warily, "You mean Charles?"

"Charles," Laurie said. "He gave the crayons around and he picked up the books afterward and the teacher said he was her helper."

"What happened?" I asked incredulously.

"He was her helper, that's all," Laurie said, and shrugged.

"Can this be true, about Charles?" I asked my husband that night. "Can something like this happen?"

"Wait and see," my husband said cynically. "When you've got a Charles to deal with, this may mean he's only plotting."

He seemed to be wrong. For over a week Charles was the teacher's helper; each day he handed things out and he picked things up; no one had to stay after school.

"The P.T.A. meeting's next week again," I told my husband one evening. "I'm going to find Charles's mother there."

"Ask her what happened to Charles," my husband said. "I'd like to know."

"I'd like to know myself," I said.

On Friday of that week things were back to normal. "You know what Charles did today?" Laurie demanded at the lunch table, in a voice slightly awed. "He told a little girl to say a word and she said it and the teacher washed her mouth out with soap and Charles laughed."

"What word?" his father asked unwisely, and Laurie said, "I'll have to whisper it to you, it's so bad." He got down off his chair and went around to his father. His father bent his head down and Laurie whispered joyfully. His father's eyes widened.

"Did Charles tell the little girl to say *that*?" he asked respectfully.

"She said it *twice*," Laurie said. "Charles told her to say it *twice*."

"What happened to Charles?" my husband asked.

"Nothing," Laurie said. "He was passing out the crayons."

Monday morning Charles abandoned the little girl and said the evil word himself three or four times, getting his mouth washed out with soap each time. He also threw chalk.

My husband came to the door with me that evening as I set out for the P.T.A. meeting. "Invite her over for a cup of tea after the meeting," he said. "I want to get a look at her."

"If only she's there," I said prayerfully.

"She'll be there," my husband said. "I don't see how they could hold a P.T.A. meeting without Charles's mother."

At the meeting I sat restlessly, scanning each comfortable matronly face, trying to determine which one hid the secret of Charles. None of them looked to me haggard enough. No one stood up in the meeting and apologized for the way her son had been acting. No one mentioned Charles.

After the meeting I identified and sought out Laurie's kindergarten teacher. She had a plate with a cup of tea and a piece of chocolate cake; I had a plate with a cup of tea and a piece of marshmallow cake. We maneuvered up to one another cautiously, and smiled.

"I've been so anxious to meet you," I said. "I'm Laurie's mother."

"We're all so interested in Laurie," she said.

"Well, he certainly likes kindergarten," I said. "He talks about it all the time."

"We had a little trouble adjusting, the first week or so," she said primly, "but now he's a fine little helper. With occasional lapses, of course."

"Laurie usually adjusts very quickly," I said. "I suppose this time it's Charles's influence."

"Charles?"

"Yes," I said, laughing, "you must have your hands full in that kindergarten, with Charles."

"Charles?" she said. "We don't have any Charles in the kindergarten."

Questions

1. Were you surprised by the ending of "Charles"? How did the author prepare the reader for the outcome? Could she have done it differently to better effect?

2. How does repetition of the name *Charles* in the following description of Laurie's return from school further reveal our understanding of Laurie?

> On Monday Laurie came home late, full of news. "Charles," he shouted as he came up the hill; I was waiting anxiously on the front steps. "Charles," Laurie yelled all the way up the hill, "Charles was bad again."

3. This story illustrates the skillful use of dialogue. What functions does it serve?

4. "Charles" differs from most of the stories in this book because of the position of the climax. Where does it occur, and how does its position in the sequence of the action relate to the total effect? (See p. 26.)

5. Applying them to "Charles," answer the questions on point of view on page 39.

Youth: A Narrative

Joseph Conrad

This could have occurred nowhere but in England, where men and sea interpenetrate, so to speak—the sea entering into the life of most men, and the men knowing something or everything about the sea, in the way of amusement, of travel, or of bread-winning.

We were sitting round a mahogany table that reflected the bottle, the claret-glasses, and our faces as we leaned on our elbows. There was a director of companies, an accountant, a lawyer, Marlow, and myself. The director had been a *Conway* boy, the accountant had served four years at sea, the lawyer—a fine crusted Tory, High Churchman, the best of old fellows, the soul of honour—had been chief officer in the P. & O. service in the good old days when mail-boats were square-rigged at least on two masts, and used to come down the China Sea before a fair monsoon with stun'sails set alow and aloft. We all began life in the merchant service. Between the five of us there was the strong bond of the sea, and also the fellowship of the craft, which no amount of enthusiasm for yachting, cruising, and so on can give, since one is only the amusement of life and the other is life itself.

Marlow (at least I think that is how he spelt his name) told the story, or rather the chronicle, of a voyage:

"Yes, I have seen a little of the Eastern seas; but what I remember best is my first voyage there. You fellows know there are those voyages that seem ordered for the illustration of life, that might stand for a symbol of existence. You fight, work, sweat, nearly kill yourself, sometimes do kill yourself, trying to accomplish something—and you can't. Not from any fault of yours. You simply can do nothing, neither great nor little—not a thing in the world—not even marry an old maid, or get a wretched 600-ton cargo of coal to its port of destination.

"It was altogether a memorable affair. It was my first voyage to the East, and my first voyage as second mate; it was also my skipper's first command. You'll admit it was time. He was sixty if a day; a little man, with a broad, not very straight back, with bowed shoulders and one leg more bandy than the other, he had that queer twisted-about appearance you see so often in men who work in the fields. He had a nut-cracker face—chin and nose trying to come together over a sunken mouth—and it was framed in iron-gray fluffy hair, that looked like a chin-strap of cotton-wool sprinkled with coal-dust. And he had blue eyes in that old face of his, which were amazingly like a boy's, with that candid expression some quite common men preserve to the end of their days by a rare internal gift of simplicity of heart and rectitude of soul. What induced him to accept me was a wonder. I had come out of a crack Australian clipper, where I had been third officer, and he seemed to have a prejudice against crack clippers as aristocratic and high-toned. He said to me, 'You know, in this ship you will have to work.' I said I had to work in every ship I had ever been in. 'Ah, but this is different, and you gentlemen out of them big ships; . . . but there! I dare say you will do. Join to-morrow.'

"I joined to-morrow. It was twenty-two years ago; and I was just twenty. How time passes! It was one of the happiest days of my life. Fancy! Second mate for the first time—a really responsible officer! I wouldn't have thrown up my new billet for a fortune. The mate looked me over carefully. He was also an old chap, but of another stamp. He had a Roman nose, a snow-white, long beard, and his name was Mahon, but he insisted that it should be pronounced Mann. He was well connected; yet there was something wrong with his luck, and he had never got on.

"As to the captain, he had been for years in coasters, then in the Mediterranean, and last in the West Indian trade. He had never been round the Capes. He could just write a kind of sketchy hand, and didn't care for writing at all. Both were thorough good seamen of course, and between those two old chaps I felt like a small boy between two grandfathers.

"The ship also was old. Her name was the *Judea*. Queer name, isn't it? She belonged to a man Wilmer, Wilcox—some name like that; but he has been bankrupt and dead these twenty years or more, and his name don't matter. She had been laid up in Shadwell basin for ever so long. You may imagine her state. She was all rust, dust, grime—soot aloft, dirt on deck. To me it was like coming out of a palace into a ruined cottage. She was about 400 tons, had a primitive windlass, wooden latches to the doors, not a bit of brass about her, and a big square stern. There was on it, below her name in big letters, a lot of scrollwork, with the gilt off, and some sort of a coat of arms, with the motto 'Do or Die' underneath. I remember it took my fancy immensely. There was a touch of romance in it, something that made me love the old thing—something that appealed to my youth!

"We left London in ballast—sand ballast—to load a cargo of coal in a northern port for Bangkok. Bangkok! I thrilled. I had been six years at sea, but had only seen Melbourne and Sydney, very good places, charming places in their way—but Bangkok!

"We worked out of the Thames under canvas, with a North Sea pilot on board. His name was Jermyn, and he dodged all day long about the galley drying his handkerchief before the stove. Apparently he never slept. He was a dismal man, with a perpetual tear sparkling at the end of his nose, who either had been in trouble, or was in trouble, or expected to be in trouble—couldn't be happy unless something went wrong. He mistrusted my youth, my common-sense, and my seamanship, and made a point of showing it in a hundred little ways. I dare say he was right. It seems to me I knew very little then, and I know not much more now; but I cherish a hate for that Jermyn to this day.

"We were a week working up as far as Yarmouth Roads, and then we got into a gale—the famous October gale of twenty-two years ago. It was wind, lightning, sleet, snow, and a terrific sea. We were flying light, and you may imagine how bad it was when I tell you we had smashed bulwarks and a flooded deck. On the second night she shifted her ballast into the lee bow, and by that time we had been blown off somewhere on the Dogger Bank. There was nothing for it but go below with shovels and try to right her, and there we were in that vast hold, gloomy like a cavern, the tallow dips stuck and flickering on the beams, the gale howling above, the ship tossing about like mad on her side; there we all were, Jermyn, the captain, every one, hardly able to keep our feet, engaged on that gravedigger's work, and trying to toss shovelfuls of wet sand up to windward. At every tumble of the ship you could see vaguely in the dim light men falling down with a great flourish of shovels. One of the ship's boys (we had two), impressed by the weirdness of the scene, wept as if his heart would break. We could hear him blubbering somewhere in the shadows.

"On the third day the gale died out, and by and by a north-country tug picked us up. We took sixteen days in all to get from London to the Tyne! When we got into dock we had lost our turn for loading, and they hauled us off to a tier where we remained for a month. Mrs. Beard (the captain's name was Beard) came from Colchester to see the old man. She lived on board. The crew of runners had left, and there remained only the officers, one boy and the steward, a mulatto who answered to the name of Abraham. Mrs. Beard was an old woman, with a face all wrinkled and ruddy like a winter apple, and the figure of a young girl. She caught sight of me once, sewing on a button, and insisted on having my shirts to repair. This was something different from the captains' wives I had known on board crack clippers. When I brought her the shirts, she said: 'And the socks? They want mending, I am sure, and John's—Captain Beard's—things are all in order now. I would be glad of something to do.' Bless the old woman. She over-hauled my outfit for me, and meantime I read for the first time *Sartor Resartus* and Burnaby's *Ride to Khiva*. I didn't understand much of the first then; but I remember I preferred the soldier to the philosopher at the time; a preference which life has only confirmed. One was a man, and the other was either more—or less. However, they are both dead and Mrs. Beard is dead, and youth, strength, genius, thoughts, achieve-ments, simple hearts—all die. . . . No matter.

"They loaded us at last. We shipped a crew. Eight able seamen and two boys. We hauled off one evening to the buoys at the dock-gates, ready to go out, and with a fair prospect of beginning the voyage next day. Mrs. Beard was to start for home by a late train. When the ship was fast we went to tea. We sat rather silent through the meal—Mahon, the old couple, and I. I finished first, and slipped away for a smoke, my cabin being in a deck-house just against the poop. It was high water, blowing fresh with a drizzle; the double dock-gates were opened, and the steam-colliers were going in and out in the darkness with their lights burning bright, a great plashing of propellers, rattling of winches, and a lot of hailing on the pier-heads. I watched the pro-cession of head-lights gliding high and of green lights gliding low in the night, when suddenly a red gleam flashed at me, vanished, came into view again, and remained. The fore-end of a steamer loomed up close. I shouted down the cabin, 'Come up, quick!' and then heard a startled voice saying afar in the dark, 'Stop her, sir.' A bell jingled. Another voice cried warningly, 'We are going right into that barque, sir.' The answer to this was a gruff 'All right,' and the next thing was a heavy crash as the steamer struck a glancing blow with the bluff of her bow about our fore-rigging. There was a moment of confusion, yelling, and running about. Steam roared. Then somebody was heard saying, 'All clear, sir.' . . . 'Are you all right?' asked the gruff voice. I had jumped forward to see the damage, and hailed back, 'I think so.' 'Easy astern,' said the gruff voice. A bell jingled. 'What steamer is that?' screamed Mahon. By that time she was no more to us than a bulky shadow manœuvring a little way off. They shouted at us some name—a woman's name, Miranda or Melissa—or some such thing. 'This means another month in this beastly hole,' said Mahon to me, as we peered with lamps about the splintered bulwarks and broken braces. 'But where's the captain?'

"We had not heard or seen anything of him all that time. We went aft to look. A doleful voice arose hailing somewhere in the middle of the dock, '*Judea*, ahoy!' . . . How the devil did he get there? . . . 'Hallo!' we shouted. 'I am adrift in our boat without oars,' he cried. A belated waterman offered his services, and Mahon struck a bargain with him for half-a-crown to tow our skipper alongside; but it was Mrs. Beard that came up the ladder first. They had been floating about the dock in that mizzly cold rain for nearly an hour. I was never so surprised in my life.

"It appears that when he heard my shout 'Come up' he understood at once what was the matter, caught up his wife, ran on deck, and across, and down into our boat, which was fast to the ladder. Not bad for a sixty-year-old. Just imagine that old fellow saving heroically in his arms that old woman—the woman of his life. He set her down on a thwart, and was ready to climb back on board when the painter came adrift somehow, and away they went together. Of course in the confusion we did not hear him shouting. He looked abashed. She said cheerfully, 'I suppose it does not matter my losing the train now?' 'No, Jenny—you go below and get warm,' he growled. Then to us: 'A sailor has no business with a wife—I say. There I was, out of the ship. Well, no harm done this time. Let's go and look at what that fool of a steamer smashed.'

"It wasn't much, but it delayed us three weeks. At the end of that time, the captain being engaged with his agents, I carried Mrs. Beard's bag to the railway-station and put her all comfy into a third-class carriage. She lowered the window to say, 'You are a good young man. If you see John—Captain Beard—without his muffler at night, just remind him from me to keep his throat well wrapped up.' 'Certainly, Mrs. Beard,' I said. 'You are a good young man; I noticed how attentive you are to John—to Captain——' The train pulled out suddenly; I took my cap off to the old woman: I never saw her again. . . . Pass the bottle.

"We went to sea next day. When we made that start for Bangkok we had been already three months out of London. We had expected to be a fortnight or so—at the outside.

"It was January, and the weather was beautiful—the beautiful sunny winter weather that has more charm than in the summer-time, because it is unexpected, and crisp, and you know it won't, it can't, last long. It's like a windfall, like a godsend, like an unexpected piece of luck.

"It lasted all down the North Sea, all down Channel; and it lasted till we were three hundred miles or so to the westward of the Lizards: then the wind went round to the sou'west and began to pipe up. In two days it blew a gale. The *Judea,* hove to, wallowed on the Atlantic like an old candle-box. It blew day after day: it blew with spite, without interval, without mercy, without rest. The world was nothing but an immensity of great foaming waves rushing at us, under a sky low enough to touch with the hand and dirty like a smoked ceiling. In the stormy space surrounding us there was as much flying spray as air. Day after day and night after night there was nothing round the ship but the howl of the wind, the tumult of the sea, the noise of water pouring over her deck. There was no rest for her and no rest for us. She tossed, she pitched, she stood on her head, she sat on her tail, she rolled, she groaned, and we had to hold on while on deck and cling to our bunks when below, in a constant effort of body and worry of mind.

"One night Mahon spoke through the small window of my berth. It opened right into my very bed, and I was lying there sleepless, in my boots, feeling as though I had not slept for years, and could not if I tried. He said excitedly:

"'You got the sounding-rod in here, Marlow? I can't get the pumps to suck. By God! it's no child's play.'

"I gave him the sounding-rod and lay down again, trying to think of various things—but I thought only of the pumps. When I came on deck they were still at it, and my watch relieved at the pumps. By the light of the lantern brought on deck to examine the sounding-rod I caught a glimpse of their weary, serious faces. We pumped all the four hours. We pumped all night, all day, all the week—watch and watch. She was working herself loose, and leaked badly—not enough to drown us at once, but enough to kill us with the work at the pumps. And while we pumped the ship was going from us piecemeal: the bulwarks went, the stanchions were torn out, the ventilators smashed, the cabin-door burst in. There was not a dry spot in the ship. She was being gutted bit by bit. The long-boat changed, as if by magic, into matchwood where she stood in her gripes. I had lashed her myself, and was rather proud of my handiwork, which had withstood so long the malice of the sea. And we pumped. And there was no break in the weather. The sea was white like a sheet of foam, like a cauldron of boiling milk; there was not a break in the clouds, no—not the size of a man's hand—no, not for so much as ten seconds. There was for us no sky, there were for us no stars, no sun, no universe—nothing but angry clouds and an infuriated sea. We pumped watch and watch, for dear life; and it seemed to last for months, for years, for all eternity, as though we had been dead and gone to a hell for sailors. We forgot the day of the week, the name of the month, what year it was, and whether we had ever been ashore. The sails blew away, she lay broadside on under a weather-cloth, the ocean poured over her, and we did not care. We turned those handles, and had the eyes of idiots. As soon as we had crawled on deck I used to take a round turn with a rope about the men, the pumps, and the mainmast, and we turned, we turned incessantly, with the water to our waists, to our necks, over our heads. It was all one. We had forgotten how it felt to be dry.

"And there was somewhere in me the thought: By Jove! this is the deuce of an adventure—something you read about; and it is my first voyage as second mate—and I am only twenty—and here I am lasting it out as well as any of these men, and keeping my chaps up to the mark. I was pleased. I would not have given up the experience for worlds. I had moments of exultation. Whenever the old dismantled craft pitched heavily with her counter high in the air, she seemed to me to throw up, like an appeal, like a defiance, like a cry to the clouds without mercy, the words written on her stern: '*Judea*, London. Do or Die.'

"O youth! The strength of it, the faith of it, the imagination of it! To me she was not an old rattletrap carting about the world a lot of coal for a freight—to me she was the endeavour, the test, the trial of life. I think of her with pleasure, with affection, with regret—as you would think of some one dead you have loved. I shall never forget her. . . . Pass the bottle.

"One night when tied to the mast, as I explained, we were pumping on, deafened with the wind, and without spirit enough in us to wish ourselves dead, a heavy sea crashed aboard and swept clean over us. As soon as I got my breath I shouted, as in duty bound, 'Keep on, boys!' when suddenly I felt something hard floating on deck strike the calf of my leg. I made a grab at it and missed. It was so dark we could not see each other's faces within a foot—you understand.

"After that thump the ship kept quiet for a while, and the thing, whatever it was, struck my leg again. This time I caught it—and it was a saucepan. At first, being stupid with fatigue and thinking of nothing but the pumps, I did not understand what I had in my hand. Suddenly it dawned upon me, and I shouted, 'Boys, the house on deck is gone. Leave this, and let's look for the cook.'

"There was a deck-house forward, which contained the galley, the cook's berth, and the quarters of the crew. As we had expected for days to see it swept away, the hands had been ordered to sleep in the cabin—the only safe place in the ship. The steward, Abraham, however, persisted in clinging to his berth, stupidly, like a mule—from sheer fright I believe, like an animal that won't leave a stable falling in an earthquake. So we went to look for him. It was chancing death, since once out of our lashings we were as exposed as if on a raft. But we went. The house was shattered as if a shell had exploded inside. Most of it had gone overboard—stove, men's quarters, and their property, all was gone; but two posts, holding a portion of the bulkhead to which Abraham's bunk was attached, remained as if by a miracle. We groped in the ruins and came upon this, and there he was, sitting in his bunk, surrounded by foam and wreckage, jabbering cheerfully to himself. He was out of his mind; completely and for ever mad, with this sudden shock coming upon the fag-end of his endurance. We snatched him up, lugged him aft, and pitched him headfirst down the cabin companion. You understand there was no time to carry him down with infinite pre-cautions and wait to see how he got on. Those below would pick him up at the bottom of the stairs all right. We were in a hurry to go back to the pumps. That business could not wait. A bad leak is an inhuman thing.

"One would think that the sole purpose of that fiendish gale had been to make a lunatic of that poor devil of a mulatto. It eased before morn-ing, and next day the sky cleared, and as the sea went down the leak took up. When it came to bending a fresh set of sails the crew de-manded to put back—and really there was nothing else to do. Boats gone, decks swept clean, cabin gutted, men without a stitch but what they stood in, stores spoiled, ship strained. We put her head for home, and—would you believe it? The wind came east right in our teeth. It blew fresh, it blew continuously. We had to beat up every inch of the way, but she did not leak so badly, the water keeping comparatively smooth. Two hours' pumping in every four is no joke—but it kept her afloat as far as Falmouth.

"The good people there live on casualties of the sea, and no doubt were glad to see us. A hungry crowd of shipwrights sharpened their chisels at the sight of that carcass of a ship. And, by Jove! they had pretty pickings off us before they were done. I fancy the owner was already in a tight place. There were delays. Then it was decided to take part of the cargo out and caulk her topsides. This was done, the repairs finished, cargo reshipped; a new crew came on board, and we went out—for Bangkok. At the end of a week we were back again.

The crew said they weren't going to Bangkok—a hundred and fifty days' passage—in a something hooker that wanted pumping eight hours out of the twenty-four; and the nautical papers inserted again the little paragraph: 'Judea. Barque. Tyne to Bangkok; coals; put back to Falmouth leaky and with crew refusing duty.'

"There were more delays—more tinkering. The owner came down for a day, and said she was as right as a little fiddle. Poor old Captain Beard looked like the ghost of a Geordie skipper—through the worry and humiliation of it. Remember he was sixty, and it was his first command. Mahon said it was a foolish business, and would end badly. I loved the ship more than ever, and wanted awfully to get to Bangkok. To Bangkok! Magic name, blessed name. Mesopotamia wasn't a patch on it. Remember I was twenty, and it was my first second-mate's billet, and the East was waiting for me.

"We went out and anchored in the outer roads with a fresh crew—the third. She leaked worse than ever. It was as if those confounded shipwrights had actually made a hole in her. This time we did not even go outside. The crew simply refused to man the windlass.

"They towed us back to the inner harbour, and we became a fixture, a feature, an institution of the place. People pointed us out to visitors as 'That 'ere barque that's going to Bangkok—has been here six months —put back three times.' On holidays the small boys pulling about in boats would hail, 'Judea, ahoy!' and if a head showed above the rail shouted, 'Where you bound to?—Bangkok?' and jeered. We were only three on board. The poor old skipper mooned in the cabin. Mahon undertook the cooking, and unexpectedly developed all a Frenchman's genius for preparing nice little messes. I looked languidly after the rigging. We became citizens of Falmouth. Every shopkeeper knew us. At the barber's or tobacconist's they asked familiarly, 'Do you think you will ever get to Bangkok?' Meantime the owner, the underwriters, and the charterers squabbled amongst themselves in London, and our pay went on. . . . Pass the bottle.

"It was horrid. Morally it was worse than pumping for life. It seemed as though we had been forgotten by the world, belonged to nobody, would get nowhere; it seemed that, as if bewitched, we would have to live for ever and ever in that inner harbour, a derision and a byword to generations of long-shore loafers and dishonest boatmen. I obtained three months' pay and a five days' leave, and made a rush for London. It took me a day to get there and pretty well another to come back—but three months' pay went all the same. I don't know what I did with it. I went to a music-hall, I believe, lunched, dined, and supped in a swell place in Regent Street, and was back in time, with nothing but a complete set of Byron's works and a new railway rug to show for three months' work. The boat-man who pulled me off to the ship said: 'Hallo! I thought you had left the old thing. *She* will never get to Bangkok.' 'That's all *you* know about it,' I said scornfully—but I didn't like that prophecy at all.

"Suddenly a man, some kind of agent to somebody, appeared with full powers. He had grog-blossoms all over his face, an indomitable energy, and was a jolly soul. We leaped into life again. A hulk came alongside, took our cargo, and then we went into dry dock to get our copper stripped. No wonder she leaked. The poor thing, strained beyond endurance by the gale, had, as if in disgust, spat out all the oakum of her lower seams. She was recaulked, new coppered, and made as tight as a bottle. We went back to the hulk and reshipped our cargo.

"Then, on a fine moonlight night, all the rats left the ship.

"We had been infested with them. They had destroyed our sails, consumed more stores than the crew, affably shared our beds and our dangers, and now, when the ship was made seaworthy, concluded to clear out. I called Mahon to enjoy the spectacle. Rat after rat appeared on our rail, took a last look over his shoulder, and leaped with a hollow thud into the empty hulk. We tried to count them, but soon lost the tale. Mahon said: 'Well, well! don't talk to me about the intelligence of rats. They ought to have left before, when we had that narrow squeak from foundering. There you have the proof how silly is the superstition about them. They leave a good ship for an old rotten hulk, where there is nothing to eat, too, the fools! . . . I don't believe they know what is safe or what is good for them, any more than you or I.'

"And after some more talk we agreed that the wisdom of rats had been grossly overrated, being in fact no greater than that of men.

"The story of the ship was known, by this, all up the Channel from Land's End to the Forelands, and we could get no crew on the south coast. They sent us one all complete from Liverpool, and we left once more—for Bangkok.

"We had fair breezes, smooth water right into the tropics, and the old *Judea* lumbered along in the sunshine. When she went eight knots everything cracked aloft, and we tied our caps to our heads; but mostly she strolled on at the rate of three miles an hour. What could you expect? She was tired—that old ship. Her youth was where mine is— where yours is—you fellows who listen to this yarn; and what friend would throw your years and your weariness in your face? We didn't grumble at her. To us aft, at least, it seemed as though we had been born in her, reared in her, had lived in her for ages, had never known any other ship. I would just as soon have abused the old village church at home for not being a cathedral.

"And for me there was also my youth to make me patient. There was all the East before me, and all life, and the thought that I had been tried in that ship and had come out pretty well. And I thought of men of old who, centuries ago, went that road in ships that sailed no better, to the land of palms, and spices, and yellow sands, and of brown nations ruled by kings more cruel than Nero the Roman, and more splendid than Solomon the Jew. The old barque lumbered on, heavy with her age and the burden of her cargo, while I lived the life of youth in ignorance and hope. She lumbered on through an interminable procession of days; and the fresh gilding flashed back at the setting sun, seemed to cry out over the darkening sea the words painted on her stern, '*Judea*, London. Do or Die.'

"Then we entered the Indian Ocean and steered northerly for Java Head. The winds were light. Weeks slipped by. She crawled on, do or die, and people at home began to think of posting us as overdue.

"One Saturday evening, I being off duty, the men asked me to give them an extra bucket of water or so—for washing clothes. As I did not wish to screw on the fresh-water pump so late, I went forward whistling, and with a key in my hand to unlock the forepeak scuttle, intending to serve the water out of a spare tank we kept there.

"The smell down below was as unexpected as it was frightful. One would have thought hundreds of paraffin-lamps had been flaring and smoking in that hole for days. I was glad to get out. The man with me coughed and said, 'Funny smell, sir.' I answered negligently, 'It's good for the health they say,' and walked aft.

"The first thing I did was to put my head down the square of the midship ventilator. As I lifted the lid a visible breath, something like a thin fog, a puff of faint haze, rose from the opening. The ascending air was hot, and had a heavy, sooty, paraffiny smell. I gave one sniff, and put down the lid gently. It was no use choking myself. The cargo was on fire.

"Next day she began to smoke in earnest. You see it was to be expected, for though the coal was of a safe kind, that cargo had been so handled, so broken up with handling, that it looked more like smithy coal than anything else. Then it had been wetted—more than once. It rained all the time we were taking it back from the hulk, and now with this long passage it got heated, and there was another case of spontaneous combustion.

"The captain called us into the cabin. He had a chart spread on the table, and looked unhappy. He said, "The coast of West Australia is near, but I mean to proceed to our destination. It is the hurricane month, too; but we will just keep our head for Bangkok, and fight the fire. No more putting back anywhere, if we all get roasted. We will try first to stifle this 'ere damned combustion by want of air.'

"We tried. We battened down everything, and still she smoked. The smoke kept coming out through imperceptible crevices; it forced itself through bulkheads and covers; it oozed here and there and everywhere in slender threads, in an invisible film, in an incomprehensible manner. It made its way into the cabin, into the forecastle; it poisoned the sheltered places on the deck, it could be sniffed as high as the mainyard. It was clear that if the smoke came out the air came in. This was disheartening. This combustion refused to be stifled.

"We resolved to try water, and took the hatches off. Enormous volumes of smoke, whitish, yellowish, thick, greasy, misty, choking, ascended as high as the trucks. All hands cleared out aft. Then the poisonous cloud blew away, and we went back to work in a smoke that was no thicker now than that of an ordinary factory chimney.

"We rigged the force-pump, got the hose along, and by and by it burst. Well, it was as old as the ship—a prehistoric hose, and past repair. Then we pumped with the feeble head-pump, drew water with buckets, and in this way managed in time to pour lots of Indian Ocean into the main hatch. The bright stream flashed in sunshine, fell into a layer of white crawling smoke, and vanished on the black surface of coal. Steam ascended mingling with the smoke. We poured salt water as into a barrel without a bottom. It was our fate to pump in that ship, to pump out of her, to pump into her; and after keeping water out of her to save ourselves from being drowned, we frantically poured water into her to save ourselves from being burnt.

"And she crawled on, do or die, in the serene weather. The sky was a miracle of purity, a miracle of azure. The sea was polished, was blue, was pellucid, was sparkling like a precious stone, extending on all sides, all round to the horizon—as if the whole terrestrial globe had been one jewel, one colossal sapphire, a single gem fashioned into a planet. And on the lustre of the great calm waters the *Judea* glided imperceptibly, enveloped in languid and unclean vapours, in a lazy cloud that drifted to leeward, light and slow; a pestiferous cloud defiling the splendour of sea and sky.

102 YOUTH: A NARRATIVE

"All this time of course we saw no fire. The cargo smouldered at the bottom somewhere. Once Mahon, as we were working side by side, said to me with a queer smile: 'Now, if she only would spring a tidy leak—like that time when we first left the Channel—it would put a stopper on this fire. Wouldn't it?' I remarked irrelevantly, 'Do you remember the rats?'

"We fought the fire and sailed the ship too as carefully as though nothing had been the matter. The steward cooked and attended on us. Of the other twelve men, eight worked while four rested. Everyone took his turn, captain included. There was equality, and if not exactly fraternity then a deal of good feeling. Sometimes a man, as he dashed a bucketful of water down the hatchway, would yell out, 'Hurrah for Bangkok!' and the rest laughed. But generally we were taciturn and serious—and thirsty. Oh! how thirsty! And we had to be careful with the water. Strict allowance. The ship smoked, the sun blazed. . . . Pass the bottle.

"We tried everything. We even made an attempt to dig down to the fire. No good, of course. No man could remain more than a minute below. Mahon, who went first, fainted there, and the man who went to fetch him out did likewise. We lugged them out on deck. Then I leaped down to show how easily it could be done. They had learned wisdom by that time, and contented themselves by fishing for me with a chain-hook tied to a broom-handle, I believe. I did not offer to go and fetch up my shovel, which was left down below.

"Things began to look bad. We put the long-boat into the water. The second boat was ready to swing out. We had also another, a 14-foot thing, on davits aft, where it was quite safe.

"Then, behold, the smoke suddenly decreased. We redoubled our efforts to flood the bottom of the ship. In two days there was no smoke at all. Everybody was on the broad grin. This was on a Friday. On Saturday no work, but sailing the ship of course, was done. The men washed their clothes and their faces for the first time in a fortnight, and had a special dinner given them. They spoke of spontaneous combustion with contempt, and implied *they* were the boys to put out combustions. Somehow we all felt as though we each had inherited a large fortune. But a beastly smell of burning hung about the ship. Captain Beard had hollow eyes and sunken cheeks. I had never noticed so much before how twisted and bowed he was. He and Mahon prowled soberly about hatches and ventilators, sniffing. It struck me suddenly poor Mahon was a very, very old chap. As to me, I was as pleased and proud as though I had helped to win a great naval battle. O! Youth!

"The night was fine. In the morning a homeward-bound ship passed us hull down—the first we had seen for months; but we were nearing the land at last, Java Head being about 190 miles off and nearly due north.

"Next day it was my watch on deck from eight to twelve. At breakfast the captain observed, 'It's wonderful how that smell hangs about the cabin.' About ten, the mate being on the poop, I stepped down on the main-deck for a moment. The carpenter's bench stood abaft the mainmast: I leaned against it sucking at my pipe, and the carpenter, a young chap, came to talk to me. He remarked, 'I think we have done very well, haven't we?' and then I perceived with annoyance the fool was trying to tilt the bench. I said curtly, 'Don't, Chips,' and immediately became aware of a queer sensation, of an absurd delusion—I seemed somehow to be in the air. I heard all round me like a pent-up breath released—as if a thousand giants simultaneously had said Phoo! —and felt a dull concussion which made my ribs ache suddenly. No doubt about it—I was in the air, and my body was describing a short parabola. But short as it was, I had the time to think several thoughts in, as far as I can remember, the following order: 'This can't be the carpenter—What is it?—Some accident—Submarine volcano?—Coals, gas!—By Jove! we are being blown up—Everybody's dead—I am falling into the after-hatch—I see fire in it.'

"The coal-dust suspended in the air of the hold had glowed dull-red at the moment of the explosion. In the twinkling of an eye, in an infinitesimal fraction of a second since the first tilt of the bench, I was sprawling full length on the cargo. I picked myself up and scrambled out. It was quick like a rebound. The deck was a wilderness of smashed timber, lying crosswise like trees in a wood after a hurricane; an immense curtain of soiled rags waved gently before me—it was the mainsail blown to strips. I thought, The masts will be toppling over directly; and to get out of the way bolted on all-fours towards the poop-ladder. The first person I saw was Mahon, with eyes like saucers, his mouth open, and the long white hair standing straight on end round his head like a silver halo. He was just about to go down when the sight of the main-deck stirring, heaving up, and changing into splinters before his eyes, petrified him on the top step. I stared at him in unbelief, and he stared at me with a queer kind of shocked curiosity. I did not know that I had no hair, no eyebrows, no eyelashes, that my young moustache was burnt off, that my face was black; one cheek laid open, my nose cut, and my chin bleeding. I had lost my cap, one of my slippers, and my shirt was torn to rags. Of all this I was not aware. I was amazed to see the ship still afloat, the poop-deck whole—and, most of all, to see anybody alive. Also the peace of the sky and the serenity of the sea were distinctly surprising. I suppose I expected to see them convulsed with horror. . . . Pass the bottle.

"There was a voice hailing the ship from somewhere—in the air, in the sky—I couldn't tell. Presently I saw the captain—and he was mad. He asked me eagerly, 'Where's the cabin-table?' and to hear such a question was a frightful shock. I had just been blown up, you understand, and vibrated with that experience—I wasn't quite sure whether I was alive. Mahon began to stamp with both feet and yelled at him, 'Good God! don't you see the deck's blown out of her?' I found my voice, and stammered out as if conscious of some gross neglect of duty, 'I don't know where the cabin-table is.' It was like an absurd dream.

"Do you know what he wanted next? Well, he wanted to trim the yards. Very placidly, and as if lost in thought, he insisted on having the foreyard squared. 'I don't know if there's anybody alive,' said Mahon, almost tearfully. 'Surely,' he said gently, 'there will be enough left to square the foreyard.'

"The old chap, it seems, was in his own berth winding up the chronometers, when the shock sent him spinning. Immediately it occurred to him—as he said afterwards—that the ship had struck something, and he ran out into the cabin. There, he saw, the cabin-table had vanished somewhere. The deck being blown up, it had fallen down into the lazarette of course. Where we had our breakfast that morning he saw only a great hole in the floor. This appeared to him so awfully mysterious, and impressed him so immensely, that what he saw and heard after he got on deck were mere trifles in comparison. And, mark, he noticed directly the wheel deserted and his barque off her course—and his only thought was to get that miserable, stripped, undecked, smouldering shell of a ship back again with her head pointing at her port of destination. Bangkok! That's what he was after. I tell you this quiet, bowed, bandy-legged, almost deformed little man was immense in the singleness of his idea and in his placid ignorance of our agitation. He motioned us forward with a commanding gesture, and went to take the wheel himself.

"Yes; that was the first thing we did—trim the yards of that wreck! No one was killed, or even disabled, but everyone was more or less hurt. You should have seen them! Some were in rags, with black faces, like coal-heavers, like sweeps, and had bullet heads that seemed closely cropped, but were in fact singed to the skin. Others, of the watch below, awakened by being shot out from their collapsing bunks, shivered incessantly, and kept on groaning even as we went about our

work. But they all worked. That crew of Liverpool hard cases had in
them the right stuff. It's my experience they always have. It is the
sea that gives it—the vastness, the loneliness surrounding their dark
stolid souls. Ah! Well! we stumbled, we crept, we fell, we barked
our shins on the wreckage, we hauled. The masts stood, but we did not
know how much they might be charred down below. It was nearly
calm, but a long swell ran from the west and made her roll. They
might go at any moment. We looked at them with apprehension. One
could not foresee which way they would fall.

"Then we retreated aft and looked about us. The deck was a tangle
of planks on edge, of planks on end, of splinters, of ruined woodwork.
The masts rose from that chaos like big trees above a matted undergrowth. The interstices of that mass of wreckage were full of something whitish, sluggish, stirring—of something that was like a greasy
fog. The smoke of the invisible fire was coming up again, was trailing,
like a poisonous thick mist in some valley choked with dead wood.
Already lazy wisps were beginning to curl upwards amongst the mass
of splinters. Here and there a piece of timber, stuck upright, resembled
a post. Half of a fife-rail had been shot through the foresail, and the
sky made a patch of glorious blue in the ignobly soiled canvas. A portion of several boards holding together had fallen across the rail, and
one end protruded overboard, like a gangway leading upon nothing,
like a gangway leading over the deep sea, leading to death—as if invit-
ing us to walk the plank at once and be done with our ridiculous
troubles. And still the air, the sky—a ghost, something invisible was
hailing the ship.

"Some one had the sense to look over, and there was the helmsman,
who had impulsively jumped overboard, anxious to come back. He
yelled and swam lustily like a merman, keeping up with the ship. We
threw him a rope, and presently he stood amongst us streaming with
water and very crestfallen. The captain had surrendered the wheel,
and apart, elbow on rail and chin in hand, gazed at the sea wistfully.
We asked ourselves, What next? I thought, Now, this is something like.
This is great. I wonder what will happen. O youth!

"Suddenly Mahon sighted a steamer far astern. Captain Beard said,
'We may do something with her yet.' We hoisted two flags, which said
in the international language of the sea, 'On fire. Want immediate
assistance.' The steamer grew bigger rapidly, and by and by spoke
with two flags on her foremast, 'I am coming to your assistance.'

"In half an hour she was abreast, to windward, within hail, and rolling slightly, with her engines stopped. We lost our composure, and

yelled all together with excitement, 'We've been blown up.' A man in a white helmet, on the bridge, cried, 'Yes! All right! all right!' and he nodded his head, and smiled, and made soothing motions with his hand as though at a lot of frightened children. One of the boats dropped in the water, and walked towards us upon the sea with her long oars. Four Calashes pulled a swinging stroke. This was my first sight of Malay seamen. I've known them since, but what struck me then was their unconcern; they came alongside, and even the bowman standing up and holding to our main-chains with the boat-hook did not deign to lift his head for a glance. I thought people who had been blown up deserved more attention.

"A little man, dry like a chip and agile like a monkey, clambered up. It was the mate of the steamer. He gave one look, and cried, 'O boys— you had better quit.'

"We were silent. He talked apart with the captain for a time— seemed to argue with him. Then they went away together to the steamer.

"When our skipper came back we learned that the steamer was the *Somerville*, Captain Nash, from West Australia to Singapore *via* Batavia with mails, and that the agreement was she should tow us to Anjer or Batavia, if possible, where we could extinguish the fire by scuttling, and then proceed on our voyage—to Bangkok! The old man seemed excited. 'We will do it yet,' he said to Mahon fiercely. He shook his fist at the sky. Nobody else said a word.

"At noon the steamer began to tow. She went ahead slim and high, and what was left of the *Judea* followed at the end of seventy fathom of tow-rope—followed her swiftly like a cloud of smoke with mast-heads protruding above. We went aloft to furl the sails. We coughed on the yards, and were careful about the bunts. Do you see the lot of us there, putting a neat furl on the sails of that ship doomed to arrive nowhere? There was not a man who didn't think that at any moment the masts would topple over. From aloft we could not see the ship for smoke, and they worked carefully, passing the gaskets with even turns. 'Harbour furl—aloft there!' cried Mahon from below.

"You understand this? I don't think one of those chaps expected to get down in the usual way. When we did I heard them saying to each other, 'Well, I thought we would come down overboard, in a lump— sticks and all—blame me if I didn't.' 'That's what I was thinking to myself,' would answer wearily another battered and bandaged scarecrow. And, mind, these were men without the drilled-in habit of obedience. To an onlooker they would be a lot of profane scallawags without a redeeming point. What made them do it—what made them obey me when I, thinking consciously how fine it was, made them drop the bunt of the foresail twice to try and do it better? What? They had no professional reputation—no examples, no praise. It wasn't a sense of duty; they all knew well enough how to shirk and laze and dodge—when they had a mind to it—and mostly they had. Was it the two pounds ten a-month that sent them there? They didn't think their pay half good enough. No; it was something in them, something inborn and subtle and everlasting. I don't say positively that the crew of a French or German merchantman wouldn't have done it, but I doubt whether it would have been done in the same way. There was a completeness in it, something solid like a principle, and masterful like an instinct—a disclosure of something secret—of that hidden something, that gift of good or evil that makes racial difference, that shapes the fate of nations.

"It was that night at ten that, for the first time since we had been fighting it, we saw the fire. The speed of the towing had fanned the smouldering destruction. A blue gleam appeared forward, shining below the wreck of the deck. It wavered in patches, it seemed to stir and creep like the light of a glowworm. I saw it first, and told Mahon. 'Then the game's up,' he said. 'We had better stop this towing, or she will burst out suddenly fore and aft before we can clear out.' We set up a yell; rang bells to attract their attention; they towed on. At last Mahon and I had to crawl forward and cut the rope with an axe. There was no time to cast off the lashings. Red tongues could be seen licking the wilderness of splinters under our feet as we made our way back to the poop.

"Of course they very soon found out in the steamer that the rope was gone. She gave a loud blast of her whistle, her lights were seen sweeping in a wide circle, she came up ranging close alongside, and stopped. We were all in a tight group on the poop looking at her. Every man had saved a little bundle or a bag. Suddenly a conical flame with a twisted top shot up forward and threw upon the black sea a circle of light, with the two vessels side by side and heaving gently in its centre. Captain Beard had been sitting on the gratings still and mute for hours, but now he rose slowly and advanced in front of us, to the mizzen-shrouds. Captain Nash hailed: 'Come along! Look sharp. I have mail-bags on board. I will take you and your boats to Singapore.'

"'Thank you! No!' said our skipper. 'We must see the last of the ship.'

" 'I can't stand by any longer,' shouted the other. 'Mails—you know.'

" 'Ay! ay! We are all right.'

" 'Very well! I'll report you in Singapore. . . . Good-bye!'

"He waved his hand. Our men dropped their bundles quietly. The steamer moved ahead, and passing out of the circle of light, vanished at once from our sight, dazzled by the fire which burned fiercely. And then I knew that I would see the East first as commander of a small boat. I thought it fine; and the fidelity to the old ship was fine. We should see the last of her. Oh, the glamour of youth! Oh, the fire of it, more dazzling than the flames of the burning ship, throwing a magic light on the wide earth, leaping audaciously to the sky, presently to be quenched by time, more cruel, more pitiless, more bitter than the sea —and like the flames of the burning ship surrounded by an impenetrable night.

"The old man warned us in his gentle and inflexible way that it was part of our duty to save for the underwriters as much as we could of the ship's gear. Accordingly we went to work aft, while she blazed forward to give us plenty of light. We lugged out a lot of rubbish. What didn't we save? An old barometer fixed with an absurd quantity of screws nearly cost me my life: a sudden rush of smoke came upon me, and I just got away in time. There were various stores, bolts of canvas, coils of rope; the poop looked like a marine bazaar, and the boats were lumbered to the gunwales. One would have thought the old man wanted to take as much as he could of his first command with him. He was very, very quiet, but off his balance evidently. Would you believe it? He wanted to take a length of old stream-cable and a kedge-anchor with him in the long-boat. We said, 'Ay, ay, sir,' deferentially, and on the quiet let the things slip overboard. The heavy medicine-chest went that way, two bags of green coffee, tins of paint— fancy, paint!—a whole lot of things. Then I was ordered with two hands into the boats to make a stowage and get them ready against the time it would be proper for us to leave the ship.

"We put everything straight, stepped the long-boat's mast for our skipper, who was to take charge of her, and I was not sorry to sit down for a moment. My face felt raw, every limb ached as if broken, I was aware of all my ribs, and would have sworn to a twist in the backbone. The boats, fast astern, lay in a deep shadow, and all around I could see the circle of the sea lighted by the fire. A gigantic flame arose forward straight and clear. It flared fierce, with noises like the whirr of wings, with rumbles as of thunder. There were cracks, detonations, and from the cone of flame the sparks flew upwards, as man is born to trouble, to leaky ships, and to ships that burn.

"What bothered me was that the ship, lying broadside to the swell and to such wind as there was—a mere breath—the boats would not keep astern where they were safe, but persisted, in a pig-headed way boats have, in getting under the counter and then swinging alongside. They were knocking about dangerously and coming near the flame, while the ship rolled on them, and, of course, there was always the danger of the masts going over the side at any moment. I and my two boat-keepers kept them off as best we could, with oars and boat-hooks; but to be constantly at it became exasperating, since there was no reason why we should not leave at once. We could not see those on board, nor could we imagine what caused the delay. The boat-keepers were swearing feebly, and I had not only my share of the work but also had to keep at it two men who showed a constant inclination to lay themselves down and let things slide.

"At last I hailed, 'On deck there,' and some one looked over. 'We're ready here,' I said. The head disappeared, and very soon popped up again. 'The captain says, All right, sir, and to keep the boats well clear of the ship.'

"Half an hour passed. Suddenly there was a frightful racket, rattle, clanking of chain, hiss of water, and millions of sparks flew up into the shivering column of smoke that stood leaning slightly above the ship. The cat-heads had burned away, and the two red-hot anchors had gone to the bottom, tearing out after them two hundred fathom of red-hot chain. The ship trembled, the mass of flame swayed as if ready to collapse, and the fore top-gallant-mast fell. It darted down like an arrow of fire, shot under, and instantly leaping up within an oar's-length of the boats, floated quietly, very black on the luminous sea. I hailed the deck again. After some time a man in an unexpectedly cheerful but also muffled tone, as though he had been trying to speak with his mouth shut, informed me, 'Coming directly, sir,' and vanished. For a long time I heard nothing but the whirr and roar of the fire. There were also whistling sounds. The boats jumped, tugged at the painters, ran at each other playfully, knocked their sides together, or, do what we would, swung in a bunch against the ship's side. I couldn't stand it any longer, and swarming up a rope, clambered aboard over the stern.

"It was as bright as day. Coming up like this, the sheet of fire facing me was a terrifying sight, and the heat seemed hardly bearable at first. On a settee cushion dragged out of the cabin Captain Beard, his legs

drawn up and one arm under his head, slept with the light playing on
him.   Do you know what the rest were busy about?   They were sitting
on deck right aft, round an open case, eating bread and cheese and
drinking bottled stout.

"On the background of flames twisting in fierce tongues above their
heads they seemed at home like salamanders, and looked like a band of
desperate pirates.   The fire sparkled in the whites of their eyes,
gleamed on patches of white skin seen through the torn shirts.   Each
had the marks as of a battle about him—bandaged heads, tied-up arms,
a strip of dirty rag round a knee—and each man had a bottle between
his legs and a chunk of cheese in his hand.   Mahon got up.   With his
handsome and disreputable head, his hooked profile, his long white
beard, and with an uncorked bottle in his hand, he resembled one of
those reckless sea-robbers of old making merry amidst violence and
disaster.   'The last meal on board,' he explained solemnly.   'We had
nothing to eat all day, and it was no use leaving all this.'   He flourished
the bottle and indicated the sleeping skipper.   'He said he couldn't
swallow anything, so I got him to lie down,' he went on; and as I
stared, 'I don't know whether you are aware, young fellow, the man had
no sleep to speak of for days—and there will be dam' little sleep in the
boats.'   'There will be no boats by and by if you fool about much
longer,' I said indignantly.   I walked up to the skipper and shook him
by the shoulder.   At last he opened his eyes, but did not move.   'Time
to leave her, sir,' I said quietly.

"He got up painfully, looked at the flames, at the sea sparkling round
the ship, and black, black as ink farther away; he looked at the stars
shining dim through a thin veil of smoke in a sky black, black as
Erebus.

" 'Youngest first,' he said.

"And the ordinary seaman, wiping his mouth with the back of his
hand, got up, clambered over the taffrail, and vanished.   Others followed.   One, on the point of going over, stopped short to drain his
bottle, and with a great swing of his arm flung it at the fire.   'Take
this!' he cried.

"The skipper lingered disconsolately, and we left him to commune
alone for a while with his first command.   Then I went up again and
brought him away at last.   It was time.   The ironwork on the poop was
hot to the touch.

"Then the painter of the long-boat was cut, and the three boats, tied
together, drifted clear of the ship.   It was just sixteen hours after the
explosion when we abandoned her.   Mahon had charge of the second

boat, and I had the smallest—the 14-foot thing. The long-boat would have taken the lot of us; but the skipper said we must save as much property as we could—for the underwriters—and so I got my first command. I had two men with me, a bag of biscuits, a few tins of meat, and a breaker of water. I was ordered to keep close to the long-boat, that in case of bad weather we might be taken into her.

"And do you know what I thought? I thought I would part company as soon as I could. I wanted to have my first command all to myself. I wasn't going to sail in a squadron if there were a chance for independent cruising. I would make land by myself. I would beat the other boats. Youth! All youth! The silly, charming, beautiful youth.

"But we did not make a start at once. We must see the last of the ship. And so the boats drifted about that night, heaving and setting on the swell. The men dozed, waked, sighed, groaned. I looked at the burning ship.

"Between the darkness of earth and heaven she was burning fiercely upon a disc of purple sea shot by the blood-red play of gleams; upon a disc of water glittering and sinister. A high, clear flame, an immense and lonely flame, ascended from the ocean, and from its summit the black smoke poured continuously at the sky. She burned furiously; mournful and imposing like a funeral pile kindled in the night, surrounded by the sea, watched over by the stars. A magnificent death had come like a grace, like a gift, like a reward to that old ship at the end of her laborious days. The surrender of her weary ghost to the keeping of stars and sea was stirring like the sight of a glorious triumph. The masts fell just before daybreak, and for a moment there was a burst and turmoil of sparks that seemed to fill with flying fire the night patient and watchful, the vast night lying silent upon the sea. At daylight she was only a charred shell, floating still under a cloud of smoke and bearing a glowing mass of coal within.

"Then the oars were got out, and the boats forming in a line moved round her remains as if in procession—the long-boat leading. As we pulled across her stern a slim dart of fire shot out viciously at us, and suddenly she went down, head first, in a great hiss of steam. The unconsumed stern was the last to sink; but the paint had gone, had cracked, had peeled off, and there were no letters, there was no word, no stubborn device that was like her soul, to flash at the rising sun her creed and her name.

"We made our way north. A breeze sprang up, and about noon all the boats came together for the last time. I had no mast or sail in mine, but I made a mast out of a spare oar and hoisted a boat-awning for a

sail, with a boat-hook for a yard. She was certainly over-masted, but I
had the satisfaction of knowing that with the wind aft I could beat the
other two. I had to wait for them. Then we all had a look at the
captain's chart, and, after a sociable meal of hard bread and water, got
our last instructions. These were simple: steer north, and keep together as much as possible. 'Be careful with that jury-rig, Marlow,'
said the captain; and Mahon, as I sailed proudly past his boat, wrinkled
his curved nose and hailed, 'You will sail that ship of yours under water
if you don't look out, young fellow.' He was a malicious old man—and
may the deep sea where he sleeps now rock him gently, rock him
tenderly to the end of time!

"Before sunset a thick rain-squall passed over the two boats, which
were far astern, and that was the last I saw of them for a time. Next
day I sat steering my cockle-shell—my first command—with nothing but
water and sky around me. I did sight in the afternoon the upper sails
of a ship far away, but said nothing, and my men did not notice her.
You see I was afraid she might be homeward bound, and I had no mind
to turn back from the portals of the East. I was steering for Java—another blessed name—like Bangkok, you know. I steered many days.

"I need not tell you what it is to be knocking about in an open boat.
I remember nights and days of calm, when we pulled, we pulled, and
the boat seemed to stand still, as if bewitched within the circle of the
sea horizon. I remember the heat, the deluge of rain-squalls that kept
us baling for dear life (but filled our water-cask), and I remember sixteen hours on end with a mouth dry as a cinder and a steering-oar over
the stern to keep my first command head on to a breaking sea. I did
not know how good a man I was till then. I remember the drawn
faces, the dejected figures of my two men, and I remember my youth
and the feeling that will never come back any more—the feeling that I
could last for ever, outlast the sea, the earth, and all men; the deceitful
feeling that lures us on to joys, to perils, to love, to vain effort—to death;
the triumphant conviction of strength, the heat of life in the handful of
dust, the glow in the heart that with every year grows dim, grows cold,
grows small, and expires—and expires, too soon, too soon—before life
itself.

"And this is how I see the East. I have seen its secret places and
have looked into its very soul; but now I see it always from a small
boat, a high outline of mountains, blue and afar in the morning; like
faint mist at noon; a jagged wall of purple at sunset. I have the feel of
the oar in my hand, the vision of a scorching blue sea in my eyes. And
I see a bay, a wide bay, smooth as glass and polished like ice, shim-

mering in the dark. A red light burns far off upon the gloom of the land, and the night is soft and warm. We drag at the oars with aching arms, and suddenly a puff of wind, a puff faint and tepid and laden with strange odours of blossoms, of aromatic wood, comes out of the still night—the first sigh of the East on my face. That I can never forget. It was impalpable and enslaving, like a charm, like a whispered promise of mysterious delight.

"We had been pulling this finishing spell for eleven hours. Two pulled, and he whose turn it was to rest sat at the tiller. We had made out the red light in that bay and steered for it, guessing it must mark some small coasting port. We passed two vessels, outlandish and high-sterned, sleeping at anchor, and, approaching the light, now very dim, ran the boat's nose against the end of a jutting wharf. We were blind with fatigue. My men dropped the oars and fell off the thwarts as if dead. I made fast to a pile. A current rippled softly. The scented obscurity of the shore was grouped into vast masses, a density of colossal clumps of vegetation, probably—mute and fantastic shapes. And at their foot the semicircle of a beach gleamed faintly, like an illusion. There was not a light, not a stir, not a sound. The mysterious East faced me, perfumed like a flower, silent like death, dark like a grave.

"And I sat weary beyond expression, exulting like a conqueror, sleepless and entranced as if before a profound, a fateful enigma.

"A splashing of oars, a measured dip reverberating on the level of water, intensified by the silence of the shore into loud claps, made me jump up. A boat, a European boat, was coming in. I invoked the name of the dead; I hailed *Judea,* ahoy! A thin shout answered.

"It was the captain. I had beaten the flagship by three hours, and I was glad to hear the old man's voice again, tremulous and tired. 'Is it you, Marlow?' 'Mind the end of that jetty, sir,' I cried.

"He approached cautiously, and brought up with the deep-sea lead-line which we had saved—for the underwriters. I eased my painter and fell alongside. He sat, a broken figure at the stern, wet with dew, his hands clasped in his lap. His men were asleep already. 'I had a terrible time of it,' he murmured. 'Mahon is behind—not very far.' We conversed in whispers, in low whispers, as if afraid to wake up the land. Guns, thunder, earthquakes would not have awakened the men just then.

"Looking round as we talked, I saw away at sea a bright light travelling in the night. 'There's a steamer passing the bay,' I said. She was not passing, she was entering, and she even came close and anchored.

YOUTH: A NARRATIVE

'I wish,' said the old man, 'you would find out whether she is English. Perhaps they could give us a passage somewhere.' He seemed nervously anxious. So by dint of punching and kicking I started one of my men into a state of somnambulism, and giving him an oar, took another and pulled towards the lights of the steamer.

"There was a murmur of voices in her, metallic hollow clangs of the engine-room, footsteps on the deck. Her ports shone, round like dilated eyes. Shapes moved about, and there was a shadowy man high up on the bridge. He heard my oars.

"And then, before I could open my lips, the East spoke to me, but it was in a Western voice. A torrent of words was poured into the enigmatical, the fateful silence; outlandish, angry words, mixed with words and even whole sentences of good English, less strange but even more surprising. The voice swore and cursed violently; it riddled the solemn peace of the bay by a volley of abuse. It began by calling me Pig, and from that went crescendo into unmentionable adjectives—in English. The man up there raged aloud in two languages, and with a sincerity in his fury that almost convinced me I had, in some way, sinned against the harmony of the universe. I could hardly see him, but began to think he would work himself into a fit.

"Suddenly he ceased, and I could hear him snorting and blowing like a porpoise. I said:

" 'What steamer is this, pray?'

" 'Eh? What's this? And who are you?'

" 'Castaway crew of an English barque burnt at sea. We came here to-night. I am the second mate. The captain is in the long-boat and wishes to know if you would give us a passage somewhere.'

" 'Oh, my goodness! I say. . . . This is the *Celestial* from Singapore on her return trip. I'll arrange with your captain in the morning, . . . and, . . . I say, . . . did you hear me just now?'

" 'I should think the whole bay heard you.'

" 'I thought you were a shore-boat. Now, look here—this infernal lazy scoundrel of a caretaker has gone to sleep again—curse him. The light is out, and I nearly ran foul of the end of this damned jetty. This is the third time he plays me this trick. Now, I ask you, can anybody stand this kind of thing? It's enough to drive a man out of his mind. I'll report him. . . . I'll get the Assistant Resident to give him the sack, by . . . ! See—there's no light. It's out, isn't it? I take you to witness the light's out. There should be a light, you know. A red light on the——'

" 'There was a light,' I said mildly.

" 'But it's out, man! What's the use of talking like this? You can see for yourself it's out—don't you? If you had to take a valuable steamer along this God-forsaken coast you would want a light, too. I'll kick him from end to end of his miserable wharf. You'll see if I don't. I will——'

" 'So I may tell my captain you'll take us?' I broke in.

" 'Yes, I'll take you. Good-night,' he said brusquely.

"I pulled back, made fast again to the jetty, and then went to sleep at last. I had faced the silence of the East. I had heard some of its language. But when I opened my eyes again the silence was as complete as though it had never been broken. I was lying in a flood of light, and the sky had never looked so far, so high, before. I opened my eyes and lay without moving.

"And then I saw the men of the East—they were looking at me. The whole length of the jetty was full of people. I saw brown, bronze, yellow faces, the black eyes, the glitter, the colour of an Eastern crowd. And all these beings stared without a murmur, without a sigh, without a movement. They stared down at the boats, at the sleeping men who at night had come to them from the sea. Nothing moved. The fronds of palms stood still against the sky. Not a branch stirred along the shore, and the brown roofs of hidden houses peeped through the green foliage, through the big leaves that hung shining and still like leaves forged of heavy metal. This was the East of the ancient navigators, so old, so mysterious, resplendent and sombre, living and unchanged, full of danger and promise. And these were the men. I sat up suddenly. A wave of movement passed through the crowd from end to end, passed along the heads, swayed the bodies, ran along the jetty like a ripple on the water, like a breath of wind on a field—and all was still again. I see it now—the wide sweep of the bay, the glittering sands, the wealth of green infinite and varied, the sea blue like the sea of a dream, the crowd of attentive faces, the blaze of vivid colour—the water reflecting it all, the curve of the shore, the jetty, the high-sterned outlandish craft floating still, and the three boats with the tired men from the West sleeping, unconscious of the land and the people and of the violence of sunshine. They slept thrown across the thwarts, curled on bottom-boards, in the careless attitudes of death. The head of the old skipper, leaning back in the stern of the long-boat, had fallen on his breast, and he looked as though he would never wake. Farther out old Mahon's face was upturned to the sky, with the long white beard spread out on his breast, as though he had been shot where he sat at the tiller; and a man, all in a heap in the bows of the boat, slept with both arms embracing the stem-head and with his cheek laid on the gunwale. The East looked at them without a sound.

"I have known its fascination since; I have seen the mysterious shores, the still water, the lands of brown nations, where a stealthy Nemesis lies in wait, pursues, overtakes so many of the conquering race, who are proud of their wisdom, of their knowledge, of their strength. But for me all the East is contained in that vision of my youth. It is all in that moment when I opened my young eyes on it. I came upon it from a tussle with the sea—and I was young—and I saw it looking at me. And this is all that is left of it! Only a moment; a moment of strength, of romance, of glamour—of youth! . . . A flick of sunshine upon a strange shore, the time to remember, the time for a sigh, and—good-bye! Night—Good-bye . . . !"

He drank.

"Ah! The good old time—the good old time. Youth and the sea. Glamour and the sea! The good, strong sea, the salt, bitter sea, that could whisper to you and roar at you and knock your breath out of you."

He drank again.

"By all that's wonderful it is the sea, I believe, the sea itself—or is it youth alone? Who can tell? But you here—you all had something out of life: money, love—whatever one gets on shore—and, tell me, wasn't that the best time, that time when we were young at sea; young and had nothing, on the sea that gives nothing, except hard knocks—and sometimes a chance to feel your strength—that only—what you all regret?"

And we all nodded at him: the man of finance, the man of accounts, the man of law, we all nodded at him over the polished table that like a still sheet of brown water reflected our faces, lined, wrinkled; our faces marked by toil, by deceptions, by success, by love; our weary eyes looking still, looking always, looking anxiously for something out of life, that while it is expected is already gone—has passed unseen, in a sigh, in a flash—together with the youth, with the strength, with the romance of illusions.

Commentary

This story is about the strength and romance of youth as remembered in age. The vivid action is narrated not as experienced but as vividly recalled, because the perceptions of youth are so sharp as to have impressed themselves firmly upon the memory. Conrad insistently makes his point that youth is resilient and exuberant. Youth is perceptive, courageous, and vigorous, but to the aged, youth is also uninitiated and romantically full of illusions. Yet the attitude of disenchanted age toward energetic youth is ironically wistful: ". . .wasn't that the best time, that time when we were young at sea; young and had nothing, on the sea that gives nothing, except hard knocks—and sometimes a chance to feel your strength . . . ?"

This contrast between youth and age is demonstrated by the narrator, Marlow, a character that is Conrad's favorite device for achieving first-person objectivity without losing the intimacy of a firsthand account (see p. 31). Marlow tells his story to four old seamen, like himself now landlocked meditators. But the Marlow of the narration is not the same Marlow as the narrator, for twenty-two years have intervened between the action and its telling.

The reminiscence is of the young Marlow's first voyage to the East, when he was twenty, a voyage "that might stand for a symbol of existence." The youthful Marlow in his first vision of the inscrutable East did not know what the mature Marlow knows now: that the mystery of the East, "perfumed like a flower, silent like death, dark like a grave," is beautiful and somber like life, which cannot last. ". . . youth, strength, genius, thoughts, achievements, simple hearts—all die . . . No matter."

The older Marlow captures the spirit of the young sailor: "I joined [the *Judea's* crew]. . . . It was one of the happiest days of my life." Yet in the next breath he makes fun of his earlier self: "Fancy! Second mate for the first time—a really responsible officer."

Again, the narrator captures the zest of his youth and then deflates it: "He [the North Sea pilot] mistrusted my youth, my common-sense, and my seamanship. . . ." followed by "I dare say he was right. It seems to me I knew very little then. . . ."

After the first storm that the *Judea* endured on the voyage, Marlow recalls: "And there was somewhere in me the thought: By Jove! this is the deuce of an adventure—something you read about; and it is my first voyage as second mate—and I am only twenty—and here I am lasting it out as well as any of these men, and keeping my chaps up to the mark." This expression of pride is in turn deflated by the older Marlow's apostrophe: "O youth! The strength of it . . . the imagination of it!" And after the first sign that the *Judea* was ill-fated, the young Marlow feels: "And then I knew that I would see the East first as commander of a small boat. I thought it fine. . . ." But the reminiscent Marlow comments in a rueful metaphor:

Oh, the glamour of youth! Oh, the fire of it, more dazzling than the flames of the burning ship, throwing a magic light on the wide earth, leaping audaciously to the sky, presently to be quenched by time, more cruel, more pitiless, more bitter than the sea—and like the flames [youth] of the burning ship [life] surrounded by an impenetrable night [ignorance, death].

Besides this employment of point of view to achieve the contrast between youth and age, Conrad uses imagery to make vivid the remembered action of the voyage. Of the night before the *Judea* was to set sail, the sense impressions convey an atmosphere of vital expectancy: the high water blows "fresh with a drizzle," and there is a "great plashing of propellers, rattling of winches." The young Marlow watches "head-lights gliding high" and "green lights gliding low." "A bell jingled." "Steam roared." "A bell jingled." With forceful parallelism and repetition, Conrad frames his images.

During a North Sea gale, later in the narrative, the wind

blew with spite, without interval, without mercy, without rest. The world was nothing but an immensity of great foaming waves rushing at us, under a sky low enough to touch with the hand and dirty like a smoked ceiling.

Meanwhile, the *Judea* "tossed, she pitched, she stood on her head, she stood on her tail, she rolled, she groaned," and the sea was white like "a cauldron of boiling milk; there was not a break in the clouds, no—not the size of a man's hand—no, not so much as ten seconds."

Before the fire, when the cargo was smouldering, the image of the smoke is rendered through olfactory, visual, and tactile sense impressions:

The smoke kept coming out . . . it oozed here and there and everywhere in slender threads, in an invisible film. . . . Enormous volumes of smoke, whitish, yellowish, thick, greasy, misty, choking, ascended as high as the trucks. . . . Then the poisonous cloud blew away, and we went back to work in a smoke that was no thicker than that of an ordinary factory chimney.

Further to heighten the action, the narrator uses irony (see p. 42) in his description: "It was our fate to pump in that ship, to pump out of her, to pump into her; and after keeping water out of her to save ourselves from being drowned, we frantically poured water into her to save ourselves from being burnt."

To describe the contrasting calm of the weather about the smouldering *Judea*, he uses metaphor:

The sky was a miracle of purity, a miracle of azure. The sea was polished, was blue, was pellucid, was sparkling like a precious stone, extending on all sides, all round to the horizon—as if the whole terrestrial globe had been one jewel, one colossal sapphire, a single gem fashioned into a planet.

Through imagery, figurative language, dialogue of short words and phrases, and a minimum of dependent clauses to impede the movement of his prose, Conrad achieves an energizing undercurrent of the vigor of action and of youth.

Questions

1. How is the fate of the *Judea* foreshadowed? When were you first aware of the impending disaster? What was the second clue?
2. What does the young Marlow's statement after the explosion reveal about his character: "I had just blown up, you understand, and vibrated with that experience" and his later thought when he is impressed by the apparent unconcern of the Malay seaman, "I thought people who had been blown up deserved more attention"?
3. What does the narrator's description of young Marlow's feeling regarding his "first command" in the cockle-shell reveal about the character of young Marlow? What does the description reveal about the older Marlow? What does it, therefore, contribute to the illumination of theme? Why does the young Marlow also make no comment to "my men" when he sees the upper sails of a ship far away?
4. Why is the narrative interrupted from time to time by the refrain "Pass the bottle" and "He drank," "He drank again"? At what point do these asides usually occur?
5. What does the author accomplish by the imagery of the fire after the explosion of the *Judea* and of the afterglow following the sinking?
6. What is the symbolism of the sea, the ship, darkness, light, and the East? (See p. 40.)

The Father

Björnstjerne Björnson

The man whose story is here to be told was the wealthiest and most influential person in his parish; his name was Thord Overaas. He appeared in the priest's study one day, tall and earnest.

"I have gotten a son," said he, "and I wish to present him for baptism."

"What shall his name be?"

"Finn—after my father."

"And the sponsors?"

They were mentioned, and proved to be the best men and women of Thord's relations in the parish.

"Is there anything else?" inquired the priest, and looked up.

The peasant hesitated a little.

"I should like very much to have him baptized by himself," said he, finally.

"That is to say on a weekday?"

"Next Saturday, at twelve o'clock, noon."

"Is there anything else?" inquired the priest.

"There is nothing else;" and the peasant twirled his cap, as though he were about to go.

Then the priest rose. "There is yet this, however," said he, and walking toward Thord, he took him by the hand and looked gravely into his eyes: "God grant that the child may become a blessing to you!"

One day sixteen years later, Thord stood once more in the priest's study.

"Really, you carry your age astonishingly well, Thord," said the priest; for he saw no change whatever in the man.

"That is because I have no troubles," replied Thord.

To this the priest said nothing, but after a while he asked: "What is your pleasure this evening?"

"I have come this evening about that son of mine who is to be confirmed tomorrow."

"He is a bright boy."

"I did not wish to pay the priest until I heard what number the boy would have when he takes his place in church tomorrow."

"He will stand number one."

"So I have heard; and here are ten dollars for the priest."

"Is there anything else I can do for you?" inquired the priest, fixing his eyes on Thord.

"There is nothing else."

Thord went out.

Eight years more rolled by, and then one day a noise was heard outside of the priest's study, for many men were approaching, and at their head was Thord, who entered first.

The priest looked up and recognized him.

"You come well attended this evening, Thord," said he.

"I am here to request that the bans may be published for my son; he is about to marry Karen Storliden, daughter of Gudmund, who stands here beside me."

"Why, that is the richest girl in the parish."

"So they say," replied the peasant, stroking back his hair with one hand.

The priest sat a while as if in deep thought, then entered the names in his book, without making any comments, and the men wrote their signatures underneath. Thord laid three dollars on the table.

"One is all I am to have," said the priest.

"I know that very well; but he is my only child, I want to do it handsomely."

The priest took the money.

"This is now the third time, Thord, that you have come here on your son's account."

"But now I am through with him," said Thord, and folding up his pocketbook, he said farewell and walked away.

The men slowly followed him.

A fortnight later, the father and son were rowing across the lake, one calm, still day, to Storliden to make arrangements for the wedding.

"This thwart is not secure," said the son, and stood up to straighten the seat on which he was sitting.

At the same moment the board he was standing on slipped from under him; he threw out his arms, uttered a shriek, and fell overboard.

"Take hold of the oar!" shouted the father, springing to his feet and holding out the oar.

But when the son had made a couple of efforts he grew stiff.

"Wait a moment!" cried the father, and began to row toward his son. Then the son rolled over on his back, gave his father one long look, and sank.

Thord could scarcely believe it; he held the boat still, and stared at the spot where his son had gone down, as though he must surely come to the surface again. There rose some bubbles, then some more, and finally one large one that burst; and the lake lay there as smooth and bright as a mirror again.

For three days and three nights people saw the father rowing round and round the spot, without taking either food or sleep; he was dragging the lake for the body of his son. And toward morning of the third day he found it, and carried it in his arms up over the hills to his farm.

It might have been about a year from that day, when the priest, late one autumn evening, heard someone in the passage outside of the door, carefully trying to find the latch. The priest opened the door, and in walked a tall, thin man, with bowed form and white hair. The priest looked long at him before he recognized him. It was Thord.

"Are you out walking so late?" said the priest, and stood still in front of him.

"Ah, yes! It is late," said Thord, and took a seat.

The priest sat down also, as though waiting. A long, long silence followed. At last Thord said:

"I have something with me that I should like to give to the poor; I want it to be invested as a legacy in my son's name."

He rose, laid some money on the table, and sat down again. The priest counted it.

"It is a great deal of money," said he.

"It is half the price of my farm. I sold it today."

The priest sat in silence. At last he asked, but gently:

"What do you propose to do now, Thord?"

"Something better."

They sat for a while, Thord with downcast eyes, the priest with his eyes fixed on Thord. Presently the priest said, slowly and softly:

"I think your son has at last brought you a true blessing."

"Yes, I think so myself," said Thord, looking up, while two big tears coursed slowly down his cheeks.

Questions

1. Read "The Father" once, keeping in mind the suggestions listed on page 21 in "The Art of Short Fiction."
2. Read "The Father" a second time with the attitudes listed on page 22; then answer the questions on pages 30, 39, and 43-44.
3. Compare and contrast this parable with the parable of "The Prodigal Son" in terms of universality and individuality.   (See p. 11.)

Pigeon Feathers

John Updike

When they moved to Firetown, things were upset, displaced, re-arranged. A red cane-back sofa that had been the chief piece in the living room at Olinger was here banished, too big for the narrow country parlor, to the barn, and shrouded under a tarpaulin. Never again would David lie on its length all afternoon eating raisins and reading mystery novels and science fiction and P. G. Wodehouse. The blue wing chair that had stood for years in the ghostly, immaculate guest bedroom, gazing through the windows curtained with dotted swiss toward the telephone wires and horse-chestnut trees and opposite houses, was here established importantly in front of the smutty little fireplace that supplied, in those first cold April days, their only heat. As a child, David had been afraid of the guest bedroom—it was there that he, lying sick with the measles, had seen a black rod the size of a yardstick jog along at a slight slant beside the edge of the bed and vanish when he screamed—and it was disquieting to have one of the elements of its haunted atmosphere basking by the fire, in the center of the family, growing sooty with use. The books that at home had gathered dust in the case beside the piano were here hastily stacked, all out of order, in the shelves that the carpenters had built along one wall below the deep-silled windows. David, at fourteen, had been more moved than a mover; like the furniture, he had to find a new place, and on the Saturday of the second week he tried to work off some of his disorientation by arranging the books.

It was a collection obscurely depressing to him, mostly books his mother had acquired when she was young: college anthologies of Greek plays and Romantic poetry, Will Durant's *Story of Philosophy*, a soft-leather set of Shakespeare with string bookmarks sewed to the bindings, *Green Mansions* boxed and illustrated with woodcuts, *I, the Tiger*, by Manuel Komroff, novels by names like Galsworthy and Ellen Glasgow and Irvin S. Cobb and Sinclair Lewis and "Elizabeth." The odor of faded taste made him feel the ominous gap between himself and his parents, the insulting gulf of time that existed before he was born. Suddenly he was tempted to dip into this time. From the heaps of books piled around him on the worn old floorboards, he picked up Volume II of a four-volume set of *The Outline of History,* by H. G. Wells. Once David had read *The Time Machine* in an anthology; this gave him a small grip on the author. The book's red binding had faded to orange-pink on the spine. When he lifted the cover, there was a sweetish, attic-like smell, and his mother's maiden name written in unfamiliar handwriting on the flyleaf—an upright, bold, yet careful signature, bearing a faint relation to the quick scrunched backslant that flowed with marvellous consistency across her shopping lists and budget accounts and Christmas cards to college friends from this same, vaguely menacing long ago.

He leafed through, pausing at drawings, done in an old-fashioned stippled style, of bas-reliefs, masks, Romans without pupils in their eyes, articles of ancient costume, fragments of pottery found in unearthed homes. He knew it would be interesting in a magazine, sandwiched between ads and jokes, but in this undiluted form history was somehow sour. The print was determinedly legible, and smug, like a lesson book. As he bent over the pages, yellow at the edges, they seemed rectangles of dusty glass through which he looked down into unreal and irrelevant worlds. He could see things sluggishly move, and an unpleasant fullness came into his throat. His mother and grandmother fussed in the kitchen; the puppy, which they had just acquired, for "protection in the country," was cowering, with a sporadic panicked scrabble of claws, under the dining table that in their old home had been reserved for special days but that here was used for every meal.

Then, before he could halt his eyes, David slipped into Wells's account of Jesus. He had been an obscure political agitator, a kind of hobo, in a minor colony of the Roman Empire. By an accident impossible to reconstruct, he (the small *h* horrified David) survived his own crucifixion and presumably died a few weeks later. A religion was founded on the freakish incident. The credulous imagination of the times retrospectively assigned miracles and supernatural pretensions to Jesus; a myth grew, and then a church, whose theology at most points was in direct contradiction of the simple, rather communistic teachings of the Galilean.

It was as if a stone that for weeks and even years had been gathering weight in the web of David's nerves snapped them and plunged through the page and a hundred layers of paper underneath. These fantastic falsehoods—plainly untrue; churches stood everywhere, the entire nation was founded "under God"—did not at first frighten him; it was the fact that they had been permitted to exist in an actual human brain. This was the initial impact—that at a definite spot in time and space a brain black with the denial of Christ's divinity had been suffered to exist; that the universe had not spit out this ball of tar but allowed it to continue in its blasphemy, to grow old, win honors, wear a hat, write books that, if true, collapsed everything into a jumble of horror. The world outside the deep-silled windows—a rutted lawn, a whitewashed barn, a walnut tree frothy with fresh green—seemed a haven from which he was forever sealed off. Hot washrags seemed pressed against his cheeks.

He read the account again. He tried to supply out of his ignorance objections that would defeat the complacent march of these black words, and found none. Survivals and misunderstandings more far-fetched were reported daily in the papers. But none of them caused churches to be built in every town. He tried to work backwards through the churches, from their brave high fronts through their shabby, ill-attended interiors back into the events at Jerusalem, and felt himself surrounded by shifting gray shadows, centuries of history, where he knew nothing. The thread dissolved in his hands. Had Christ ever come to him, David Kern, and said, "Here. Feel the wound in My side"? No; but prayers had been answered. What prayers? He had prayed that Rudy Mohn, whom he had purposely tripped so he cracked his head on their radiator, not die, and he had not died. But for all the blood, it was just a cut; Rudy came back the same day, wearing a bandage and repeating the same teasing words. He could never have died. Again, David had prayed for two separate war-effort posters he had sent away for to arrive tomorrow, and though they did not, they did arrive, some days later, together, popping through the clacking letter slot like a rebuke from God's mouth: *I answer your prayers in My way, in My time.* After that, he had made his prayers less definite, less susceptible of being twisted into a scolding. But what a tiny, ridiculous coincidence this was, after all, to throw into battle against H. G. Wells's engines of knowledge! Indeed, it proved the enemy's point: Hope bases vast premises on foolish accidents, and reads a word where in fact only a scribble exists.

His father came home. Though Saturday was a free day for him, he had been working. He taught school in Olinger and spent all his days performing, with a curious air of panic, needless errands. Also, a city boy by birth, he was frightened of the farm and seized any excuse to get away. The farm had been David's mother's birthplace; it had been her idea to buy it back. With an ingenuity and persistence unparalleled in her life, she had gained that end, and moved them all here—her son, her husband, her mother. Granmom, in her prime, had worked these fields alongside her husband, but now she dabbled around the kitchen futilely, her hands waggling with Parkinson's disease. She was always in the way. Strange, out in the country, amid eighty acres, they were crowded together. His father expressed his feelings of discomfort by conducting with Mother an endless argument about organic farming. All through dusk, all through supper, it rattled on.

"Elsie, I *know,* I know from my education, the earth is nothing but chemicals. It's the only damn thing I got out of four years of college, so don't tell me it's not true."

"George, if you'd just walk out on the farm you'd know it's not true. The land has a *soul.*"

"Soil, has, no, soul," he said, enunciating stiffly, as if to a very stupid class. To David he said, "You can't argue with a femme. Your mother's a real femme. That's why I married her, and now I'm suffering for it."

"*This* soil has no soul," she said, "because it's been killed with superphosphate. It's been burned bare by Boyer's tenant farmers." Boyer was the rich man they had bought the farm from. "It used to have a soul, didn't it, Mother? When you and Pop farmed it?"

"Ach, yes; I guess." Granmom was trying to bring a forkful of food to her mouth with her less severely afflicted hand. In her anxiety she brought the other hand up from her lap. The crippled fingers, dull red in the orange light of the kerosene lamp in the center of the table, were welded by paralysis into one knobbed hook.

"Only human indi-vidu-als have souls," his father went on, in the same mincing, lifeless voice. "Because the Bible tells us so." Done eating, he crossed his legs and dug into his ear with a match miserably; to get at the thing inside his head he tucked in his chin, and his voice came out low-pitched at David. "When God made your mother, He made a real femme."

"George, don't you read the papers? Don't you know that between the chemical fertilizers and the bug sprays we'll all be dead in ten years? Heart attacks are killing every man in the country over forty-five."

He sighed wearily; the yellow skin of his eyelids wrinkled as he hurt himself with the match. "There's no connection," he stated, spacing his words with pained patience, "between the heart—and chemical fertilizers. It's alcohol that's doing it. Alcohol and milk. There is too much—cholesterol—in the tissues of the American heart. Don't tell me about chemistry, Elsie; I majored in the damn stuff for four years."

"Yes and I majored in Greek and I'm not a penny wiser. Mother, put your waggler *away!*" The old woman started, and the food dropped from her fork. For some reason, the sight of her bad hand at the table cruelly irritated her daughter. Granmom's eyes, worn bits of crazed crystal embedded in watery milk, widened behind her cockeyed spectacles. Circles of silver as fine as thread, they clung to the red notches they had carved over the years into her little white beak. In the orange flicker of the kerosene lamp her dazed misery seemed infernal. David's mother began, without noise, to cry. His father did not seem to have eyes at all; just jaundiced sockets of wrinkled skin. The steam of food clouded the scene. It was horrible but the horror was particular and familiar, and distracted David from the formless dread that worked, sticky and sore, within him, like a too large wound trying to heal.

He had to go to the bathroom, and took a flashlight down through the wet grass to the outhouse. For once, his fear of spiders there felt trivial. He set the flashlight, burning, beside him, and an insect alighted on its lens, a tiny insect, a mosquito or flea, made so fine that the weak light projected its X-ray onto the wall boards: the faint rim of its wings, the blurred strokes, magnified, of its long hinged legs, the dark cone at the heart of its anatomy. The tremor must be its heart beating. Without warning, David was visited by an exact vision of death: a long hole in the ground, no wider than your body, down which you are drawn while the white faces above recede. You try to reach them but your arms are pinned. Shovels pour dirt into your face. There you will be forever, in an upright position, blind and silent, and in time no one will remember you, and you will never be called. As strata of rock shift, your fingers elongate, and your teeth are distended sideways in a great underground grimace indistinguishable from a strip of chalk. And the earth tumbles on, and the sun expires, and unaltering darkness reigns where once there were stars.

Sweat broke out on his back. His mind seemed to rebound off a solidness. Such extinction was not another threat, a graver sort of danger, a kind of pain; it was qualitatively different. It was not even a conception that could be voluntarily pictured; it entered him from outside. His protesting nerves swarmed on its surface like lichen on a meteor. The skin of his chest was soaked with the effort of rejection. At the same time that the fear was dense and internal, it was dense and all around him; a tide of clay had swept up to the stars; space was crushed into a mass. When he stood up, automatically hunching his shoulders to keep his head away from the spider webs, it was with a numb sense of being cramped between two huge volumes of rigidity. That he had even this small freedom to move surprised him. In the narrow shelter of that rank shack, adjusting his pants, he felt—his first spark of comfort—too small to be crushed.

But in the open, as the beam of the flashlight skidded with frightened quickness across the remote surfaces of the barn and the grape arbor and the giant pine that stood by the path to the woods, the terror descended. He raced up through the clinging grass pursued, not by one of the wild animals the woods might hold, or one of the goblins his superstitious grandmother had communicated to his childhood, but by spectres out of science fiction, where gigantic cinder moons fill half the turquoise sky. As David ran, a gray planet rolled inches behind his neck. If he looked back, he would be buried. And in the momentum of his terror, hideous possibilities—the dilation of the sun, the triumph of the insects, the crabs on the shore in *The Time Machine*—wheeled out of the vacuum of make-believe and added their weight to his impending oblivion.

He wrenched the door open; the lamps within the house flared. The wicks burning here and there seemed to mirror one another. His mother was washing the dishes in a little pan of heated pump-water; Granmom fluttered near her elbow apprehensively. In the living room —the downstairs of the little square house was two long rooms—his father sat in front of the black fireplace restlessly folding and unfolding a newspaper as he sustained his half of the argument. "Nitrogen, phosphorus, potash: these are the three replaceable constituents of the soil. One crop of corn carries away hundreds of pounds of"—he dropped the paper into his lap and ticked them off on three fingers —"nitrogen, phosphorus, potash."

"Boyer didn't grow corn."

"*Any* crop, Elsie. The human animal—"

"You're killing the *earth*worms, George!"

"The human animal, after thousands and *thou*sands of years, learned methods whereby the chemical balance of the soil may be maintained. Don't carry me back to the Dark Ages."

"When we moved to Olinger the ground in the garden was like slate. Just one summer of my cousin's chicken dung and the earthworms came back."

"I'm sure the Dark Ages were a fine place to the poor devils born in them, but I don't want to go there. They give me the creeps." Daddy stared into the cold pit of the fireplace and clung to the rolled newspaper in his lap as if it alone were keeping him from slipping backwards and down, down.

Mother came into the doorway brandishing a fistful of wet forks. "And thanks to your DDT there soon won't be a bee left in the country. When I was a girl here you could eat a peach without washing it."

"It's primitive, Elsie. It's Dark Age stuff."

"Oh what do *you* know about the Dark Ages?"

"I know I don't want to go back to them."

David took from the shelf, where he had placed it this afternoon, the great unabridged Webster's Dictionary that his grandfather had owned. He turned the big thin pages, floppy as cloth, to the entry he wanted, and read

soul . . . 1. An entity conceived as the essence, substance, animating principle, or actuating cause of life, or of the individual life, esp. of life manifested in psychical activities; the vehicle of individual existence, separate in nature from the body and usually held to be separable in existence.

The definition went on, into Greek and Egyptian conceptions, but David stopped short on the treacherous edge of antiquity. He needed to read no further. The careful overlapping words shingled a temporary shelter for him. "Usually held to be separable in existence"— what could be fairer, more judicious, surer?

His father was saying, "The modern farmer can't go around sweeping up after his cows. The poor devil has thousands and *thou*sands of acres on his hands. Your modern farmer uses a scientifically-arrived-at mixture, like five-ten-five, or six-twelve-six, or *three*-twelve-six, and spreads it on with this wonderful modern machinery which of course we can't afford. Your modern farmer can't *afford* medieval methods."

Mother was quiet in the kitchen; her silence radiated waves of anger.

"No now Elsie; don't play the femme with me. Let's discuss this calmly like two rational twentieth-century people. Your organic farming nuts aren't attacking five-ten-five; they're attacking the chemical fertilizer crooks. The monster firms."

A cup clinked in the kitchen. Mother's anger touched David's face;

his cheeks burned guiltily. Just by being in the living room he was associated with his father. She appeared in the doorway with red hands and tears in her eyes, and said to the two of them, "I knew you didn't want to come here but I didn't know you'd torment me like this. You talked Pop into his grave and now you'll kill me. Go ahead, George, more power to you; at least I'll be buried in good ground." She tried to turn and met an obstacle and screamed, "Mother, stop hanging on my *back!* Why don't you go to *bed?*"

"Let's all go to bed," David's father said, rising from the blue wing chair and slapping his thigh with a newspaper. "This reminds me of death." It was a phrase of his that David had heard so often he never considered its sense.

Upstairs, he seemed to be lifted above his fears. The sheets on his bed were clean. Granmom had ironed them with a pair of flatirons saved from the Olinger attic; she plucked them hot off the stove alternately, with a wooden handle called a goose. It was a wonder, to see how she managed. In the next room, his parents grunted peaceably; they seemed to take their quarrels less seriously than he did. They made comfortable scratching noises as they carried a little lamp back and forth. Their door was open a crack, so he saw the light shift and swing. Surely there would be, in the last five minutes, in the last second, a crack of light, showing the door from the dark room to another, full of light. Thinking of it this vividly frightened him. His own dying, in a specific bed in a specific room, specific walls mottled with wallpaper, the dry whistle of his breathing, the murmuring doctors, the nervous relatives going in and out, but for him no way out but down into the funnel. *Never touch a doorknob again.* A whisper, and his parents' light was blown out. David prayed to be reassured. Though the experiment frightened him, he lifted his hands high into the darkness above his face and begged Christ to touch them. Not hard or long: the faintest, quickest grip would be final for a lifetime. His hands waited in the air, itself a substance, which seemed to move through his fingers; or was it the pressure of his pulse? He returned his hands to beneath the covers uncertain if they had been touched or not. For would not Christ's touch *be* infinitely gentle.

Through all the eddies of its aftermath, David clung to this thought about his revelation of extinction: that there, in the outhouse, he had struck a solidness qualitatively different, a rock of horror firm enough to support any height of construction. All he needed was a little help; a word, a gesture, a nod of certainty, and he would be sealed in, safe.

The assurance from the dictionary had melted in the night. Today was Sunday, a hot fair day. Across a mile of clear air the church bells called, *Celebrate, celebrate.* Only Daddy went. He put on a coat over his rolled-up shirtsleeves and got into the little old black Plymouth parked by the barn and went off, with the same pained hurried grimness of all his actions. His churning wheels, as he shifted too hastily into second, raised plumes of red dust on the dirt road. Mother walked to the far field, to see what bushes needed cutting. David, though he usually preferred to stay in the house, went with her. The puppy followed at a distance, whining as it picked its way through the stubble but floundering off timidly if one of them went back to pick it up and carry it. When they reached the crest of the far field, his mother asked, "David, what's troubling you?"

"Nothing. Why?"

She looked at him sharply. The greening woods crosshatched the space beyond her half-gray hair. Then she showed him her profile, and gestured toward the house, which they had left a half-mile behind them. "See how it sits in the land? They don't know how to build with the land any more. Pop always said the foundations were set with the compass. We must try to get a compass and see. It's supposed to face due south; but south feels a little more *that* way to me." From the side, as she said these things, she seemed handsome and young. The smooth sweep of her hair over her ear seemed white with a purity and calm that made her feel foreign to him. He had never regarded his parents as consolers of his troubles; from the beginning they had seemed to have more troubles than he. Their confusion had flattered him into an illusion of strength; so now on this high clear ridge he jealously guarded the menace all around them, blowing like a breeze on his fingertips, the possibility of all this wide scenery sinking into darkness. The strange fact that though she came to look at the brush she carried no clippers, for she had a fixed prejudice against working on Sundays, was the only consolation he allowed her to offer.

As they walked back, the puppy whimpering after them, the rising dust behind a distant line of trees announced that Daddy was speeding home from church. When they reached the house he was there. He had brought back the Sunday paper and the vehement remark, "Dobson's too intelligent for these farmers. They just sit there with their mouths open and don't hear a thing the poor devil's saying."

"What makes you think farmers are unintelligent? This country was made by farmers. George Washington was a farmer."

"They are, Elsie. They are unintelligent. George Washington's dead. In this day and age only the misfits stay on the farm. The lame, the halt, the blind. The morons with one arm. Human garbage. They remind me of death, sitting there with their mouths open."

"My *father* was a farmer."

"He was a frustrated man, Elsie. He never knew what hit him. The poor devil meant so well, and he never knew which end was up. Your mother'll bear me out. Isn't that right, Mom? Pop never knew what hit him?"

"Ach, I guess not," the old woman quavered, and the ambiguity for the moment silenced both sides.

David hid in the funny papers and sports section until one-thirty. At two, the catechetical class met at the Firetown church. He had transferred from the catechetical class of the Lutheran church in Olinger, a humiliating comedown. In Olinger they met on Wednesday nights, spiffy and spruce, in the atmosphere of a dance. Afterwards, blessed by the brick-faced minister from whose lips the word "Christ" fell like a burning stone, the more daring of them went with their Bibles to a luncheonette and smoked. Here in Firetown, the girls were dull white cows and the boys narrow-faced brown goats in old men's suits, herded on Sunday afternoons into a threadbare church basement that smelled of stale hay. Because his father had taken the car on one of his endless errands to Olinger, David walked, grateful for the open air and the silence. The catechetical class embarrassed him, but today he placed hope in it, as the source of the nod, the gesture, that was all he needed.

Reverend Dobson was a delicate young man with great dark eyes and small white shapely hands that flickered like protesting doves when he preached; he seemed a bit misplaced in the Lutheran ministry. This was his first call. It was a split parish; he served another rural church twelve miles away. His iridescent green Ford, new six months ago, was spattered to the windows with red mud and rattled from bouncing on the rude back roads, where he frequently got lost, to the malicious satisfaction of many. But David's mother liked him, and, more pertinent to his success, the Haiers, the sleek family of feed merchants and innkeepers and tractor salesmen who dominated the Firetown church, liked him. David liked him, and felt liked in turn; sometimes in class, after some special stupidity, Dobson directed toward him out of those wide black eyes a mild look of disbelief, a look that, though flattering, was also delicately disquieting.

Catechetical instruction consisted of reading aloud from a work book-let answers to problems prepared during the week, problems like, "I

am the _____, the _____, and the _____, saith the Lord." Then
there was a question period in which no one ever asked any questions.
Today's theme was the last third of the Apostles' Creed. When the
time came for questions, David blushed and asked, "About the Resurrection of the Body—are we conscious between the time when we die
and the Day of Judgment?"

Dobson blinked, and his fine little mouth pursed, suggesting that
David was making difficult things more difficult. The faces of the
other students went blank, as if an indiscretion had been committed.

"No, I suppose not," Reverend Dobson said.

"Well, where is our soul, then, in this gap?"

The sense grew, in the class, of a naughtiness occurring. Dobson's
shy eyes watered, as if he were straining to keep up the formality of
attention, and one of the girls, the fattest, simpered toward her twin,
who was a little less fat. Their chairs were arranged in a rough circle.
The current running around the circle panicked David. Did everybody
know something he didn't know?

"I suppose you could say our souls are asleep," Dobson said.

"And then they wake up, and there is the earth like it always is, and
all the people who have ever lived? Where will Heaven be?"

Anita Haier giggled. Dobson gazed at David intently, but with an
awkward, puzzled flicker of forgiveness, as if there existed a secret
between them that David was violating. But David knew of no secret.
All he wanted was to hear Dobson repeat the words he said every Sunday morning. This he would not do. As if these words were unworthy
of the conversational voice.

"David, you might think of Heaven this way: as the way the goodness Abraham Lincoln did lives after him."

"But is Lincoln conscious of it living on?" He blushed no longer
with embarrassment but in anger; he had walked here in good faith and
was being made a fool.

"Is he conscious now? I would have to say no; but I don't think it
matters." His voice had a coward's firmness; he was hostile now.

"You don't."

"Not in the eyes of God, no." The unction, the stunning impudence,
of this reply sprang tears of outrage in David's eyes. He bowed them
to his book, where short words like Duty, Love, Obey, Honor, were
stacked in the form of a cross.

"Were there any other questions, David?" Dobson asked with renewed gentleness. The others were rustling, collecting their books.

"No." He made his voice firm, though he could not bring up his eyes.

"Did I answer your question fully enough?"

"Yes."

In the minister's silence the shame that should have been his crept over David: the burden and fever of being a fraud were placed upon *him*, who was innocent, and it seemed, he knew, a confession of this guilt that on the way out he was unable to face Dobson's stirred gaze, though he felt it probing the side of his head.

Anita Haier's father gave him a ride down the highway as far as the dirt road. David said he wanted to walk the rest, and figured that his offer was accepted because Mr. Haier did not want to dirty his bright blue Buick with dust. This was all right; everything was all right, as long as it was clear. His indignation at being betrayed, at seeing Christianity betrayed, had hardened him. The straight dirt road reflected his hardness. Pink stones thrust up through its packed surface. The April sun beat down from the center of the afternoon half of the sky; already it had some of summer's heat. Already the fringes of weeds at the edges of the road were bedraggled with dust. From the reviving grass and scruff of the fields he walked between, insects were sending up a monotonous, automatic chant. In the distance a tiny figure in his father's coat was walking along the edge of the woods. His mother. He wondered what joy she found in such walks; to him the brown stretches of slowly rising and falling land expressed only a huge exhaustion.

Flushed with fresh air and happiness, she returned from her walk earlier than he had expected, and surprised him at his grandfather's Bible. It was a stumpy black book, the boards worn thin where the old man's fingers had held them; the spine hung by one weak hinge of fabric. David had been looking for the passage where Jesus says to the one thief on the cross, "Today shalt thou be with me in paradise." He had never tried reading the Bible for himself before. What was so embarrassing about being caught at it, was that he detested the apparatus of piety. Fusty churches, creaking hymns, ugly Sunday-school teachers, and their stupid leaflets—he hated everything about them but the promise they held out, a promise that in the most perverse way, as if the homeliest crone in the kingdom were given the Prince's hand, made every good and real thing, ball games and jokes and pert-breasted girls, possible. He couldn't explain this to his mother. There was no time. Her solicitude was upon him.

"David, what are you doing?"

"Nothing."

"What are you doing at Grandpop's Bible?"

"Trying to read it. This is supposed to be a Christian country, isn't it?"

She sat down on the green sofa, which used to be in the sun parlor at Olinger, under the fancy mirror. A little smile still lingered on her face from the walk. "David, I wish you'd talk to me."

"What about?"

"About whatever it is that's troubling you. Your father and I have both noticed it."

"I asked Reverend Dobson about Heaven and he said it was like Abraham Lincoln's goodness living after him."

He waited for the shock to strike her. "Yes?" she said, expecting more.

"That's all."

"And why didn't you like it?"

"Well; don't you see? It amounts to saying there isn't any Heaven at all."

"I don't see that it amounts to that. What do you want Heaven to be?"

"Well, I don't know. I want it to be *some*thing. I thought he'd tell me what it was. I thought that was his job." He was becoming angry, sensing her surprise at him. She had assumed that Heaven had faded from his head years ago. She had imagined that he had already entered, in the secrecy of silence, the conspiracy that he now knew to be all around him.

"David," she asked gently, "don't you ever want to rest?"

"No. Not forever."

"David, you're so young. When you get older, you'll feel differently."

"Grandpa didn't. Look how tattered this book is."

"I never understood your grandfather."

"Well I don't understand ministers who say it's like Lincoln's goodness going on and on. Suppose you're not Lincoln?"

"I think Reverend Dobson made a mistake. You must try to forgive him."

"It's not a *question* of his making a mistake! It's a question of dying and never moving or seeing or hearing anything ever again."

"But"—in exasperation—"darling, it's so *greedy* of you to want more. When God has given us this wonderful April day, and given us this farm, and you have your whole life ahead of you—"

"You think, then, that there is God?"

"Of course I do"—with deep relief, that smoothed her features into a reposeful oval. He had risen and was standing too near her for his comfort. He was afraid she would reach out and touch him.

"He made everything? You feel that?"

"Yes."

"Then who made Him?"

"Why, Man. Man." The happiness of this answer lit up her face radiantly, until she saw his gesture of disgust. She was so simple, so illogical; such a femme.

"Well that amounts to saying there is none."

Her hand reached for his wrist but he backed away. "David, it's a mystery. A miracle. It's a miracle more beautiful than any Reverend Dobson could have told you about. You don't say houses don't exist because Man made them."

"No. God has to be different."

"But, David, you have the *evidence*. Look out the window at the sun; at the fields."

"Mother, good grief. Don't you see"—he rasped away the roughness in his throat—"if when we die there's nothing, all your sun and fields and what not are all, ah, *horror?* It's just an ocean of horror."

"But David, it's not. It's so clearly not that." And she made an urgent opening gesture with her hands that expressed, with its sugges-tion of a willingness to receive his helplessness, all her grace, her gentle-ness, her love of beauty, gathered into a passive intensity that made him intensely hate her. He would not be wooed away from the truth. *I am the Way, the Truth* . . .

"No," he told her. "Just let me alone."

He found his tennis ball behind the piano and went outside to throw it against the side of the house. There was a patch high up where the brown stucco that had been laid over the sandstone masonry was crum-bling away; he kept trying with the tennis ball to chip more pieces off. Superimposed upon his deep ache was a smaller but more immediate worry; that he had hurt his mother. He heard his father's car rattling on the straightaway, and went into the house, to make peace before he arrived. To his relief, she was not giving off the stifling damp heat of her anger, but instead was cool, decisive, maternal. She handed him an old green book, her college text of Plato.

"I want you to read the Parable of the Cave," she said.

"All right," he said, though he knew it would do no good. Some story by a dead Greek just vague enough to please her. "Don't worry about it, Mother."

"I *am* worried. Honestly, David, I'm sure there will be something for us. As you get older, these things seem to matter a great deal less."

"That may be. It's a dismal thought, though."

His father bumped at the door. The locks and jambs stuck here. But before Granmom could totter to the latch and let him in, he had knocked it open. He had been in Olinger dithering with track meet tickets. Although Mother usually kept her talks with David a confidence, a treasure between them, she called instantly, "George, David is worried about death!" ·

He came to the doorway of the living room, his shirt pocket bristling with pencils, holding in one hand a pint box of melting ice cream and in the other the knife with which he was about to divide it into four sections, their Sunday treat. "Is the kid worried about death? Don't give it a thought, David. I'll be lucky if I live till tomorrow, and I'm not worried. If they'd taken a buckshot gun and shot me in the cradle I'd be better off. The *world*'d be better off. Hell, I think death is a wonderful thing. I look forward to it. Get the garbage out of the way. If I had the man here who invented death, I'd pin a medal on him."

"Hush, George. You'll frighten the child worse than he is."

This was not true; he never frightened David. There was no harm in his father, no harm at all. Indeed, in the man's steep self-disgust the boy felt a kind of ally. A distant ally. He saw his position with a certain strategic coldness. Nowhere in the world of other people would he find the hint, the nod, he needed to begin to build his fortress against death. They none of them believed. He was alone. In that deep hole.

❖   ❖   ❖

In the months that followed, his position changed little. School was some comfort. All those sexy, perfumed people, wisecracking, chewing gum, all of them doomed to die, and none of them noticing. In their company David felt that they would carry him along into the bright, cheap paradise reserved for them. In any crowd, the fear ebbed a little; he had reasoned that somewhere in the world there must exist a few people who believed what was necessary, and the larger the crowd, the greater the chance that he was near such a soul, within calling distance, if only he was not too ignorant, too ill-equipped, to spot him. The sight of clergymen cheered him; whatever they themselves thought, their collars were still a sign that somewhere, at some time, someone had recognized that we cannot, *cannot*, submit to death. The sermon topics posted outside churches, the flip, hurried pieties of disc jockeys, the cartoons in magazines showing angels or devils—on such scraps he kept alive the possibility of hope.

For the rest, he tried to drown his hopelessness in clatter and jostle. The pinball machine at the luncheonette was a merciful distraction; as he bent over its buzzing, flashing board of flippers and cushions, the weight and constriction in his chest lightened and loosened. He was grateful for all the time his father wasted in Olinger. Every delay postponed the moment when they must ride together down the dirt road into the heart of the dark farmland, where the only light was the kerosene lamp waiting on the dining-room table, a light that drowned their food in shadow and made it sinister.

He lost his appetite for reading. He was afraid of being ambushed again. In mystery novels people died like dolls being discarded; in science fiction enormities of space and time conspired to crush the humans; and even in P. G. Wodehouse he felt a hollowness, a turning away from reality that was implicitly bitter, and became explicit in the comic figures of futile clergymen. All gaiety seemed minced out on the skin of a void. All quiet hours seemed invitations to dread.

Even on weekends, he and his father contrived to escape the farm; and, when, some Saturdays, they did stay home, it was to do something destructive—tear down an old henhouse or set huge brush fires that threatened, while Mother shouted and flapped her arms, to spread to the woods. Whenever his father worked, it was with rapt violence; when he chopped kindling, fragments of the old henhouse boards flew like shrapnel and the ax-head was always within a quarter of an inch of flying off the handle. He was exhilarating to watch, sweating and swearing and sucking bits of saliva back into his lips.

School stopped. His father took the car in the opposite direction, to a highway construction job where he had been hired for the summer as a timekeeper, and David was stranded in the middle of acres of heat and greenery and blowing pollen and the strange, mechanical humming that lay invisibly in the weeds and alfalfa and dry orchard grass.

For his fifteenth birthday his parents gave him, with jokes about him being a hillbilly now, a Remington .22. It was somewhat like a pinball machine to take it out to the old kiln in the woods where they dumped their trash, and set up tin cans on the kiln's sandstone shoulder and shoot them off one by one. He'd take the puppy, who had grown long legs and a rich coat of reddish fur—he was part chow. Copper hated the gun but loved the boy enough to accompany him. When the flat acrid crack rang out, he would race in terrified circles that would tighten and tighten until they brought him, shivering, against David's legs. Depending upon his mood, David would shoot again or drop to his knees and comfort the dog. Giving this comfort to a degree returned comfort to him. The dog's ears, laid flat against his skull in fear, were folded so intricately, so—he groped for the concept—*surely*. Where the dull-studded collar made the fur stand up, each hair showed a root of soft white under the length, black-tipped, of the metal-color that had lent the dog its name. In his agitation Copper panted through nostrils that were elegant slits, like two healed cuts, or like the key-holes of a dainty lock of black, grained wood. His whole whorling, knotted, jointed body was a wealth of such embellishments. And in the smell of the dog's hair David seemed to descend through many finely differentiated layers of earth: mulch, soil, sand, clay, and the glittering mineral base.

But when he returned to the house, and saw the books arranged on the low shelves, fear returned. The four adamant volumes of Wells like four thin bricks, the green Plato that had puzzled him with its queer softness and tangled purity, the dead Galsworthy and "Eliza-beth," Grandpa's mammoth dictionary, Grandpa's Bible, the Bible that he himself had received on becoming a member of the Firetown Lutheran Church—at the sight of these, the memory of his fear re-awakened and came around him. He had grown stiff and stupid in its embrace. His parents tried to think of ways to entertain him.

"David, I have a job for you to do," his mother said one evening at the table.

"What?"

"If you're going to take that tone perhaps we'd better not talk."

"What tone? I didn't take any tone."

"Your grandmother thinks there are too many pigeons in the barn."

"Why?" David turned to look at his grandmother, but she sat there staring at the burning lamp with her usual expression of bewilderment.

Mother shouted, "Mom, he wants to know why!"

Granmom made a jerky, irritable motion with her bad hand, as if generating the force for utterance, and said, "They foul the furniture."

"That's right," Mother said. "She's afraid for that old Olinger furni-ture that we'll never use. David, she's been after me for a month about those poor pigeons. She wants you to shoot them."

"I don't want to kill anything especially," David said.

Daddy said, "The kid's like you are, Elsie. He's too good for this world. Kill or be killed, that's my motto."

His mother said loudly, "Mother, he doesn't want to do it."

"Not?" The old lady's eyes distended as if in horror, and her claw descended slowly to her lap.

"Oh, I'll do it, I'll do it tomorrow," David snapped, and a pleasant crisp taste entered his mouth with the decision.

"And I had thought, when Boyer's men made the hay, it would be better if the barn doesn't look like a rookery," his mother added need-lessly.

A barn, in day, is a small night. The splinters of light between the dry shingles pierce the high roof like stars, and the rafters and cross-beams and built-in ladders seem, until your eyes adjust, as mysterious as the branches of a haunted forest. David entered silently, the gun in one hand. Copper whined desperately at the door, too frightened to come in with the gun yet unwilling to leave the boy. David stealthily turned, said "Go away," shut the door on the dog, and slipped the bolt across. It was a door within a door; the double door for wagons and tractors was as high and wide as the face of a house.

The smell of old straw scratched his sinuses. The red sofa, half-hidden under its white-splotched tarpaulin, seemed assimilated into this smell, sunk in it, buried. The mouths of empty bins gaped like caves. Rusty oddments of farming—coils of baling wire, some spare tines for a harrow, a handleless shovel—hung on nails driven here and there in the thick wood. He stood stock-still a minute; it took a while to sepa-rate the cooing of the pigeons from the rustling in his ears. When he had focused on the cooing, it flooded the vast interior with its throaty, bubbling outpour: there seemed no other sound. They were up behind the beams. What light there was leaked through the shingles and the dirty glass windows at the far end and the small round holes, about as big as basketballs, high on the opposite stone side walls, under the ridge of the roof.

A pigeon appeared in one of these holes, on the side toward the house. It flew in, with a battering of wings, from the outside, and waited there, silhouetted against its pinched bit of sky, preening and cooing in a throbbing, thrilled, tentative way. David tiptoed four steps to the side, rested his gun against the lowest rung of a ladder pegged between two upright beams, and lowered the gunsight into the bird's tiny, jauntily cocked head. The slap of the report seemed to come off the stone wall behind him, and the pigeon did not fall. Neither did it fly. Instead it stuck in the round hole, pirouetting rapidly and nodding its head as if in frantic agreement. David shot the bolt back and forth

and had aimed again before the spent cartridge had stopped jingling
on the boards by his feet. He eased the tip of the sight a little lower,
into the bird's breast, and took care to squeeze the trigger with perfect
evenness. The slow contraction of his hand abruptly sprang the bullet;
for a half-second there was doubt, and then the pigeon fell like a handful of rags, skimming down the barn wall into the layer of straw that
coated the floor of the mow on this side.

Now others shook loose from the rafters, and whirled in the dim air
with a great blurred hurtle. of feathers and noise. They would go for
the hole; he fixed his sight on the little moon of blue, and when a
pigeon came to it, shot him as he was walking the ten inches of stone
that would have carried him into the open air. This pigeon lay down
in that tunnel of stone, unable to fall either one way or the other, although he was alive enough to lift one wing and cloud the light. It
would sink back, and he would suddenly lift it again, the feathers
flaring. His body blocked that exit. David raced to the other side of
the barn's main aisle, where a similar ladder was symmetrically placed,
and rested his gun on the same rung. Three birds came together to this
hole; he got one, and two got through. The rest resettled in the rafters.

There was a shallow triangular space behind the cross beams supporting the roof. It was here they roosted and hid. But either the
space was too small, or they were curious, for now that his eyes were at
home in the dusty gloom David could see little dabs of gray popping in
and out. The cooing was shriller now; its apprehensive tremolo made
the whole volume of air seem liquid. He noticed one little smudge of
a head that was especially persistent in peeking out; he marked the
place, and fixed his gun on it, and when the head appeared again, had
his finger tightened in advance on the trigger. A parcel of fluff slipped
off the beam and fell the barn's height onto a canvas covering some
Olinger furniture, and where its head had peeked out there was a fresh
prick of light in the shingles.

Standing in the center of the floor, fully master now, disdaining to
steady the barrel with anything but his arm, he killed two more that
way. He felt like a beautiful avenger. Out of the shadowy ragged
infinity of the vast barn roof these impudent things dared to thrust their
heads, presumed to dirty its starred silence with their filthy timorous
life, and he cut them off, tucked them back neatly into the silence. He
had the sensation of a creator; these little smudges and flickers that he
was clever to see and even cleverer to hit in the dim recesses of the
rafters—out of each of them he was making a full bird. A tiny peek,

probe, dab of life, when he hit it, blossomed into a dead enemy, falling with good, final weight.

The imperfection of the second pigeon he had shot, who was still lifting his wing now and then up in the round hole, nagged him. He put a new clip into the stock. Hugging the gun against his body, he climbed the ladder. The barrel sight scratched his ear; he had a sharp, garish vision, like a color slide, of shooting himself and being found tumbled on the barn floor among his prey. He locked his arm around the top rung—a fragile, gnawed rod braced between uprights—and shot into the bird's body from a flat angle. The wing folded, but the impact did not, as he had hoped, push the bird out of the hole. He fired again, and again, and still the little body, lighter than air when alive, was too heavy to budge from its high grave. From up here he could see green trees and a brown corner of the house through the hole. Clammy with the cobwebs that gathered between the rungs, he pumped a full clip of eight bullets into the stubborn shadow, with no success. He climbed down, and was struck by the silence in the barn. The remaining pigeons must have escaped out the other hole. That was all right; he was tired of it.

He stepped with his rifle into the light. His mother was coming to meet him, and it tickled him to see her shy away from the carelessly held gun. "You took a chip out of the house," she said. "What were those last shots about?"

"One of them died up in that little round hole and I was trying to shoot it down."

"Copper's hiding behind the piano and won't come out. I had to leave him."

"Well don't blame me. *I* didn't want to shoot the poor devils."

"Don't smirk. You look like your father. How many did you get?"

"Six."

She went into the barn, and he followed. She listened to the silence. Her hair was scraggly, perhaps from tussling with the dog. "I don't suppose the others will be back," she said wearily. "Indeed, I don't know why I let Mother talk me into it. Their cooing was such a comforting noise." She began to gather up the dead pigeons. Though he didn't want to touch them, David went into the mow and picked up by its tepid, horny, coral-colored feet the first bird he had killed. Its wings unfolded disconcertingly, as if the creature had been held together by threads that now were slit. It did not weigh much. He retrieved the one on the other side of the barn; his mother got the three in the middle and led the way across the road to the little southern slope of land that went down toward the foundations of the vanished tobacco shed. The ground was too steep to plant and mow; wild strawberries grew in the tangled grass. She put her burden down and said, "We'll have to bury them. The dog will go wild."

He put his two down on her three; the slick feathers let the bodies slide liquidly on one another. He asked, "Shall I get you the shovel?"

"Get it for yourself; *you* bury them. They're your kill. And be sure to make the hole deep enough so he won't dig them up." While he went to the tool shed for the shovel, she went into the house. Unlike her, she did not look up, either at the orchard to the right of her or at the meadow on her left, but instead held her head rigidly, tilted a little, as if listening to the ground.

He dug the hole, in a spot where there were no strawberry plants, before he studied the pigeons. He had never seen a bird this close before. The feathers were more wonderful than dog's hair, for each filament was shaped within the shape of the feather, and the feathers in turn were trimmed to fit a pattern that flowed without error across the bird's body. He lost himself in the geometrical tides as the feathers now broadened and stiffened to make an edge for flight, now softened and constricted to cup warmth around the mute flesh. And across the surface of the infinitely adjusted yet somehow effortless mechanics of the feathers played idle designs of color, no two alike, designs executed, it seemed, in a controlled rapture, with a joy that hung level in the air above and behind him. Yet these birds bred in the millions and were exterminated as pests. Into the fragrant open earth he dropped one broadly banded in slate shades of blue, and on top of it another, mottled all over in rhythms of lilac and gray. The next was almost wholly white, but for a salmon glaze at its throat. As he fitted the last two, still pliant, on the top, and stood up, crusty coverings were lifted from him, and with a feminine, slipping sensation along his nerves that seemed to give the air hands, he was robed in this certainty: that the God who had lavished such craft upon these worthless birds would not destroy His whole Creation by refusing to let David live forever.

Commentary

Between childhood and adulthood, adolescence is a period of *disorientation*, a key word in "Pigeon Feathers," one of the most moving as well as skillfully wrought stories in this collection. "David, at fourteen, had been more moved than a mover; like the furniture, he had to find a new place, and on the Saturday of the second week he tried to work off some of his *disorientation* by arranging the books."

The external action of the story revolves around a family's move back to the farm and their difficult adjustment to this old but to them, new, way of life. This external action closely parallels the internal action, the boy David's removal from the unquestioning faith of childhood to the tormented search for reality, man's eternal dilemma, "Why must I live only to die?" David struggles to achieve order out of disorder.

Many adolescents find science and mathematics satisfying studies because in them the students find orderliness. At their stage of development, the humanities, and the study of literature in particular, are frustrating, sometimes distasteful and depressing. The reason is that the ideas found in literature are directly related to life and death and are in the nature of questions that do not seem to have clear-cut, orderly answers. In his mother's books, left over from her college days, David finds questions and answers that contradict what he had found in the Bible and in the books of humor, adventure, and science fiction he had read as a child.

Furthermore, in his Sunday-school class, the Reverend Dobson disappoints David with what seem to be illogical and nebulous answers about immortality. During the year of David's life that the story covers, every experience intensifies his growing fear that death will be the end of living, of consciousness, of not only his body but also his soul. His childhood's innocent confidence is profoundly shaken, and even his parents begin to appear somewhat less than wise.

Using the third-person-central point of view (see p. 35), the author has made David the central character. The youth emerges as a unique, precocious individual but also as the universal adolescent. His parents and grandmother, as we see them through David's acute perceptions, also emerge as fully developed characters, unique in their particularity but recognizably universal. Each has come to terms with the *fact* as well as *idea* of mortality in his own way.

David's father "taught school in Olinger and spent all his days performing, with a curious air of panic, needless errands." A city boy, he is frightened of the farm—a setting in which the elemental facts of life and death are eloquently stark. He seems to reduce every argument to terms of chemistry, his college major, and presumably the subject he has been teaching: "I *know* . . . the earth is nothing but chemicals," he tells David's mother. This knowledge is the only thing he got out of four years of college. "Soil, has, no, soul," he carefully enunciates, punctuating each word for emphasis. Furthermore, he has taken a belligerent attitude toward life and death: "I think death is a wonderful thing. I look forward to it. Get the garbage out of the way. If I had the man here who invented death, I'd pin a medal on him."

He does not help David very much with this bitter, ironic attitude. David's mother, with her background of a college major in Greek, on the other hand, does not dismiss David's questions so readily as his father does. She does believe in *soul*—that the soil has it, that all living creatures have it. Her heart opens to David as she becomes aware of his struggle. She has been through it herself; that is why she is determined to get back to fundamental things, close to the soil. "David, I wish you'd talk to me," she offers.

But her answers to his questions are not very helpful either. "David, don't you ever want to rest?" she asks him. Then, "David, you're so young. When you get older, you'll feel differently." But just as she has agreed that she, too, believes in God and that He made everything, to David's question, "Then who made Him?" she replies, "Why, Man. Man." To the boy, this answer is the same as saying there is nothing after death. "It's just an ocean of horror." She hands him Plato's Parable of the Cave to read, and she closes the conversation, "As you get older, these things seem to matter a great deal less." Small comfort!

Granmom's attitude toward death, on the other hand, is the resignation of the aged to the cyclic pattern of life and death. "Granmom, in her prime, had worked these fields alongside her husband, but now she dabbled around the kitchen futilely, her hands waggling with Parkinson's disease." She constantly gets on her daughter's nerves. She is always in the way. Her fingers are crippled by paralysis into one knobbed hook. She wears a "usual expression of bewilderment." Her usefulness in life finished, Granmom certainly is bewildered and has no answer for the groping youth.

Yet, strangely, it is Granmom, representing the most extreme degree of age that is juxtaposed to the boy's youth, that precipitates the event which will enable him to arrive at a resolution for his preoccupation with death. Granmom does not want the pigeons to "foul the furniture" stored in the barn—discarded furniture, including the symbolic old red couch of David's childhood, cozy comfort, that has been replaced in the farmhouse by the symbolic formal, cold, blue wing chair that used to be in the guest room in the Olinger house. To David his mother assigns the task of killing the pigeons with the new Remington .22 he had received for his fifteenth birthday. What irony to ask

David to *kill* when he is fighting so feverishly the futile battle against
the *idea* of death!

"I don't want to kill anything especially," he says.

"The kid's like you are, Elsie," comments his father. "He's too good
for this world. Kill or be killed, that's my motto."

David's mother starts to relent, but Granmom's cryptic "Not?"
moves David to decision. He will kill the pigeons tomorrow.

The beautifully described scene in the barn is the climax to the
story, for here David comes to terms with the terrifying *idea* of death
by facing the *fact* of death. He finds the answer to his questions at
last, by himself, in the lovely orderliness of nature, symbolized by the
blue, lilac, gray, white, and salmon feathers he examines so carefully:

The feathers were more wonderful than dog's hair, for each filament was
shaped within the shape of the feather, and the feathers in turn were
trimmed to fit a pattern that flowed without error across the bird's body.
He lost himself in the geometrical tides as the feathers now broadened and
stiffened to make an edge for flight, now softened and constricted to cup
warmth around the mute flesh. And across the surface of the infinitely adjusted yet somehow effortless mechanics of the feathers played idle designs
of color, no two alike, designs executed, it seemed, in a controlled rapture,
with a joy that hung level in the air above and behind him.

It is ironic that by observing scientifically, David finds the order he
has been seeking. Scientific observation had raised his nagging
doubts. Now, coupled with faith, his observations lead him to his
own conclusion: "the God who had lavished such craft upon these
worthless birds would not destroy His whole Creation by refusing to
let David live forever."

His conclusion may not suffice for the rest of his life, but it has
brought David to another threshold in man's eternal search for the
answers to the questions the humanities ask.

Questions

1. Every detail in a short story should be relevant to its theme. Some
   details represent a "free choice" to the author. He may use any
   objects he likes as long as they are plausible, even though exactly
   what they are may not be important. David's mother has a collection of old books she read in college. But the author does not say
   just that David read adult books that contradicted what he had
   formerly believed. John Updike is very specific in naming the

books. What kind of books are they? How does mention of the particular books contribute to the theme?

2. David notes the difference between his mother's signature in her old books and the way she writes shopping lists and Christmas cards now. Why is the contrast significant, and how is this detail relevant to the theme?

3. Why is the opening sentence of "Pigeon Feathers" like a key that opens the door to the world and meaning of the story?

4. The setting and atmosphere of a work of fiction contribute to its total effect. Why does this story have a farm for its setting?

5. Why is it that except for the Reverend Dobson all the characters are members of a single family unit?

6. Why are there no other characters in the story of David's own generation? Mention is made only of the catechetical class: girls —"dull white cows"—and boys—"narrow-faced brown goats in old men's suits."

7. David's formal education is scarcely mentioned in the story. There are the mere statements "School was some comfort" and "School stopped." Why is school so insignificant?

8. How does the story illustrate the controversy between the humanities and science?

9. Compare and contrast the nature of David's observation of the tiny insect that lighted on the lens of his flashlight with that of his observation of the pigeon feathers. Why does the one fill him with fear and the other with faith in God and himself?

10. What do the references to Copper, the puppy, contribute to the effect of the whole story?

11. Consider the attitudes of the four adults toward death. Discuss whether each is so entirely wrong that David rejects all their attitudes?

Youth and Age: General Questions

1. How do "Charles," "Youth," and "The Father" illustrate what age can learn from youth? In what other ways can adults learn from children and youth?

2. As a contrast, how does "Pigeon Feathers" illustrate what youth can learn from age? In what other ways is it possible for children and youth to learn from adults?

3. Discuss the mother-child relationships in "Charles" and "Pigeon Feathers." How does the point of view (see p. 31) from which

each story is told re-create a different aspect of the mother-child relationship?

4. Compare and contrast the ways that the father in Björnson's story is reconciled to the idea of death with the ways that David in "Pigeon Feathers" comes to an understanding of death. To what extent do the two characters accept death? What does the age of each have to do with his acceptance?

5. "Charles" and "The Father" are short-short stories, whereas "Youth" and "Pigeon Feathers" can be considered novelettes (see p. 18). Why does the content—character, action, theme—of the latter two require more detailed treatment than that of short-short stories?

6. How does the richness of imagery in "Youth" and "Pigeon Feathers" contribute to the individuality of each story? In what way do the imagery and symbolism (see p. 38) in each illustrate characteristics of youth?

7. How does the use of dialogue in "Charles" and "The Father" not only help to compress action and reveal character but also to elucidate the idea of youth and age?

8. On the basis of the four stories, explain how youth and age are interdependent in some respects, yet irreconcilable in others.

MORE STORIES ABOUT YOUTH AND AGE

"A Christmas Memory" by Truman Capote
"A Worn Path" by Eudora Welty
"Blackberry Winter" by Robert Penn Warren
"For Esme, with Love and Squalor" by J. D. Salinger
"I Want to Know Why" by Sherwood Anderson
"My First Two Women" by Nadine Gordimer
"My Oedipus Complex" by Frank O'Connor
"The Lumber-Room" by Saki (H. H. Munro)
"The Rocking-Horse Winner" by D. H. Lawrence
"Thus I Refute Beelzy" by John Collier

Man and Nature

Introduction

Man's relationship with nature raises many questions. Can man control nature? Is nature hostile, benign, or indifferent toward man? How can man co-operate with nature? As man, through science, learns more about the mysteries of nature, will his respect for or fear of nature be the greater? Is nature itself beautiful or ugly, or does it become so, depending on man's attitude toward it?

In the enigmatic Japanese short story "Autumn Mountain," the beauty of nature in the eyes of a painter who beholds the mountains is captured on canvas. But many years later, after the painter has been almost forgotten, is it the painting itself that is sought after or the view through a window of the mountains that inspired the painting?

In "Action," about mountains in another part of the world, C. E. Montague illustrates man's fascination with nature, his desire to climb a snowy, icy mountain peak "because it is there" or because he wishes to court danger. The story also reveals the appalling odds against mere human beings who challenge the majesty and relentlessness of nature. "Action" also provides an insight into the interrelationship between nature and human nature—how endurance against the threat of nature can make human life more precious.

Still another story about the contest between man, on one hand, and the snow and ice of nature, on the other, is Jack London's Alaskan tale "To Build a Fire." This story also deals with another kind of man's experiences with nature, his relationship with mute animals. Man tames animals, befriending those he makes his pets, using the strength of those he domesticates to assist him in his work. But sometimes man misuses the strength of animals, as London demonstrates.

The mortality of animals and other living creatures besides man and the regeneration of matter are still another aspect of nature that concerns man. In "The Fair Young Willowy Tree," through fantasy (see p. 17) the author combines the romantic and the realistic to illus-

trate the ambivalent attitudes of man toward nature as well as of man
toward man.

Another kind of relationship between man and nature is that in
which nature teaches man his own worth in the design of the universe.
In "Pigeon Feathers," the story in the Youth and Age section of this
book, for example, the young hero, David, learns from nature through
his observation of the orderly beauty of the pigeon feathers, and
hence, the orderliness and purposefulness of all living things, including
himself.

The student story "Leatherback" in a later section of this anthology
also examines the question of man's responsibility or irresponsibility
in the age-old conflict between the human and animal worlds.   And
another student story, "Noontide of the First Day," traces the experiences with nature, both delightful and terrifying, that a small boy has
during the course of a spring morning's walk outdoors.

The Fair Young Willowy Tree

A. E. Coppard

At the side of a long road winding high over a lonely moor stood a fair young willowy tree. Alone it grew on the verge of the road, the one tree in that solitary place; there was no other within the compass of an eye, not a hedge or house or bush to greet a stumbling traveller, only the vast hummocks of the moorland.

The tree was a little scattery sort of thing but it was graceful. When soft breezes played she waved her arms happily to the sky, but in squally weather she shrank from the wind and squealed at its roughness. The fogs, too, wearied her, so that she drooped and wept; often she sighed at the loneliness of her lot and longed for a companion.

"If only I had a friend to give me greetings and to talk with about the great matters of the world I should be the happiest of creatures; but I am alone, alone, all alone."

She grew and grew until she was twelve feet high and then one day, while peeping from her topmost twigs, she saw far down the road a wagon filled with huge black poles, and a gang of men beside it engaged in merry activities. They returned the next day and the next and for many more days; each day seemed to bring them all nearer to her and at last she was able to see what it was they were about. They were digging pits by the roadside and hoisting a tall black pole in every one, and along the tops of the poles they were hanging bright wires for a new telegraph line. Oh joy! Wild with delight and hope, she watched the lengthening column of tall black poles advancing steadily across the lonely moor, ever nearer and nearer, until at last they were so close that she could hear the shouts of the men and the thumping of their gear as they shovelled and dug. When they were close at hand the men came and dug a hole just beside the fair young willowy tree and hoisted a sturdy blackamoor of a pole upright in it, then filled in the hole and rammed the earth tight at its foot. They put back the turf so neatly, left the pole standing beside her, and went on, farther and farther, planting giant poles across the moor.

The fair young willowy tree was filled with gladness.

"Now at last I have a dear companion!" and she laughed and spoke to the sturdy telegraph pole.

For a while the poor thing was gloomy, he was new to that country and felt lost in his surroundings, but he soon settled down and became friendly. Unhappily, however, a nasty odour of tar drifted from him to the fair young willowy tree whenever the wind was set to her quarter, and this offended her delicate senses. At such times she shrank from his neighbourhood as far as her station would permit—though this of course was not very far; indeed, it was not far enough for her happiness, and she would rail at her companion for a stinking interloper.

"Oh what a stench you have brought to the flavour of this highway!" she complained to the telegraph pole. "I cannot bear your company; you are a common low thing, stuck there and reeking with smells and defiling my air. And look at your stupid stumpy arms, and your skinny wires that groan and moan without stopping! What am I to do about it!"

"Alas!" the pole sighed. "It is true that my appearance is nothing to boast about now; in my figure I take no pride; but I am not now as once I was. You should have seen me then! Oh no indeed, I have been maimed and put to uses I was never educated for. I have travelled the wide world over, but I take no credit for that—have you ever travelled, my dear?"

"No," replied she. "I should scorn it. I do not want to go elsewhere. This is my real home."

"Oh, but it broadens the mind," he said. "One should travel when one is young. I did."

"I have no wish to travel." The fair young willowy tree tossed her head disdainfully and at the same time looked most beautiful with her trim leaves and sweet slender boughs.

"No, of course not," the sturdy pole answered. "Neither had I. I was reared in the northern land beyond the sea. I had a thousand companions around me there, and I had my branches too, but I was not graceful and delicate like you—I was only sturdy and brave. All the same, you could not have endured the life, you could not have survived the fury of the weather and the bitterness of those crags where I had my home. My! How the wind came screaming over the icy isles! All day long and all year long the roaring waves came crashing upon our shore and I could watch the swirl of the last foot of foam hissing at the last foot of shingle. Oh, so good! So good! But you, my dear—your delicate body would have soon perished there, yes, indeed. It did not daunt me, though; nothing could uproot me."

"How vain you are!" taunted the fair young willowy tree. "I love the wind. I do not fear it, it is my joy. I hold out my arms and it embraces me and I hear the voices of angels, the sun pours its beams among my leaves."

So then the tall black pole began to brag of his travels: "I have travelled the wide world over, by ship and by wagon."

But the fair young willowy tree only laughed at him: "Pooh! You had to be carried! You had no choice. You were cut down and sold. A fine traveller indeed! You cannot travel now, you are just a post stuck in the ground, you can neither turn nor move. Ha, ha, ha!"

Such hilarity vexed him, it was so unkind, and he retorted sourly: "And how, pray, did you come to be rooted where you are? You cannot travel anywise at all, you cannot stir from this spot. You did not plant yourself, you have no will, no pride, no use—you have only vanity!"

"No use!" she cried indignantly. "No use! Listen!" she shook her branches and a sweet bird appeared upon one of the swaying boughs and began to sing its song, for in the bosom of the fair young willowy tree it had woven a nest, and in the nest were five golden eggs.

"You see, stupid thing! Birds come to me for shelter and love. What bird would ever, or could ever, build its nest upon you!"

"But, but, but," the sturdy pole protested, "such birds are of no account. In my country birds are as big as hounds; eagles, condors, alabatrosses; even the swan is just nothing."

"But can they sing, any of them!" cried she.

"Now why," the pole asked, "should an eagle sing? Do be reasonable. Tiny birds hop about and chipper and eat worms, or they go into private gardens and dig up the seeds, or steal the cherries before anyone else can pick them. It is dreadful, they are a great nuisance until the cat catches them. That is the only thing cats are good for."

Time and again they would squabble, which was a pity because
they had no other friends, not a hedge nor a house nor a bush nor
a tree, and the other poles were as poles apart, businesslike fellows
with no nonsense about them. She was often petulant and over-
bearing, yet she was so very young and beautiful that he always
soon forgave her and in the pleasant summer breezes she would
dance for him alone. When the foggy autumn weather hung over
them, and she was drooping in despair as her leaves fell from her,
and her twigs dripped with weeping, he would comfort her childish
tears.

How solitary they were! Sometimes in all a week only a coach
would go by—but then it would be a coach of blue with yellow
wheels and four white galloping horses and a man in red to blow
the long copper horn! If the day were fine the passengers might
even be singing, and that was most sweet to hear.

"How good it is! Yes, yes, it is grand!" the sturdy pole would
say, although his heart was despairing for he had begun to be in
love with the fair young willowy tree and saw no hope for himself.

Or a flock of sheep might cross the road at evening chased by a
shepherd whistling and a dog that harried them. How their tough
little hoofs scattered the dust!

"This is most enjoyable and exciting," he would cry. "Life is
sweet, is it not, my dear? Tell me now, what would you like best
to be in all the world?" And he was hoping she might say she would
like to be his wife!

"To be? Oh, if I could have my choice," laughed the fair young
willowy tree, "I would like to feel bright flowers growing upon
me everywhere, blossoms on every twig, of many different colours
—yes, and each flower to turn at last into a yellow quince. What
now would you most care to be?"

"Me? If I could have my choice," he answered, "I would be
the mast on some tall leaning ship, with my white sails trimmed
and my ropes to hold me fast, so I could peer far down into the
crystal waters and note the wonders of the deep."

"Of the deep!"

"Yes. The billowing forests that are there, the vast ocean fungi,
the caverns in the coral, the dreaming weed swaying in its dream;
sponges like palaces, the fish going and coming all in silver and gold
like princes' children."

"No, I would rather be as I am," said the fair young willowy
tree. And that was wise of her, for then she could wave her arms

merrily in the way she most liked to do, day in, day out, and every day, and dance as well as her station allowed—although that was not so very well because she was rooted in the soil. All the same, that does not matter if nobody sees you. There was only herself to please, and the sturdy pole had grown so fond of her that he thought it was perfection. One bright day he summoned up his courage and said:

"I would like to marry you."

"Oh, but you are dead," said she. "Aren't you? You have no twigs, no branches, only those stupid wires; you are not even alive."

"I may be dead, young lady," was his sorrowful rejoinder, "but I am still useful."

"Not useful to yourself, Mr. Pole."

"To others." He sighed. "The dead are of no use to themselves."

"Nor useful to me. I am alive, alive!" she cried. "Pray do not speak of this again, it upsets me. I have other hopes for myself."

"You have certainly little else," he retorted with an insolent sniff.

That made her quite angry and she cried out: "Why are you so stupid, tell me that, you fool!"

"Pardon me," he loftily replied, "is that a serious question?"

"You can make what you like of it."

"Well, I can't make sense of it," said he.

"Try again, you great big blackamoor," she said in her most aggravating tone.

"Is it a joke?" he asked. "I am quite unable to laugh at it."

"But who wants you to laugh! I am only asking you a simple question."

"I am not a dictionary," the proud pole responded.

"And I don't think that so very funny either!" said the fair young willowy tree. Oh, she was very furious! And most provoking.

But the sturdy pole went on: "Let me tell you it is honourable and good to be useful when you are dead. And I am not really dead, not yet. I am only half dead. You see, I have been painted with the nasty-smelling stuff in order to preserve me for a span of usefulness, and I am glad of it too, for otherwise I should have been chopped up for a fire probably."

"Ugh! Do not speak of fire!" She quivered to her very roots. "I hate it. I abominate it. The very thought of it makes me tremble."

"But fire is good," said he soothingly. "In a way it is very valuable. It has a long history, it is most useful and is highly esteemed in the highest circles."

"I don't care," she answered, "I hate it!   I hate it!"

"And those wires you dislike so, which I carry on my shoulders: they are my veins!   My life blood!   Without them I should be nothing at all.   They carry the news of the great world and, do you know, sometimes I can actually hear them whisper the messages from the King!"

"I have my own veins," said she.   "I have no need of messages and news.   I can dance with my branches in the rays of the sun, I can whistle with the wind, I have a hundred arms, I have more twigs than there are stars in the sky, my leaves are full of joy and they dream in the moonlight."

"Ah, my dear," murmured the poor black pole, "ah, my dear." It was all he could say, and he did not propose to hear any more.

Time, which cannot hold back, passed over the moor in the breath of happy winds, in the flight of gloomy clouds.   Lone as the sky itself, the heather on the moor budded, bloomed, and faded.   Sharp winter came harrying the world, and the fair young willowy tree lost her leaves again; they flew away from her and she shivered forlorn in the icy blast.   But the tall black pole did not shiver.   Valiant and unconcerned, even when the snow pillowed itself thickly round half his spine, he did his duty without complaint.

Not until Shrovetide did the young tree recover her spirits and begin to grow gay again.   At Eastertide she was quite lighthearted, for her twigs were covered with tough little purple buds.   By Whitsuntide the buds had broken into tender twinkling leaves, the birds were at nest again in her bosom, and she sang in the wind and danced in the sun, and her leaves dreamed in the moonlight. Moreover, she grew, she was shaping into a tall tree; her topmost branches strained upwards, and one day the sturdy pole felt her highest twigs tapping against the wires close to his head, very tenderly, very soothingly,—Oh, it was most blissful.   And she was joyful too; they became the dearest of friends and dreamed in the moonlight together, all the bright year, all spring, all summer, all autumn.

And then, one day, an officer of state was passing by and he saw that the branches of the fair young willowy tree were mingled with the wires of the telegraph.

"That is dangerous," said he.   "That cannot be allowed.   I must attend to that."

And he sent a man with a shining broad axe, who cut down the fair young willowy tree without a word of apology.   Not content with that, the man hacked off her beautiful arms, hewed her trunk into seven separate pieces, piled her remains in a heap together on the spot where once she grew, and went away and left her there.

Thus it was, and there she lay, destroyed and forgotten, until many months afterward, when cold, cold hours were blighting the moor and a poor tinker man came traveling along who saw the heap of fuel and settled down there and, wanting a fire to thaw the ice from his bones, burned the remains of the fair young willowy tree into fine white ash and little black cinders. And when the fire was done and all was cold again, he travelled on, leaving the ashes there. For long after he was gone the heap of ash remained, black and sad, the winter through, at the foot of the sturdy pole. The poor pole almost wept to see it, but he could not quite weep—he could only stand and mourn.

By and by the spring came again. And the birds came, but alas, the fair young willowy tree was gone, quite gone; only the heap of ash remained. And even then the grass around was growing so high that it soon covered up the ashes, and then no one, not even the sturdy pole, could see it any more.

And so he forgot her.

Questions

1. Read the story once, following the suggestions listed on page 21 in the chapter "The Art of Short Fiction."
2. Read the story a second time, with the attitudes listed on page 22; then answer the questions on pages 30, 39-40, and 43-44.
3. Analyze the sentence in this story: "Time, which cannot hold back, passed over the moor in the breath of happy winds, in the flight of gloomy clouds." How does the sentence reflect the romantic-realistic dualism of the story? How does it relate to the theme of Man and Nature in general?

Autumn Mountain

Ryūnosuké Akutagawa

And speaking of Ta Ch'ih, have you ever seen his Autumn Mountain painting?"

One evening, Wang Shih-ku, who was visiting his friend Yün Nant'ien, asked this question.

"No, I have never seen it. And you?"

Ta Ch'ih, together with Mei-tao-jen and Huang-hao-shan-ch'iao, had been one of the great painters of the Mongol dynasty. As Yün Nant'ien replied, there passed before his eyes images of the artist's famous works, the Sandy Shore painting and the Joyful Spring picture scroll.

"Well, strange to say," said Wang Shih-ku, "I'm really not sure whether or not I have seen it. In fact. . . ."

"You don't know whether you have seen it or you haven't?" said Yün Nan-t'ien, looking curiously at his guest. "Do you mean that you've seen an imitation?"

"No, not an imitation. I saw the original. And it is not I alone who have seen it. The great critics Yen-k'o and Lien-chou both became involved with the Autumn Mountain." Wang Shih-ku sipped his tea and smiled thoughtfully. "Would it bore you to hear about it?"

"Quite the contrary," said Yün Nan-t'ien, bowing his head politely. He stirred the flame in the copper lamp.

* * *

At that time [began Wang Shih-ku] the old master Yüan Tsai was still alive. One evening while he was discussing paintings with Yen-k'o, he asked him whether he had ever seen Ta Ch'ih's Autumn Mountain. As you know, Yen-k'o made a veritable religion of Ta Ch'ih's painting and was certainly not likely to have missed any of his works. But he had never set eyes on this Autumn Mountain.

"No, I haven't seen it," he answered shamefacedly, "and I've never even heard of its existence."

"In that case," said Yüan Tsai, "please don't miss the first opportunity

you have of seeing it. As a work of art it's on an even higher level than
his Summer Mountain or Wandering Storm. In fact, I'm not sure that
it isn't the finest of all Ta Ch'ih's paintings."

"Is it really such a masterpiece? Then I must do my best to see it.
May I ask who owns this painting?"

"It's in the house of a Mr. Chang in the County of Jun. If you ever
have occasion to visit the Chin-shan Temple, you should call on him
and see the picture. Allow me to give you a letter of introduction."

As soon as Yen-k'o received Yüan Tsai's letter, he made plans to set
out for the County of Jun. A house which harbored so precious a
painting as this would, he thought, be bound to have other great works
of different periods. Yen-k'o was quite giddy with anticipation as he
started out.

When he reached the County of Jun, however, he was surprised to
find that Mr. Chang's house, though imposing in structure, was dilapidated. Ivy was coiled about the walls, and in the garden grass and
weeds grew rank. As the old man approached, chicken, ducks, and
other barnyard fowl looked up, as if surprised to see any stranger enter
here. For a moment he could not help doubting Yüan Tsai's words and
wondering how a masterpiece of Ta Ch'ih's could possibly have found
its way into such a house. Upon a servant's answering his knock, he
handed over the letter, explaining that he had come from far in the
hope of seeing the Autumn Mountain.

He was led almost immediately into the great hall. Here again,
though divans and tables of red sandalwood stood in perfect order, a
moldy smell hung over everything and an atmosphere of desolation had
settled even on the tiles. The owner of the house, who now appeared,
was an unhealthy-looking man; but he had a pleasant air about him
and his pale face and delicate hands bore signs of nobility. Yen-k'o,
after briefly introducing himself, lost no time in telling his host how
grateful he would be if he might be shown the famous Ta Ch'ih painting. There was an urgency in the master's words, as if he feared that
were he not to see the great painting at once, it might somehow vanish
like a mist.

Mr. Chang assented without hesitation and had the painting hung
on the bare wall of the great hall.

"This," he said, "is the Autumn Mountain to which you refer."

At first glance Yen-k'o let out a gasp of admiration. The dominant
color was a dark green. From one end to the other a river ran its
twisting course; bridges crossed the river at various places and along
its banks were little hamlets. Dominating it all rose the main peak of

the mountain range, before which floated peaceful wisps of autumn cloud. The mountain and its neighboring hills were fresh green, as if newly washed by rain, and there was an uncanny beauty in the red leaves of the bushes and thickets scattered along their slopes. This was no ordinary painting, but one in which both design and color had reached an apex of perfection. It was a work of art instinct with the classical sense of beauty.

"Well, what do you think of it? Does it please you?" said Mr. Chang, peering at Yen-k'o with a smile.

"Oh, it is truly of godlike quality!" cried Yen-k'o, while he stared at the picture in awe. "Yüan Tsai's lavish praise was more than merited. Compared to this painting, everything I have seen until now seems second-rate."

"Really? You find it such a masterpiece?"

Yen-k'o could not help turning a surprised look at his host. "Can you doubt it?"

"Oh no, it isn't that I have any doubts," said Mr. Chang, and he blushed with confusion like a schoolboy. Looking almost timidly at the painting, he continued: "The fact is that each time I look at this picture I have the feeling that I am dreaming, though my eyes are wide open. I cannot help feeling that it is I alone who see its beauty, which is somehow too intense for this world of ours. What you just said brought back these strang feelings."

But Yen-k'o was not much impressed by his host's evident attempt at self-vindication. His attention was absorbed by the painting, and Mr. Chang's speech seemed to him merely designed to hide a deficiency in critical judgment.

Soon after, Yen-k'o left the desolate house.

❊   ❊   ❊

As the weeks passed, the vivid image of the Autumn Mountain remained fresh in Yen-k'o's mind [continued Wang Shih-ku after accepting another cup of tea]. Now that he had seen Ta Ch'ih's masterpiece, he felt ready to give up anything whatsoever to possess it. Inveterate collector that he was, he knew that not one of the great works that hung in his own house—not even Li Ying-ch'iu's Floating Snowflakes, for which he had paid five hundred taels of silver—could stand comparison with that transcendent Autumn Mountain.

While still sojourning in the County of Jun, he sent an agent to the Chang house to negotiate for the sale of the painting. Despite repeated overtures, he was unable to persuade Mr. Chang to enter into any arrangement. On each occasion that pallid gentleman would reply that while he deeply appreciated the master's admiration of the Autumn Mountain and while he would be quite willing to lend the painting, he must ask to be excused from actually parting with it.

These refusals only served to strengthen the impetuous Yen-k'o's resolve. "One day," he promised himself, "that great picture will hang in my own hall." Confident of the eventual outcome, he finally resigned himself to returning home and temporarily abandoning the Autumn Mountain.

About a year later, in the course of a further visit to the County of Jun, he tried calling once more at the house of Mr. Chang. Nothing had changed: the ivy was still coiled in disorder about the walls and fences, and the garden was covered with weeds. But when the servant answered his knock, Yen-k'o was told that Chang was not in residence. The old man asked if he might have another look at the Autumn Mountain despite the owner's absence, but his importunacy was of no avail: the servant repeated that he had no authority to admit anyone until his master returned. As Yen-k'o persisted, the man finally shut the door in his face. Overcome with chagrin, Yen-k'o had to leave the house and the great painting that lay somewhere in one of the dilapidated rooms.

✤   ✤   ✤

Wang Shih-ku paused for a moment.

"All that I have related so far," he said, "I heard from the master Yen-k'o himself."

"But tell me," said Yün Nan-t'ien, stroking his white beard, "did Yen-k'o ever really see the Autumn Mountain?"

"He said that he saw it. Whether or not he did, I cannot know for certain. Let me tell you the sequel, and then you can judge for yourself."

Wang Shih-ku continued his story with a concentrated air, and now he was no longer sipping his tea.

✤   ✤   ✤

When Yen-k'o told me all this [said Wang Shih-ku] almost fifty years had passed since his visits to the County of Jun. The master Yüan Tsai was long since dead and Mr. Chang's large house had already passed into the hands of two successive generations of his family. There was no telling where the Autumn Mountain might be—nor if the best parts of the scroll might not have suffered hopeless deterioration. In the course of our talk old Yen-k'o described that mysterious painting so vividly that I was almost convinced I could see it before my eyes. It was not the details that had impressed the master but the indefinable beauty of the picture as a whole. Through the words of Yen-k'o, that beauty had entered into my heart as well as his.

It happened that, about a month after my meeting with Yen-k'o, I had myself to make a journey to the southern provinces, including the County of Jun. When I mentioned this to the old man, he suggested that I go and see if I could not find the Autumn Mountain. "If that painting ever comes to light again," he said, "it will indeed be a great day for the world of art."

Needless to say by this time I also was anxious to see the painting, but my journey was crowded and it soon became clear that I would not find time to visit Mr. Chang's house. Meanwhile, however, I happened to hear a report that the Autumn Mountain had come into the hands of a certain nobleman by the name of Wang. Having learned of the painting, Mr. Wang had despatched a messenger with greetings to Chang's grandson. The latter was said to have sent back with the messenger not only the ancient family documents and the great ceremonial cauldron which had been in the family for countless generations, but also a painting which fitted the description of Ta Ch'ih's Autumn Mountain. Delighted with these gifts, Mr. Wang had arranged a great banquet for Chang's grandson, at which he had placed the young man in the seat of honor and regaled him with the choicest delicacies, gay music, and lovely girls; in addition he had given him one thousand pieces of gold.

On hearing this report I almost leaped with joy. Despite the vicissitudes of half a century, it seemed that the Autumn Mountain was still safe! Not only that, but it actually had come within my range. Taking along only the barest necessities, I set out at once to see the painting.

I still vividly remember the day. It was a clear, calm afternoon in early summer and the peonies were proudly in bloom in Mr. Wang's garden. On meeting Mr. Wang, my face broke into a smile of delight even before I had completed my ceremonial bow. "To think that the Autumn Mountain is in this very house!" I cried. "Yen-k'o spent all those years in vain attempts to see it again—and now I am to satisfy my own ambition without the slightest effort. . . ."

"You come at an auspicious time," replied Mr. Wang. "It happens that today I am expecting Yen-k'o himself, as well as the great critic Lien-chou. Please come inside, and since you are the first to arrive you shall be the first to see the painting."

Mr. Wang at once gave instructions for the Autumn Mountain to be hung on the wall. And then it all leaped forth before my eyes: the little villages on the river, the flocks of white cloud floating over the valley, the green of the towering mountain range which extended into the distance like a succession of folding-screens—the whole world, in fact, that Ta Ch'ih had created, a world far more wonderful than our own. My heart seemed to beat faster as I gazed intently at the scroll on the wall.

These clouds and mists and hills and valleys were unmistakably the work of Ta Ch'ih. Who but Ta Ch'ih could carry the art of drawing to such perfection that every brush-stroke became a thing alive? Who but he could produce colors of such depth and richness, and at the same time hide all mechanical trace of brush and paint? And yet . . . and yet I felt at once that this was not the same painting that Yen-k'o had seen once long ago. No, no, a magnificent painting it surely was, yet just as surely not the unique painting which he had described with such religious awe!

Mr. Wang and his entourage had gathered around me and were watching my expression, so I hastened to express my enthusiasm. Naturally I did not want him to doubt the authenticity of his picture, yet it was clear that my words of praise failed to satisfy him. Just then Yen-k'o himself was announced—he who had first spoken to me of this Autumn Mountain. As the old man bowed to Mr. Wang, I could sense the excitement inside him, but no sooner had his eyes settled on the scroll than a cloud seemed to pass before his face.

"What do you think of it, Master?" asked Mr. Wang, who had been carefully observing him. "We have just heard the teacher Wang Shih-ku's enthusiastic praise, but . . ."

"Oh, you are, sir, a very fortunate man to have acquired this painting," answered Yen-k'o promptly. "Its presence in your house will add luster to all your other treasures."

Yen-k'o's courteous words only seemed to deepen Mr. Wang's anxiety; he, like me, must have heard in them a note of insincerity. I think we were all a bit relieved when Lien-chou, the famous critic, made his appearance at this juncture. After bowing to us, he turned to the scroll and stood looking at it silently, chewing his long mustaches.

"This, apparently, is the same painting that the master Yen-k'o last saw half a century ago," Mr. Wang explained to him. "Now I would much like to hear your opinion of the work. Your candid opinion," Mr. Wang added, forcing a smile.

Lien-chou sighed and continued to look at the picture. Then he took a deep breath and, turning to Mr. Wang, said: "This, sir, is probably Ta Ch'is's greatest work. Just see how the artist has shaded those clouds.

What power there was in his brush! Note also the color of his trees. And then that distant peak which brings the whole composition to life." As he spoke, Lien-chou pointed to various outstanding features of the painting, and needless to say, a look of relief, then of delight, spread over Mr. Wang's face.

Meanwhile I secretly exchanged glances with Yen-k'o. "Master," I whispered, "is that the real Autumn Mountain?" Almost imperceptibly the old man shook his head, and there was a twinkle in his eyes.

"It's all like a dream," he murmured. "I really can't help wondering if that Mr. Chang wasn't some sort of hobgoblin."

❀ ❀ ❀

"So that is the story of the Autumn Mountain," said Wang Shih-ku after a pause, and took a sip of his tea. "Later on it appears that Mr. Wang made all sorts of exhaustive enquiries. He visited Mr. Chang, but when he mentioned to him the Autumn Mountain, the young man denied all knowledge of any other version. So one cannot tell if that Autumn Mountain which Yen-k'o saw all those years ago is not even now hidden away somewhere. Or perhaps the whole thing was just a case of faulty memory on an old man's part. It would seem unlikely, though, that Yen-k'o's story about visiting Mr. Chang's house to see the Autumn Mountain was not based on solid fact."

"Well, in any case the image of that strange painting is no doubt engraved forever on Yen-k'o's mind. And on yours too."

"Yes," said Wang Shih-ku, "I still see the dark green of the mountain rock, as Yen-k'o described it all those years ago. I can see the red leaves of the bushes as if the painting were before my eyes this very moment."

"So even if it never existed, there is not really much cause for regret!" The two men laughed and clapped their hands with delight.

Notes

The Japanese title of this Chinese story told by a Japanese author is *Shuzan-zu*. It is about a famous painting of ancient China whose origin is mythical. The story is ironic (see p. 42) because the painting that it is really about, as distinguished from the painting that is actually seen by the narrator—the old teacher Wang Shih-ku—seems to be a figment of the critic Yen-k'o's imagination. The two old men, Wang Shih-ku and Yün Nan-t'ien, by the end of the story, however, "laughed and clapped their hands with delight." It does not matter whether the painting Yen-k'o thought he saw ever existed or whether it is the same painting that Wang Shih-ku and Yen-k'o see fifty years later. What is important is that Yen-k'o's memory of what he thought he had seen and Wang Shih-ku's visualization of the painting Yen-k'o had described have given both men an impression of unforgettable beauty, even if that beauty exists only in their minds.

Questions

1. Which kinds of point of view are used for this story and the story within the story? (See p. 31.) How does this complex method of narration in a relatively short story lend to the legendary quality of the strange painting as well as of the story itself?
2. Does Wang Shih-ku really think that the painting Yen-k'o told him about really exists? Consider what Wang Shih-ku says to Yün Nan-t'ien in the opening dialogue.
3. Compare the third-person description of the painting Yen-k'o saw at Mr. Chang's house with Wang Shih-ku's first-person description of the painting he saw at Mr. Wang's house. What details in the first description are missing in the second? Why? What details of "that strange painting" are "engraved forever" on Yen-k'o's and Wang Shih-ku's minds? Why?
4. Compare the descriptions of the gardens and homes of Mr. Chang and Mr. Wang. To what effect do the gardens and homes serve as settings for the Autumn Mountain painting?
5. What do the paintings of Ta Ch'ih indicate about the artist's attitude toward nature? Is beauty in nature inherent in nature itself? Or is it true that "beauty is in the eyes of the beholder"? Explain your answers.
6. Applying them to this story, answer the questions that appear on pages 30 and 43-44 of the chapter "The Art of Short Fiction."

To Build a Fire

Jack London

Day had broken cold and gray, exceedingly cold and gray, when the man turned aside from the main Yukon trail and climbed the high earthbank, where a dim and little-traveled trail led eastward through the fat spruce timberland. It was a steep bank, and he paused for breath at the top, excusing the act to himself by looking at his watch. It was nine o'clock. There was no sun nor hint of sun, though there was not a cloud in the sky. It was a clear day, and yet there seemed an intangible pall over the face of things, a subtle gloom that made the day dark, and that was due to the absence of sun. This fact did not worry the man. He was used to the lack of sun. It had been days since he had seen the sun, and he knew that a few more days must pass before that cheerful orb, due south, would just peep above the sky line and dip immediately from view.

The man flung a look back along the way he had come. The Yukon lay a mile wide and hidden under three feet of ice. On top of this ice were as many feet of snow. It was all pure white, rolling in gentle undulations where the ice jams of the freeze-up had formed. North and south, as far as his eye could see, it was unbroken white, save for a dark hairline that curved and twisted from around the spruce-covered island to the south, and that curved and twisted away into the north, where it disappeared behind another spruce-covered island. This dark hairline was the trail—the main trail—that led south five hundred miles to the Chilcoot Pass, Dyea, and salt water; and that led north seventy miles to Dawson, and still on to the north a thousand miles to Nulato, and finally to St. Michael on Bering Sea, a thousand miles and half a thousand more.

But all this—the mysterious, far-reaching hairline trail, the absence of sun from the sky, the tremendous cold, and the strangeness and weirdness of it all—made no impression on the man. It was not because he was long used to it. He was a newcomer in the land, a *chechaquo*, and this was his first winter. The trouble with him was that he was without imagination. He was quick and alert in the things of life, but only in the things, and not in the significances. Fifty degrees below zero meant eighty-odd degrees of frost. Such fact impressed him as being cold and uncomfortable, and that was all. It did not lead him to meditate upon his frailty as a creature of temperature, and upon man's frailty in general, able only to live within certain narrow limits of heat and cold; and from there on it did not lead him to the conjectural field of immortality and man's place in the universe. Fifty degrees below zero stood for a bite of frost that hurt and that must be guarded against by the use of mittens, ear flaps, warm moccasins, and thick socks. Fifty degrees below zero was to him just precisely fifty degrees below zero. That there should be anything more to it than that was a thought that never entered his head.

As he turned to go on, he spat speculatively. There was a sharp, explosive crackle that startled him. He spat again. And again, in the air, before it could fall to the snow, the spittle crackled. He knew that at fifty below, spittle crackled on the snow, but this spittle had crackled in the air. Undoubtedly it was colder than fifty below—how much colder he did not know. But the temperature did not matter. He was bound for the old claim on the left fork of Henderson Creek, where the boys were already. They had come over across the divide from the Indian Creek country, while he had come the roundabout way to take a look at the possibilities of getting out logs in the spring from the islands in the Yukon. He would be in camp by six o'clock; a bit after dark, it was true, but the boys would be there, a fire would be going, and a hot supper would be ready. As for lunch, he pressed his hand against the protruding bundle under his jacket. It was also under his shirt, wrapped up in a handkerchief and lying against the naked skin. It was the only way to keep the biscuits from freezing. He smiled agreeably to himself as he thought of those biscuits, each cut open and sopped in bacon grease, and each enclosing a generous slice of fried bacon.

He plunged in among the big spruce trees. The trail was faint. A foot of snow had fallen since the last sled had passed over, and he was glad he was without a sled, traveling light. In fact, he carried nothing but the lunch wrapped in the handkerchief. He was surprised, however, at the cold. It certainly was cold, he concluded, as he rubbed his numb nose and cheekbones with his mittened hand. He was a warm-whiskered man, but the hair on his face did not protect the high cheekbones and the eager nose that thrust itself aggressively into the frosty air.

At the man's heels trotted a dog, a big native husky, the proper wolf dog, gray coated and without any visible or temperamental difference from its brother, the wild wolf. The animal was depressed by the tremendous cold. It knew that it was no time for traveling. Its instinct told it a truer tale than was told to the man by the man's judgment. In reality, it was not merely colder than fifty below zero; it was colder than sixty below, than seventy below. It was seventy-five below zero. Since the freezing point is thirty-two above zero, it meant that one hundred and seven degrees of frost obtained. The dog did not know anything about thermometers. Possibly in its brain there was no sharp consciousness of a condition of very cold such as was in the man's brain. But the brute had its instinct. It experienced a vague but menacing apprehension that subdued it and made it slink along at the man's heels, and that made it question eagerly every unwonted movement of the man as if expecting him to go into camp or to seek shelter somewhere and build a fire. The dog had learned fire, and it wanted fire, or else to burrow under the snow and cuddle its warmth away from the air.

The frozen moisture of its breathing had settled on its fur in a fine powder of frost, and especially were its jowls, muzzle, and eyelashes whitened by its crystaled breath. The man's red beard and mustache were likewise frosted, but more solidly, the deposit taking the form of ice and increasing with every warm, moist breath he exhaled. Also, the man was chewing tobacco, and the muzzle of ice held his lips so rigidly that he was unable to clear his chin when he expelled the juice. The result was that a crystal beard of the color and solidity of amber was increasing its length on his chin. If he fell down it would shatter itself, like glass, into brittle fragments. But he did not mind the appendage. It was the penalty all tobacco chewers paid in that country, and he had been out before in two cold snaps. They had not been so cold as this, he knew, but by the spirit thermometer at Sixty Mile he knew they had been registered at fifty below and at fifty-five.

He held on through the level stretch of woods for several miles, crossed a wide flat of niggerheads, and dropped down a bank to the frozen bed of a small stream. This was Henderson Creek, and he knew he was ten miles from the forks. He looked at his watch. It was ten o'clock. He was making four miles an hour, and he calculated that he would arrive at the forks at half-past twelve. He decided to celebrate that event by eating his lunch there.

The dog dropped in again at his heels, with a tail drooping discouragement, as the man swung along the creek bed. The furrow of the old sled trail was plainly visible, but a dozen inches of snow covered the marks of the last runners. In a month no man had come up or down that silent creek. The man held steadily on. He was not much given to thinking, and just then particularly he had nothing to think about save that he would eat lunch at the forks and that at six o'clock he would be in camp with the boys. There was nobody to talk to, and, had there been, speech would have been impossible because of the ice muzzle on his mouth. So he continued monotonously to chew tobacco and to increase the length of his amber beard.

Once in a while the thought reiterated itself that it was very cold and that he had never experienced such cold. As he walked along he rubbed his cheekbones and nose with the back of his mittened hand. He did this automatically, now and again changing hands. But rub as he would, the instant he stopped his cheekbones went numb, and the following instant the end of his nose went numb. He was sure to frost his cheeks; he knew that, and experienced a pang of regret that he had not devised a nose strap of the sort Bud wore in cold snaps. Such a strap passed across the cheeks, as well, and saved them. But it didn't matter much, after all. What were frosted cheeks? A bit painful, that was all; they were never serious.

Empty as the man's mind was of thoughts, he was keenly observant, and he noticed the changes in the creek, the curves and bends and timber jams, and always he sharply noted where he placed his feet. Once, coming around a bend, he shied abruptly, like a startled horse, curved away from the place where he had been walking, and retreated several paces back along the trail. The creek he knew was frozen clear to the bottom—no creek could contain water in that arctic winter— but he knew also that there were springs that bubbled out from the hillsides and ran along under the snow and on top of the ice of the creek. He knew that the coldest snaps never froze these springs, and he knew likewise their danger. They were traps. They hid pools of water under the snow that might be three inches deep, or three feet. Sometimes a skin of ice half an inch thick covered them, and in turn was covered by the snow. Sometimes there were alternate layers of water and ice skin, so that when one broke through he kept on breaking through for a while, sometimes wetting himself to the waist.

That was why he had shied in such panic. He had felt the give under his feet and heard the crackle of a snow-hidden ice skin. And to get his feet wet in such a temperature meant trouble and danger. At the very least it meant delay, for he would be forced to stop and build a fire, and under its protection to bare his feet while he dried his

socks and moccasins.   He stood and studied the creek bed and its
banks, and decided that the flow of water came from the right.   He
reflected awhile, rubbing his nose and cheeks, then skirted to the left,
stepping gingerly and testing the footing for each step.   Once clear of
the danger, he took a fresh chew of tobacco and swung along at his
four-mile gait.

In the course of the next two hours he came upon several similar
traps.   Usually the snow above the hidden pools had a sunken, candied
appearance that advertised the danger.   Once again, however, he had
a close call; and once, suspecting danger, he compelled the dog to go
on in front.   The dog did not want to go.   It hung back until the man
shoved it forward, and then it went quickly across the white, unbroken surface.   Suddenly it broke through, floundered to one side,
and got away to firmer footing.   It had wet its forefeet and legs, and
almost immediately the water that clung to it turned to ice.   It made
quick efforts to lick the ice off its legs, then dropped down in the
snow and began to bite out the ice that had formed between the toes.
This was a matter of instinct.   To permit the ice to remain would mean
sore feet.   It did not know this.   It merely obeyed the mysterious
prompting that arose from the deep crypts of its being.   But the man
knew, having achieved a judgment on the subject, and he removed
the mitten from his right hand and helped tear out the ice particles.
He did not expose his fingers more than a minute, and was astonished
at the swift numbness that smote them.   It certainly was cold.   He
pulled on the mitten hastily, and beat the hand savagely across his
chest.

At twelve o'clock the day was at its brightest.   Yet the sun was
too far south on its winter journey to clear the horizon.   The bulge
of the earth intervened between it and Henderson Creek, where the
man walked under a clear sky at noon and cast no shadow.   At half-
past twelve, to the minute, he arrived at the forks of the creek.   He
was pleased at the speed he had made.   If he kept it up, he would
certainly be with the boys by six.   He unbuttoned his jacket and
shirt and drew forth his lunch.   The action consumed no more than a
quarter of a minute, yet in that brief moment the numbness laid hold
of the exposed fingers.   He did not put the mitten on, but, instead,
struck the fingers a dozen sharp smashes against his leg.   Then he sat
down on a snow-covered log to eat.   The sting that followed upon the
striking of his fingers against his leg ceased so quickly that he was
startled.   He had had no chance to take a bite of biscuit.   He struck
the fingers repeatedly and returned them to the mitten, baring the

other hand for the purpose of eating. He tried to take a mouthful, but the ice muzzle prevented. He had forgotten to build a fire and thaw out. He chuckled at his foolishness, and as he chuckled he noted the numbness creeping into the exposed fingers. Also, he noted that the stinging which had first come to his toes when he sat down was already passing away. He wondered whether the toes were warm or numb. He moved them inside the moccasins and decided that they were numb.

He pulled the mitten on hurriedly and stood up. He was a bit frightened. He stamped up and down until the stinging returned into the feet. It certainly was cold, was his thought. That man from Sulphur Creek had spoken the truth when telling how cold it sometimes got in the country. And he had laughed at him at the time! That showed one must not be too sure of things. There was no mistake about it, it *was* cold. He strode up and down, stamping his feet and thrashing his arms, until reassured by the returning warmth. Then he got out matches and proceeded to make a fire. From the undergrowth, where high water of the previous spring had lodged a supply of seasoned twigs, he got his firewood. Working carefully from a small beginning, he soon had a roaring fire, over which he thawed the ice from his face and in the protection of which he ate his biscuits. For the moment the cold of space was outwitted. The dog took satisfaction in the fire, stretching out close enough for warmth and far enough away to escape being singed.

When the man had finished, he filled his pipe and took his comfortable time over a smoke. Then he pulled on his mittens, settled the ear flaps of his cap firmly about his ears, and took the creek trail up the left fork. The dog was disappointed and yearned back toward the fire. This man did not know cold. Possibly all the generations of his ancestry had been ignorant of cold, of real cold, of cold one hundred and seven degrees below freezing point. But the dog knew; all its ancestry knew, and it had inherited the knowledge. And it knew that it was not good to walk abroad in such fearful cold. It was the time to lie snug in a hole in the snow and wait for a curtain of cloud to be drawn across the face of outer space whence this cold came. On the other hand, there was no keen intimacy between the dog and the man. The one was the toil-slave of the other, and the only caresses it had ever received were the caresses of the whiplash and of harsh and menacing throat sounds that threatened the whip lash. So the dog made no effort to communicate its apprehension to the man. It was not concerned in the welfare of the man; it was for its own sake that it yearned back toward the fire. But the man whistled, and spoke to it with the sound of whiplashes, and the dog swung in at the man's heels and followed after.

The man took a chew of tobacco and proceeded to start a new amber beard. Also, his moist breath quickly powdered with white his mustache, eyebrows, and lashes. There did not seem to be so many springs on the left fork of the Henderson, and for half an hour the man saw no signs of any. And then it happened. At a place where there were no signs, where the soft, unbroken snow seemed to advertise solidity beneath, the man broke through. It was not deep. He wet himself halfway to the knees before he floundered out to the firm crust.

He was angry, and cursed his luck aloud. He had hoped to get into camp with the boys at six o'clock, and this would delay him an hour, for he would have to build a fire and dry out his footgear. This was imperative at that low temperature—he knew that much; and he turned aside to the bank, which he climbed. On top, tangled in the underbrush about the trunks of several small spruce trees, was a high-water deposit of dry firewood—sticks and twigs, principally, but also larger portions of seasoned branches and fine, dry, last-year's grasses. He threw down several large pieces on top of the snow. This served for a foundation and prevented the young flame from drowning itself in the snow it otherwise would melt. The flame he got by touching a match to a small shred of birch bark that he took from his pocket. This burned even more readily than paper. Placing it on the foundation, he fed the young flame with wisps of dry grass and with the tiniest dry twigs.

He worked slowly and carefully, keenly aware of his danger. Gradually, as the flame grew stronger, he increased the size of the twigs with which he fed it. He squatted in the snow, pulling the twigs out from their entanglement in the brush and feeding directly to the flame. He knew there must be no failure. When it is seventy-five below zero, a man must not fail in his first attempt to build a fire—that is, if his feet are wet. If his feet are dry, and he fails, he can run along the trail for half a mile and restore his circulation. But the circulation of wet and freezing feet cannot be restored by running when it is seventy-five below. No matter how fast he runs, the wet feet will freeze the harder.

All this the man knew. The old-timer on Sulphur Creek had told him about it the previous fall, and new he was appreciating the advice. Already all sensation had gone out of his feet. To build the fire he had been forced to remove his mittens, and the fingers had quickly gone numb. His pace of four miles an hour had kept his heart pumping blood to the surface of his body and to all the extremities. But the instant he stopped, the action of the pump eased down. The cold of space smote the unprotected tip of the planet, and he, being on that unprotected tip, received the full force of the blow. The blood of his body recoiled before it. The blood was alive, like the dog, and like the dog it wanted to hide away and cover itself up from the fearful cold. So long as he walked four miles an hour, he pumped that blood, willy-nilly, to the surface; but now it ebbed away and sank down into the recesses of his body. The extremities were the first to feel its absence. His wet feet froze the faster, and his exposed fingers numbed the faster, though they had not yet begun to freeze. Nose and cheeks were already freezing, while the skin of all his body chilled as it lost its blood.

But he was safe. Toes and nose and cheeks would be only touched by the frost, for the fire was beginning to burn with strength. He was feeding it with twigs the size of his finger. In another minute he would be able to feed it with branches the size of his wrist, and then he could remove his wet footgear, and, while it dried, he could keep his naked feet warm by the fire, rubbing them at first, of course, with snow. The fire was a success. He was safe. He remembered the advice of the old-timer on Sulphur Creek, and smiled. The old-timer had been very serious in laying down the law that no man must travel alone in the Klondike after fifty below. Well, here he was; he had had the accident; he was alone; and he had saved himself. Those old-timers were rather womanish, some of them, he thought. All a man had to do was to keep his head, and he was all right. Any man who was a man could travel alone. But it was surprising, the rapidity with which his cheeks and nose were freezing. And he had not thought his fingers could go lifeless in so short a time. Lifeless they were, for he could scarcely make them move together to grip a twig, and they seemed remote from his body and from him. When he touched a twig, he had to look and see whether or not he had hold of it. The wires were pretty well down between him and his finger ends.

All of which counted for little. There was the fire, snapping and crackling and promising life with every dancing flame. He started to untie his moccasins. They were coated with ice; the thick German socks were like sheaths of iron halfway to the knees; and the moccasin strings were like rods of steel all twisted and knotted as by some conflagration. For a moment he tugged with his numb fingers, then, realizing the folly of it, he drew his sheath knife.

But before he could cut the strings, it happened. It was his own fault or, rather, his mistake. He should not have built the fire under the spruce tree. He should have built it in the open. But it had been easier to pull the twigs from the brush and drop them directly on the fire. Now the tree under which he had done this carried a weight of snow on its boughs. No wind had blown for weeks, and each bough was fully freighted. Each time he had pulled a twig he had communicated a slight agitation to the tree—an imperceptible agitation, so far as he was concerned, but an agitation sufficient to bring about the disaster. High up in the tree one bough capsized its load of snow. This fell on the boughs beneath, capsizing them. This process continued, spreading out and involving the whole tree. It grew like an avalanche, and it descended without warning upon the man and the fire, and the fire was blotted out! Where it had burned was a mantle of fresh and disordered snow.

The man was shocked. It was as though he had just heard his own sentence of death. For a moment he sat and stared at the spot where the fire had been. Then he grew very calm. Perhaps the old-timer on Sulphur Creek was right. If he had only had a trail mate he would have been in no danger now. The trail mate could have built the fire. Well, it was up to him to build the fire over again, and this second time there must be no failure. Even if he succeeded, he would most likely lose some toes. His feet must be badly frozen by now, and there would be some time before the second fire was ready.

Such were his thoughts, but he did not sit and think them. He was busy all the time they were passing through his mind. He made a new foundation for a fire, this time in the open, where no treacherous tree could blot it out. Next, he gathered dry grasses and tiny twigs from the high-water flotsam. He could not bring his fingers together to pull them out, but he was able to gather them by the handful. In this way he got many rotten twigs and bits of green moss that were undesirable, but it was the best he could do. He worked methodically, even collecting an armful of the larger branches to be used later when the fire gathered strength. And all the while the dog sat and watched him, a certain yearning wistfulness in its eyes, for it looked upon him as the fire provider, and the fire was slow in coming.

When all was ready, the man reached in his pocket for a second piece of birch bark. He knew the bark was there, and, though he could not feel it with his fingers, he could hear its crisp rustling as he fumbled for it. Try as he would, he could not clutch hold of it. And all the time, in his consciousness, was the knowledge that each instant his feet were freezing. This thought tended to put him in a panic, but he fought against it and kept calm. He pulled on his mittens with his teeth, and thrashed his arms back and forth, beating his hands with all his might against his sides. He did this sitting down, and he stood up to do it; and all the while the dog sat in the snow, its wolf brush of a tail curled around warmly over its forefeet, its sharp wolf ears pricked forward intently as it watched the man. And the man, as he beat and thrashed with his arms and hands, felt a great surge of envy as he regarded the creature that was warm and secure in its natural covering.

After a time he was aware of the first faraway signals of sensation in his beaten fingers. The faint tingling grew stronger till it evolved into a stinging ache that was excruciating, but which the man hailed with satisfaction. He stripped the mitten from his right hand and fetched forth the birch bark. The exposed fingers were quickly going numb again. Next he brought out his bunch of sulphur matches. But the tremendous cold had already driven the life out of his fingers. In his effort to separate one match from the others, the whole bunch fell in the snow. He tried to pick it out of the snow, but failed. The dead fingers could neither touch nor clutch. He was very careful. He drove the thought of his freezing feet, and nose, and cheeks, out of his mind, devoting his whole soul to the matches. He watched, using the sense of vision in place of that of touch, and when he saw his fingers on each side of the bunch, he closed them—that is, he willed to close them, for the wires were down, and the fingers did not obey. He pulled the mitten on the right hand, and beat it fiercely against his knee. Then, with both mittened hands, he scooped the bunch of matches, along with much snow, into his lap. Yet he was no better off.

After some manipulation he managed to get the bunch between the heels of his mittened hands. In this fashion he carried it to his mouth. The ice crackled and snapped when by a violent effort he opened his mouth. He drew the lower jaw in, curled the upper lip out of the way, and scraped the bunch with his upper teeth in order to separate a match. He succeeded in getting one, which he dropped on his lap. He was no better off. He could not pick it up. Then he devised a way. He picked it up in his teeth and scratched it on his leg. Twenty times he scratched before he succeeded in lighting it. As it flamed he held it with his teeth to the birch bark. But the burning brimstone went up his nostrils and into his lungs, causing him to cough spasmodically. The match fell into the snow and went out.

The old-timer on Sulphur Creek was right, he thought in the moment of controlled despair that ensued: after fifty below, a man should travel with a partner. He beat his hands, but failed in exciting any sensation. Suddenly he bared both hands, removing the mittens with his teeth. He caught the whole bunch between the heels of his hands. His arm muscles not being frozen enabled him to press the hand heels tightly against the matches. Then he scratched the bunch along his leg. It flared into flame, seventy sulphur matches at once! There was no wind to blow them out. He kept his head to one side to escape the strangling fumes, and held the blazing bunch to the birch bark. As he so held it, he became aware of sensation in his hand. His flesh was burning. He could smell it. Deep down below the surface he could feel it. The sensation developed into pain that grew acute. And still he endured it, holding the flame of the matches clumsily to the bark that would not light readily because his own burning hands were in the way, absorbing most of the flame.

At last, when he could endure no more, he jerked his hands apart. The blazing matches fell sizzling into the snow, but the birch bark was alight. He began laying dry grasses and the tiniest twigs on the flame. He could not pick and choose, for he had to lift the fuel between the heels of his hands. Small pieces of rotten wood and green moss clung to the twigs, and he bit them off as well as he could with his teeth. He cherished the flame carefully and awkwardly. It meant life, and it must not perish. The withdrawal of blood from the surface of his body now made him begin to shiver, and he grew more awkward. A large piece of green moss fell squarely on the little fire. He tried to poke it out with his fingers, but his shivering frame made him poke too far, and he disrupted the nucleus of the little fire, the burning grasses and tiny twigs separating and scattering. He tried to poke them together again, but in spite of the tenseness of the effort, his shivering got away with him, and the twigs were hopelessly scattered. Each twig gushed a puff of smoke and went out. The fire provider had failed. As he looked apathetically about him, his eyes chanced on the dog sitting across the ruins of the fire from him in the snow, making restless, hunching movements, slightly lifting one forefoot and then the other, shifting its weight back and forth on them with wistful eagerness.

The sight of the dog put a wild idea into his head. He remembered the tale of the man, caught in a blizzard, who killed a steer and crawled inside the carcass, and so was saved. He would kill the dog and bury his hands in the warm body until the numbness went out of them. Then he could build another fire. He spoke to the dog, calling it to him; but in his voice was a strange note of fear that frightened the animal, who had never known the man to speak in such way before. Something was the matter, and its suspicious nature sensed danger—it knew not what danger, but somewhere, somehow, in its brain arose an apprehension of the man. It flattened its ears down at the sound of the man's voice, and its restless, hunching movements and the liftings and shiftings of its forefeet became more pronounced; but it would not come to the man. He got on his hands and knees and crawled toward the dog. This unusual posture again excited suspicion, and the animal sidled mincingly away.

The man sat up in the snow for a moment and struggled for calmness. Then he pulled on his mittens, by means of his teeth, and got upon his feet. He glanced down at first in order to assure himself that he was really standing up, for the absence of sensation in his feet left him unrelated to the earth. His erect position in itself started to drive the webs of suspicion from the dog's mind; and when he spoke peremptorily, with the sound of whiplashes in his voice, the dog rendered its customary allegiance and came to him. As it came within reaching distance, the man lost his control. His arms flashed out to the dog, and he experienced genuine surprise when he discovered that his hands could not clutch, that there was neither bend nor feeling in the fingers. He had forgotten for the moment that they were frozen and that they were freezing more and more. All this happened quickly, and before the animal could get away, he encircled its body with his arms. He sat down in the snow, and in this fashion held the dog, while it snarled and whined and struggled.

But it was all he could do, hold its body encircled in his arms and sit there. He realized that he could not kill the dog. There was no way to do it. With his helpless hands he could neither draw nor hold his sheath knife nor throttle the animal. He released it, and it plunged wildly away, with tail between its legs, and still snarling. It halted forty feet away and surveyed him curiously, with ears sharply pricked forward. The man looked down at his hands in order to locate them, and found them hanging on the ends of his arms. It struck him as curious that one should have to use his eyes in order to find out where his hands were. He began thrashing his arms back and forth, beating the mittened hands against his sides. He did this for five minutes, violently, and his heart pumped enough blood up to the surface to put a stop to his shivering. But no sensation was aroused in the hands. He had an impression that they hung like weights on the ends of his arms, but when he tried to run the impression down, he could not find it.

A certain fear of death, dull and oppressive, came to him. This fear quickly became poignant as he realized that it was no longer a mere matter of freezing his fingers and toes, or of losing his hands and feet, but that it was a matter of life and death with the chances against him. This threw him into a panic, and he turned and ran up the creek bed along the old, dim trail. The dog joined in behind and kept up with him. He ran blindly, without intention, in fear such he he had never known in his life. Slowly, as he ploughed and floundered through the snow, he began to see things again—the banks of the creek, the old timber jams, the leafless aspens, and the sky. The running made him feel better. He did not shiver. Maybe, if he ran on, his feet would thaw out; and, anyway, if he ran far enough, he would reach camp and the boys. Without doubt he would lose some fingers and toes and some of his face; but the boys would take care of him, and save the rest of him when he got there. And at the same time there was another thought in his mind that said he would never get to the camp and the boys; that it was too many miles away, that the freezing had too great a start on him, and that he would soon be stiff and dead. This thought he kept in the background and refused to consider. Sometimes it pushed itself forward and demanded to be heard, but he thrust it back and strove to think of other things.

It struck him as curious that he could run at all on feet so frozen that he could not feel them when they struck the earth and took the weight of his body. He seemed to himself to skim along above the surface, and to have no connection with the earth. Somewhere he had once seen a winged Mercury, and he wondered if Mercury felt as he felt when skimming over the earth.

His theory of running until he reached camp and the boys had one flaw in it: he lacked the endurance. Several times he stumbled, and finally he tottered, crumpled up, and fell. When he tried to rise, he failed. He must sit and rest, he decided, and next time he would merely walk and keep on going. As he sat and regained his breath, he noted that he was feeling quite warm and comfortable. He was not shivering, and it even seemed that a warm glow had come to his chest and trunk. And yet, when he touched his nose or cheeks, there was no sensation. Running would not thaw them out. Nor would it thaw out his hands and feet. Then the thought came to him that the frozen portions of his body must be extending. He tried to keep this thought down, to forget it, to think of something else; he was aware of the panicky feeling that it caused, and he was afraid of the panic. But the thought asserted itself, and persisted, until it produced a vision of his body totally frozen. This was too much, and he made another wild run along the trail. Once he slowed down to a walk, but the thought of the freezing extending itself made him run again.

And all the time the dog ran with him, at his heels. When he fell down a second time, it curled its tail over its forefeet and sat in front of him, facing him, curiously eager and intent. The warmth and security of the animal angered him, and he cursed it till it flattened down its ears appeasingly. This time the shivering came more quickly upon the man. He was losing in his battle with the frost. It was creeping into his body from all sides. The thought of it drove him on, but he ran no more than a hundred feet, when he staggered and pitched headlong. It was his last panic. When he had recovered his breath and control, he sat up and entertained in his mind the conception of meeting death with dignity. However, the conception did not come to him in such terms. His idea of it was that he had been making a fool of himself, running around like a chicken with its head cut off—such was the simile that occurred to him. Well, he was bound to freeze anyway, and he might as well take it decently. With this new-found peace of mind came the first glimmerings of drowsiness. A good idea, he thought, to sleep off to death. It was like taking an anesthetic. Freezing was not so bad as people thought. There were lots worse ways to die.

He pictured the boys finding his body next day. Suddenly he found himself with them, coming along the trail and looking for himself. And, still with them, he came around a turn in the trail and found himself lying in the snow. He did not belong with himself any more, for even then he was out of himself, standing with the boys and looking at himself in the snow. It certainly was cold, was his thought. When he got back to the States he could tell the folks what real cold was. He drifted on from this to a vision of the old-timer on Sulphur Creek. He could see him quite clearly, warm and comfortable, and smoking a pipe.

"You were right, old hoss; you were right," the man mumbled to the old-timer of Sulphur Creek.

Then the man drowsed off into what seemed to him the most comfortable and satisfying sleep he had ever known. The dog sat facing him and waiting. The brief day drew to a close in a long, slow twilight. There were no signs of a fire to be made, and, besides, never in the dog's experience had it known a man to sit like that in the snow and make no fire. As the twilight drew on, its eager yearning for the fire mastered it, and with a great lifting and shifting of forefeet, it whined softly, then flattened its ears down in anticipation of being chidden by the man. But the man remained silent. Later, the dog whined loudly. And still later it crept close to the man and caught the scent of death. This made the animal bristle and back away. A little longer it delayed, howling under the stars that leaped and danced and shone brightly in the cold sky. Then it turned and trotted up the trail in the direction of the camp it knew, where were the other food providers and fire providers.

Questions

1. Setting is relatively unimportant in many modern short stories, serving as a mere background for character in action. In some stories, however, man's environment or his encounters with nature are essential to development of character and motivation of action. In "To Build a Fire," setting becomes the most important element. How does setting affect character and action in this story? How is it related to theme? How does the language Jack London uses emphasize the importance of the setting?
2. What are the opposing forces that create the conflict in "To Build a Fire"? (See p. 25.)
3. Explain how the dog is presented—as a character or a symbol or both. Why is the dog essential to the story? Why is he with the man to begin with?
4. In what way does the title suggest the theme of the story?
5. The theme is stated in the third paragraph. Would the story be more interesting to the reader had the theme been less explicitly conveyed? Why or why not?
6. In the first paragraph the narrator says: "This fact [absence of the sun] did not worry the man. . . . He was used to the lack of sun." In the third paragraph, the narrator says: "But all this . . . the absence of sun from the sky . . . made no impression on the man. It was not because he was long used to it." How can the apparent contradiction be explained?
7. What may a reader conclude about the appropriateness of the sentence structure and diction of the story to its content? Consider, for example, such phrases as: "that cheerful orb"; "he did not mind the appendage [on his chin]"; "he had a close call"; the dog "merely obeyed the mysterious prompting that arose from

the deep crypts of its being"; "For the moment the cold of space was outwitted"; "He did this sitting down, and he stood up to do it."

8. Do you at any point admire the man in "To Build a Fire"? Discuss whether you feel any sympathy for him.

9. Why does the man not have a name? What criticism of what kind of human beings is implied by the story?

10. At what point in the action is the outcome foreshadowed? What would be the effect on the whole story if the man had been able to reach "the boys"? (See p. 28.)

11. Trace the series of mistakes the man made. How could he have avoided making any of them?

12. What is the relevance of the frequent references to "the old-timer on Sulphur Creek" to the theme of the story?

Action

C. E. Montague

I

When Christopher Bell was just fifty-two he woke up, one September morning, to feel a slight numbness all down his right side. Some of the numbness was in his right arm; a good deal of it in his right thigh, along its outside, rather less in his right foot; and just a little in his head —all over the hinterland of his right ear.

It seemed a big percentage of a man to "go to sleep" at one time. He lay still for a minute, to let it pass off. But it didn't. So he began to speculate. When he got up, would he be able to stand? And to walk straight? Would his head go on working all right, with that bit of it stiff? Just how hard a punch would it turn out to be, that some god or devil had given him in the night?

He tried. Yes, he could stand, walk, dress, and shave. No portion of him was absolutely on strike. But the numbness went on. And somehow he couldn't feel sure that some part of the right flank of his body or brain would not give way, without notice, and give him a cropper. You never know how deliciously sure you have been of yourself, of every scrap of yourself, all the days of your health, till some small gadget inside you is put out of action: Bell made this deep reflection while going downstairs to his solitary breakfast. He kept one hand on the banisters.

II

Christopher Bell was the reigning sovereign of a respectable dynasty of "merchant princes" in Manchester. For several generations his clan had embraced the higher civilization so far as English public schools and universities lead to such embraces. He had read with understanding and relish, and he had travelled with open eyes. He could value the great things in the arts and in science—indeed, in the whole ampler life of the race. And always, till now, his blood had pretty well bubbled with health. He had rowed, run, swum, and ridden well. To his body, at forty years old, the war had brought a second boyhood of happy absorption in efforts merely physical.

Halfway through the war, the wife he had loved in every tissue of body and soul had died of something brought on by too passionate overwork for the cause. The news came to Bell in a hospital where he had just begun to grow a new skin on a face and hands well flayed and charred by chemical warfare. He could not see at the time, so a nurse read the telegram out. His face was buried deep in a canary-coloured mask of wadding stained with picric acid, so the nurse could not see how he took it—only knew that he thanked her very civilly through the little blowhole left for his mouth. I fancy Bell was hanging on hard to the thought that he still had two children, a boy and a girl, both in their teens. Soldiers, even educated ones, are apt to grow sentimental, especially when wounded. Bell, the war widower, lay, week by week, behind his fancy-dress mask, staying his mind on an ingenious vision of an improved world, to come after the war. He saw it as a young man and a young woman standing in summer twilight, under the stars, with their eyes all a-shine at the loveliness of the life which it had taken so much pain and shame to make possible for them.

Many soldiers hugged these quaint fancies, in their bad times. They helped, for the moment. It was afterward that they had to be paid for. In the foul enervatory air that filled England and Europe just after the war, Bell's boy and girl drifted feebly into failure. Both were married lovelessly now, each to another small waste product of that waste-producing time. Somewhere out of Bell's sight these forefeited objects of his pride and joy were shuffling punily through life. He gathered that they were rather ashamed of him as an old slow-coach provincial.

Bell was not given to wallowing in self-pity. Still, as you see, he had had his losses, like another.

III

Your merchant prince, in these days, is prone to lose heart, get himself up as an owner of land and beeves, and melt weakly into the common herd of squires who know not, poor fellows, what it is to go on 'Change. Bell was different. He had pride. He stuck, as his father had done, to his post among the garrison of the smutty city that had done well by them. He lived where he could hear the Town Hall clock strike twelve when the traffic was quiet at night, and northwind blowing. He liked the sound, he was so oddly civic a person.

To this old-fashioned hobby Bell added some cheap habits less rare in rich men. He stood on guard against his wealth, lest it should cut him off from the sight and sound of ordinary and unprincely men, for whom his regard had been redoubled by four years of living with them in the war. Because of this fad he nearly always went in to the city by tram. This morning he walked the three hundred yards from his house to the tram's stopping place with deliberate caution. He could not be sure of that sleepy right leg. He was still distrusting it temperately when he had taken his seat and was tendering his fare to town.

The conductor rejected the tender, at sight. "We doan't taäke boottons," he said with civil composure.

Bell examined the bright disk that he had offered as a sixpence.

Behold! a silvery trouser button. Last night it had come off and he had slipped it into a pocket. He put his finger tips ruefully up to his eyes. "I'm sorry," he said to the man, as he gave the right coin.

"It's aal reet, sir," the conductor said quietly. Once he saw that no pulling of legs had been intended, his tact and sympathy were perfect.

He passed on to collect other fares. But a new care remained in Bell's mind. Sight, too? Was that going? Sight, touch, the whole sensory business, losing precision, entering on the long slope to decay— the silver cord going loose and the golden bowl cracking? When a man who has known how to read feels the first clap of the hand of Time on his shoulder, he has plenty of ready prompters to ruefulness; so many excellent poets have found handsome words for the mists and mellow poignancy of man's autumn, the lapse from' old vigour and vision into mere drug-takers' dreams while we are led down the avenue lined with overblown roses, to lie in the dust at its end.

Bell kept his head. But his memory was beginning to bulge with lovely quotations not conducive to high spirits—"Bare ruined choirs where late the sweet birds sang," and all that lot.

IV

The morning's office work did him good, while it lasted. He had more than most men of the gift of forgetting himself in the excitement of getting a job to come right—any old job, the dictating of letters, anything. And just now the affairs of his firm were of quite stirring interest. Like many others it had been making large losses for several years. Bell's game was to keep these losses as low as he could without stopping the work and wages of a moorland villageful of people who spun and wove cotton for Bell to sell for less than it cost to make it.

This unacquisitive practice brought Bell into great infamy. Most of his fellow employers wanted to close all the factories down, or half close them down, and leave the work-people to live on their fat. So Bell was an arrant traitor to them. Still, he was an employer: and so, to ardent Socialist eyes, he was a sucker of blood, ex officio. This lively crossfire of censures braced Bell. If it had to be woe unto you when all men spoke well of you, it might be safer when everyone slated you hard. Anyhow it livened you up, like a good stinging wind that has blown across snow. While he schemed to find some not quite ruinous sale for the stuff that piled itself up at the mills, Bell could forget the thing that had clawed him in its clutch during the night.

But the clouds returned after the rain: luncheon time set his mind free to worry, the way your sore tongue returns and returns to the amusement of hurting itself on the sharp point of a tooth lately broken. He lunched at the club; and twice in the one hour it took him, his mind accused younger members of paying him the pestilential kind of un-arguing deference which is really the civil refusal of youth to keep its communications open with age. Could they have noticed the way he walked down the stairs—a canny way, like a horse's when it is afraid on a slippery slope? One younger man opened the door of the billiard room for him. Damn these good manners that ain't good at all.

Going home at twilight, in the tram, Bell thought over all this so absorbedly that he kept his legs crossed the whole way. So, when he stood up, to get off, his right leg had gone clean asleep. It was only asleep in the common and blameless way. Still, he couldn't know that, at first. For all he could tell, a second stroke might have fallen, and this time a real knockout. Of course he kept his fears dark; still, he stepped off the car with such unconcealable care that the conductor slipped a friendly hand under his arm and led him slowly to the safety of the footpath, like a blind man or a drunk.

When Bell had walked a few yards by himself the extra numbness was gone. But the other numbness remained. And so did the feel of that patiently guarding hand under his arm. Of course he had not needed it. Still, perhaps he would, presently, "Mene, mene, etc."—every wall seemed to be covered with sinister shreds of writing. An object for everybody's protection, a call on everyone's forbearance—that was the kind of pest that he might become. Soon, too, perhaps. This kind of plague crept on and on. It never turned back. Five years might bring an invalid chair and a male nurse to put him to bed and to see that he was carted securely about from place to place, to sprawl in the sun—Mentone, the Canaries, Egypt, all the places to which the passé butterflies of our commonwealth were brought to lie out and doze in the warmth when too much eating and idling had brought them back all the way to the status of larvæ. Disgusting!

V

Bell gazed steadily into this smiling future, while eating his dinner alone. From the table he went straight, like a man who knew what he needed, to that shelf in his study on which there were all his pet Alpine books. No other sport had ever so wholly ravished his soul as mountaineering. On the high snows it seemed as if magical fires were lit in your blood; the flame of life burned amazingly; something was added unto a man as divine as whatever it is that makes its way into the vapid juice of a fruit and turns it to wine. Nowhere else in the world was the taste of success so wholly and indefeasibly sweet as it was on the tip of some spire of granite and ice that had all but turned you back in despair by the Daphnean rigour of its resistance. There, uplifted on the swell of the round earth, you could see how men had come to dream Gardens of Eden and Ages of Gold.

He took from the shelf a great climber's narratives of his greatest adventures. Two of these, in especial, could always entrance Bell as soon as he had read a few lines: their vividness gave him an almost physical sense of what they described. Each was a case of cutting steps up a long and extremely steep slope of ice. And in each case the slope had, at one point, ceased even to slope. For just a few feet of its height it had become as vertical as the wall of a house: each man of the party had had to hold himself in to the perpendicular wall, by sheer strength and good hand-hold, against gravitation.

In each case the party had come safely through. But with how big a margin of safety, as engineers say? Bell wondered. A pretty big one, he fancied. Few good climbers slipped in really difficult places; all their faculties were bent up too intently for that, with danger about; they were above their own everyday form. But what if such a party were to try paring and paring away at that pretty wide margin? Something like an experiment, that! To what untold heights of achievement might not the party attain before all the margin was gone! And of course the party might be a party of one.

Bell had once had a holiday dream of climbing a crag that grew steeper and steeper till it was vertical first, and then overhung, more and more, but still he climbed on and on because the crag beetled out over a warm summer sea, so that, when he lost hold in the end, he would only fall from one pleasure into another, out of a mountaineer's paradise into a swimmer's. Cut out the old fear of death in that way, or some other, and—why, you could do anything.

As he sat back with the open book on his knees, a light wind stirred the trees in the garden. It may have been this that called up another old notion of his. This one had visited him in a wood close to Arras, in 1916. During some dark windless weeks of that autumn the unfallen leaves had been fading inertly from green to a dull rusty red, and so down to a dead russet brown; the whole burning heart of the year was collapsing into shabby ashes. Then a night of frost came and then a gale on a day of broken sunshine thrown wildly about between clouds. As the gale stripped the trees it had seemed almost to blow them aflame; sparks of brave yellow flew in the air; the dun beech leaves took light and fell lustrously. Somehow the sight had filled Bell, at the time, with a wish that, when he had to go, he might do it like that—all a-stir and a-glow, by one of the "violent" deaths, as most of the easy ones seemed to be called. Anything but to lie on a bed in a hushed room, with the lights low and life's jolly noises shut out, and people whispering among the shadows. One wrench for the undecayed body, and then unbreakable sleep—what end could equal it?

Now, almost suddenly, these several notions ran into one, as rain-drops do on a newly wet window. Here was the moment to put into practice that old and sound choice of his between the long decrepitude of the flesh and the one clean cut and summary pang that saved you it all. Suicide? Oh! no. But just to carry on, right to the end, the piquant experiment of paring and paring away that limiting and re-straining margin of safety which mountaineers, even the boldest, keep in reserve. Had not all things conspired to free him from too much love of remaining alive—bereavement and baulked hope and now this first lick of fire from heaven, soon to blast the whole of him by degrees? Why, fate had brought him the fulfilment of his old dream. No preci-pice in the world would now have an abhorred death waiting at its foot—merely a warm, quiet sea of painless forgetfulness.

Only—he must be quick, before the accursed thing that was setting to work on him could pith so much of the vigour out of his body that he could not make his own way to a place—already he had a good place in his mind—where he might try the thing out.

VI

At the end of September a savoursome blend of jollity and melan-choly pervades the little Val d'Anniviers. The summer hotels of Zinal, at the head of the valley, are closing. Down the bridle path, through

forests of fir, the hotel staffs stream along joyously, laden with the
year's vintage of tips, to their snug winter homes in the Rhone Valley
below. Reconverted, after four months of restraint and disguise, into
young, natural Swiss men and women, they caper like Alpine cows let
out in the spring. Shouting, chaffing, and singing, they seem to flout
with their merriment Nature's yearly menace to marmots and men.
And Nature answers them back. Almost hour by hour the new snow
creeps down the forested slopes of the valley and grizzles more of its
firs; the morning dew lies late, and even at noon the weakening sun
hangs lazily low above the main chain of the Alps. You feel, all about
you, a big closing-in, the rustle of a heavy curtain falling upon a good
time that is played out at last.

As Bell walked the six miles up from Cissoye to Zinal, he breasted
that jovial current of waiters and chambermaids thawed and rehu-
manized. Jove! they were good to see and to hear, with their jokes and
catches and bold, friendly, unobsequious looks at any man and brother
they met. But everything was good in this place. Even the smell of
Vissoye and its pigs, as he passed, had been the smell of the best holiday of his boyhood. How he had liked life—every bit of it, coloured or
plain, the high lights and the low! Even the jars had been part of the
makings of the incomparable adventure. He wondered whether the
mere feel of things—common things, all sorts of things—could ever have
given anyone else such raptures of secret contentment as they had given
to him.

He had made sure of a room at Zinal. He dined by the light of one
lamp in a corner of the hotel's dining room, now empty and shadowy.
An elderly woman waited upon him; everyone else in the house had
gone down the valley; she had been left for a week or two more, to
cook, wait, make a bed, and draw out a bill for anyone mad enough to
turn up so belatedly. Bell had known her for thirty years—ever since
her marriage to an old guide of his, recently killed on the Meije. She
told him how their son Pierre was now a guide too, rather to her alarm.
She seemed amazingly glad to see Bell, as if he were a bit of some good
old world that had been slipping away. And he——? she asked. Was
he making a *grande course*, as always? Surely not, at this time of year?

He fenced with her apt, friendly questions. He felt like a liar. Indeed, he was one, pretty well; for he fully meant to deceive. He would
go for a walk by himself, he said, after breakfast to-morrow—perhaps
to the Arpitetta Alp only, perhaps rather farther.

She looked at him sadly, with peasant directness. "All alone now!"
she said simply. "And once it was you and Madame—and Gaspard and

me. Ah! the good times." She had all humanity's fate in her face, like
an old woman drawn by Rembrandt—hopes and happy love and then
the dust of the day, dimming the roses, and then great loneliness and
unconsolable tears. Would Monsieur have coffee? she asked.

Bell could face her no longer. It was too treacherous. No, he said,
he would want nothing more. Let her go to bed early, like all the good
marmots. So would he, too, when he had smoked a little end of
tobacco.

When she was gone, he sat by a fire of log she had lit for him in the
small smoking room. To his surprise he found he had nothing to do.
There could be no saying good-bye, no specious last letter to write, no
will to be made, no manifesto of any sort to be left. People do not do
such things just before unforeseen accidents—for the wood must look
raw at the break. A real good tip for the widow of Gaspard would
have to be left in an obvious place: that was all.

It went beyond having nothing to do. There was nothing to think.
He had no fear of post-mortem torture to busy his brain, for the God
of his faith was no fiend. He was equally void of covetous hopes of a
sensational "good time" when the breath should be out of his body.
So far he might have expected his mind to be free. The strange thing
was to find how much of one's usual matter for thought is taken away
if, in twenty hours or so, one will have nothing whatever to fix up or to
see to, no house or business to run, no social beat to patrol, no arts or
letters to care for, nor "public duties" to mind. It was a release. But
it was a queer one—a kind of vacuous and disquieting freedom, such as
a man might attain who was suddenly let off the pressure of gravitation,
so that he needn't keep his feet down to the earth any more—in fact,
couldn't press on it hard if he tried, and so couldn't get any purchase for
putting forth his strength upon anything at all. Bell's released mind
did its best to think firmly of what he was going to do the next day.
But no firmness came: the levers of thought could not find any fulcrum;
they worked at a loss feebly and fumblingly.

He brought over the lamp to review the Inn's tiny library—two shelves
freakishly peopled with the printed leavings of guests lettered, half-let-
tered, unlettered, conventional, independent, and odd. There was the
common aphrodisiac novel of commerce; there was *The Vicar of Wakefield*, all golden sunshine and wit; there were Nat Gould and the wise,
humane book of the great William James on the incessant endeavour
of men to find or to imagine some larger life on which to rest the frail
and soon-tired figure of their own. Yes, that was it: something to lean

against; something sure not to give when you put your whole weight on it, in any state of yourself; that was where peace and strength were to be had; nowhere else. So he fancied, at least; he could not be sure; he was still in that vacuum where his thoughts had no pivot to work on; the wheels did not bite on the road; the cogs would not engage; he thought and he felt, but gropingly, not with the sure and eager drive of a mind and heart that have found themselves by forgetting themselves.

VII

The place that Bell had picked for his purpose was on the west side of the Schallijoch. The Schallijoch, as you may know, is a dip in the ridge that joins the Weisshorn to the Schallihorn. Even the lowest point of the dip is more than 12,000 feet high. The last part of the rise to the ridge from the west is up one of the steepest slopes of ice that are climbed. That is, if you mount it where it is least steep. At some other points it is steeper than any slope that is climbed, or thought to be climbable. The surface of this wall of ice undulates like a sheet of hammered copper—here a concave patch and there a convex one. Though the wall, at its steepest, leans back from the straight, as a whole, it has parts—the upper halves of these hollows and lower of these bulges —at which it is vertical for some feet at a time; and at two or three parts it even overhangs slightly. These last, avoided by climbers happily wedded to life, were what Bell had in mind. He would start up the wall at the steepest part he could find; as he went on, he would make, at each stage, for the point where there seemed to be most an overhang. He would do the thing honestly—try all that was in him to bring the climb off, reach the ridge and prove that, in this small matter, man could do more than he knew. With careful timing he would be up, if up at all, about dusk. In that unlikely event he would carry the test a step further and try to come down his ice ladder by feel, in the dark, instead of descending the gentle snow slopes on the eastern side of the pass.

He worked out a time-table. Three hours' work up to the Arpitetta Alp from Zinal. Three more up from the Alp to the foot of the final ice wall. Half an hour for eating; another half hour for sundries. Four for the ultimate work on the wall. Eleven hours in all. Tomorrow's evening dusk would be over by seven. He would push off at eight in the morning.

VIII

Probably you would have thought him rather a pleasant sight as he quitted Zinal—the outward figure of a hale, fit mountaineer; just a little stricken with years, but vigorous; brindled but not at all bald; leanly and brownly good-looking, turning out by himself, with his ax under his arm and a little luncheon in his pocket, for a walk among the feet of sporting old friends like the Weisshorn and Rothhorn. How can you tell by the looks of a man that he would not feel the point of a pin if you ran it into his thigh, or that this exemption from pain is causing any disturbance of his spirits?

Nobody was to be seen at the emerald Alp of Arpitetta. Like the almost deserted Zinal, like yesterday's valley path streaming with walkers carrying bundles, the empty hovels on the Alp recalled the sight of a whole countryside in flight before the army of an invader. The ashes left from the cheesemaker's fire were wet with drippings from the roof; the rough wooden crane used for swinging the cauldron over the flames flapped in a draught from the door. Outside, the intoxicant beauty of gentian and orchis was over for the year; the rich grass had spread back over the trodden mud of the milking place; but snow was lying a few hundred feet higher up. The invader was near.

Bell's legs were liking the work. The numb one was numb, but it did not give out; it would not let him down. By one o'clock he had reached the tail end—some would call it the snout—of the big Weisshorn Glacier, eaten his rations, and set a first foot on the rough convex swell of honeycombed ice with water flushing out its millions of cells; for the sun was on it. He pawed the stuff tenderly with his ax. Perdition catch his soul but he did love it—strong as iron, carvable as cheese: what genius could have conceived so delicious a union of opposites if, by some disaster, no glaciers had been made.

By three o'clock he was through the freak shapes of the ice fall, across the snowfield above it, and close to the wall that he sought. Yes, its great width and height had the wavy surface that he remembered. It showed like a vast relief map of some low-rolling downland, modelled in ice and then set up to stand on its edge. Off to his right, as he looked up, the general angle was easiest. That was the regular way— very steep but quite practicable. That was of no use for his purpose. Far away to his left the slope looked ferocious enough. But down it an almost continuous fall of stones of all sizes, broken away from the sun-warmed rocks of the Weisshorn, came sliding and hissing, or bounding and smashing explosively. That was no use either. That way would be suicide, not experiment.

He soon saw what he wanted—almost directly above him. There, nearly all the way up to the ridge, the ice was steep and bare and blue, and the face of it waved more at this place than anywhere else. Several broad bosses of rocks must have underlain the smooth surface. Over these the close-fitting ice swelled like a stocking upon a bent knee. Up to the centre of each of these bosses it bulged out overhangingly; just above each centre it would recede at a more merciful angle; but nowhere in the whole thousand feet of ascent would a man have a foothold to stand on, unless he made it.

Bell conscientiously tightened each boot lace and puttee string. Then he set off for the point where he had descried the best overhangs. It was halfway, as he judged, to the top of the wall. If he should conquer that one, then he would look for another, more bulgy.

He cut his steps with almost fanatical care. He had a disagreeable sense of doing something furtive: he couldn't help asking himself, against his own will, "What if somebody saw?" Damn somebody, another part of him said. Still, he cut every step as if he defied the whole solar system to say that it was not the work of a good craftsman bent upon keeping alive. So, he rose slowly. It took a good two hours' work to mount a third of the way to the ridge. But then he was close to what mattered more—the great bulge that he was making for.

The bulge stood out like a gigantic blister upon the face of the ice. It must have been forty feet in diameter and it jutted so much that a stone dropped from its outermost point would only have touched the slope again some fifty feet lower. So the climax had come. To reach that outermost point he would have to climb for about twenty feet as you climb up the under side of a ladder that leans against a wall. And he would have to make the ladder, rung by rung, as he climbed it— fashion each rung out of the ice with his ax, held in one hand, while with the other hand and both feet he clung to three of the rungs made already, and held up the body against the drag of its weight. Every rung would have to be made like a letter box in a door, big enough for the toe of a boot to go in, but so shaped that, when a hand entered, the fingers could bend down inside and grip as you grip the top of a fence. The grand, the crucial question was how long one hand and one arm could hold the body in to the projecting ice wall. For what part of the two hours or so that the other labouring hand might require to cut that fantastical staircase? Of course, if his ax should slip out of his hand, or if one step should break, that would end the affair. But away with the thought of any such bungling.

The moment the overhang started Bell discovered the theory of gravitation to be exceedingly true. The work was amazingly hard.

When he had carved five letter boxes, and used them, an hour had gone. He carved five more and observed that daylight was failing. Behind his back an unsensational sunset was going on at its ease. His left hand was chilled almost dead with all the ice it had gripped; his right wrist was swollen and sore with the intensity of the ax work; his right knee had begun to shake as uncontrollably as chattering teeth; he heard his breath as if it were somebody else's: it made a dry rustling noise, like a bird struggling silently in the hand.

The centre of the boss was now, he reckoned, some eight feet above his head. Beyond it he could see nothing as yet but a tranquil sky with a rose-coloured flush dying out of it. Five letter boxes more, he thought, might take him up to the nipple of this frozen breast and bring the receding slope of its upper half into his sight. It was just at this point that it struck him as a clear, sober matter of fact that he could not get up those eight feet. His strength was running out fast: one more good letter box was all that he could conceive himself able to make. He made it, hacking away with slow, painful strokes, his ax handle slippery with his sweat. He reached up his left hand to grab the new hold and dragged a foot up to its new place below. Then, just to go down fighting, he went through the movements of starting to chip out yet another step. Second by second the effort held out: his strokes were the taps of a child; his wrist felt like breaking; yet somehow he finished the hole and forced his left hand to rise up to it; then he even hauled up in its turn a right foot of infinite weight; the poor quivering knee had to straighten out next, and did it, after a long, doubtful struggle. But that was the end, he felt, of all possible effort.

By this time all his senses had the morbid exultation that will sometimes come of fierce physical effort. His mind was at leisure, after a fashion. He was fully aware of the sunset; he did not miss the charm of its sabbatical calm; the majesty and mystery of mountains were still there, all right. A verse he had liked as a boy came into his head, as beautiful things that have built themselves into your mind are apt to do at a crisis—as people who once went to church will cry out "Oh! God" when a smash comes.

> "And here indeed might death be fair
> If death be dying into air
> And souls evanished mix with the
> Illumined sky, eternal sea."

But no pretty dying for him, if death could be still headed off. He started desperately to try again, sweating and straining. No good: the feeble strokes of his ax scarcely scratched the bare ice; his left hand was frost-bitten now, past feeling anything. Only five feet to relative safety, but five more than any spur worn by his will could drive the spent body. "I'm done," he said, and ceased to struggle upward.

IX

Some innate impulse to take the thing well and not let human dignity down at a pinch kept him resolved to hold on, foot and hand, to the last moment possible.

While he clung so, the sun left him. A high Alpine sunset is sudden, like tropical ones. A cold, sharp-edged shadow raced up from the valley, chasing the sunlight before it. Pursuer and fugitive scudded up over the tops of the firs and across the bright green of the Alp Bell had passed, and then up the ice fall and on up the wall till the shadow came down like a great frigid hand on the sweaty back of his neck. Next moment the last warmth and light fleeted up out of sight, over the bulge. As his gaze followed, his cheeks felt the sting of a few falling granules of ice; little chips of it, rather; even a few rather big ones. A trickle of ice scraps seemed to be sliding down the upper half of the bulge, to dive into space on reaching its centre—most of them clear of his back.

Queer! Was an ice avalanche coming? No need to suppose it, though. Glaciers, crushed and huddled things, always heaving and cracking, played curious tricks and ground out all sorts of freak rubbish. Oh! let the ice do what it liked, all his business with it was done; all that he could now attend to was a kind of dream noise, big, muted and almost asleep, that the torrent was making, enormously far off, down in the blackening trench of the valley—that and a kind of emotional dream of himself, the dying man doing his best to take leave as was meet—a figure at which he could look, as it were, from outside, and dreamily feel it to be rather touching.

Into this semidream there managed to enter, also, a sound more abrupt—a little noise like the low startled cry that some women give when they see a horse fall or a big window is smashed. The cry worked itself into his dream, but also it roused him. "Getting light-headed," he thought. But he wasn't. Almost as quick as that thought, a new sound, a light hissing rub, rushed down to his ears and an ice ax slid over the bulge overhead and out into the air: it whizzed past the back of his head.

To anyone versed in high mountains an ice ax loose and falling in any such place is a portent of horror, like a child's pony galloping riderless home or a boat adrift, bottom uppermost, in a Thames lasher. It means that somebody may have just lost the power to move, without help, at a place where a man unable to move will soon be unable to live. Suddenly Bell's mind took eyes to itself; it saw a party of some sort above him, trying to cut its way down the ice wall, straight toward the deadly bulge that now beetled over himself. At this hour! And by such a route! They must be mad; so he thought—forgetting himself. And now one of them was disabled—perhaps had disabled the whole of his party—tethered it to the ice wall. The idea was frightful to Bell.

Another sound came. From somewhere not far overhead there broke, like an explosion, the singular cry that Swiss peasants and some mountaineers employ as a long-distance hail. No other noise of purely human production will carry so far. Harsh, wild, and long, it starts, as the noise of a rocket does, at its maximum loudness, and then wails itself out in a dying fall that has an effect of collapse into despair. Though commonly uttered on quite cheerful occasions, it might be the passionate scream of some wretched animal terrified by the solitude of a desolate place and trying to empty, into one impetuous lamentation, all its burden of loneliness and desire.

Bell held his breath as the sinking shriek thinned away into silence. Then he counted off the seconds half aloud, by guesswork, as bomb throwers learned how to do in the war. The count ran to seven— eight—nine—and, just as Bell was muttering "Ten," the great yell smashed into the silence again. Yes: he had expected that. Someone above was in the last extremity of danger—was trying the last shift of all, the most all-but-hopeless of all—was sending out the Alpine signal of distress into this stone and snow desert where autumn and night had joined to make it utterly certain that no answer could come. It was like praying to God, for dear life, that a well of fresh water might open itself in the dry middle of the Sahara.

X

Up to that point of time, as you have seen, Bell had been the kind of dual creature that most of us are for nearly the whole of our days. Part of him had toiled, sweated, and ached, and another part of him had been sorry for that one. But, from the moment the second yell came, this twofold arrangement was somehow abolished. All craving or need for any part of himself to be troubled about any other was over; now there was nothing at all to work out any more, no next move to be consciously planned, nor hesitant will to be coaxed or hustled, nor any plaguey choice to be made. All of the man was one unit at last, and it lived intently and intensely, moved by some force which it had no more desire to question than flames have to ask, "Why burn upward?"

The next mystery was that out of the mind so suddenly lightened there seemed, as it were, to overflow lightness into Bell's body of lead. Strangely empowered, his left foot was rising already to thrust itself into the next letter box; almost gaily his right arm, freed from its preoccupation with pain, was beginning to hack a new hand hold above. How long it took him to make he could not have told, then or after. For time, too, was abolished; long trains of executive, practical thought could run on to their end instantaneously; courses, whole courses, of study of relevant things—of the state of the ice, minute changes of gradient, the swift regelation following sundown—were carried out without any sense of duration. One of the revelatory trances had come, in which even a plain man sees for once that an eternity need not be long and that in a single moment he may have everlasting life.

A minor, but still a piquant, discovery was that he had never really known till now what it was to cut a good sizable strip off that old margin of safety which he had imagined himself to have all but used up. His new letter boxes were marvels of sketchy adequacy; they were high art in the skimpiness of the means that they took to their end; triumphs of confident "cheek" to Nature, they bluffed that august power quite wittily. Almost before the vocalist overhead had completed the long S O S of the mountains—it takes three minutes in all—Bell had his chest up to the dead centre of the bulge and saw what he had come for.

Some thirty feet higher up, a woman in mountain kit, with no ax and no hold for hand or foot, was dangling at a long rope's end. Her body revolved a little as it hung against the steep ice, but she was making no voluntary movement. The rope constricting her chest was held with one straining hand by a man perched eighty feet higher up. He was clearly unable to move, hand or foot, without being dragged off his stance by the weight of the woman. He stood on one foot—his right: it seemed to be firmly placed on a tiny step; and a little above his hand he had the pick of his ax driven well into the ice. To the steel bracket thus formed by the ax head the man was holding on stoutly with his right hand.

The sorry sight explained itself. The woman must have been cutting steps down the slope; she must have slipped from a step, and dropped her ax with the shock. The man had checked her fall well, but both were hung up as immovably as a couple of stoats nailed to a gamekeeper's door. And now the rope must be slowly killing the woman. Just as Bell's head topped the bulge she called out in a strangled voice to the man: "Can you cut the rope, Teddy? I'm done, anyhow. Think of the kiddies. You *must*." The man held on.

Bell gave tongue as loud as the dry brown fur lining his mouth would allow. "Well held, sir," he roared. "It's all right, I'm coming."

Not once in a long and respectable Alpine career had Bell thought he would ever entrust his person to ledges quite so narrow as those on which he made the rest of his way up to that pendent woman. And yet he had never, in any hard place, felt such absolute freedom from any uneasiness. As he romped up, he sang out, at intervals: "There in three minutes," "Just two minutes more," "Only one minute more," "Half a shake—I'm just there." Then he arrived. He cut a big step close to where the woman's feet hung, planted his own firmly on it, and then stooping and straightening up again, took the weight of her, sitting, on his right shoulder. Lest she be fainting he put up his right hand behind her, to hold her in place.

She was no fainter, though she was white, yellow, greenish—all the bad colours that beauty itself may have to put on in bad times. "She's a good 'un," Bell thought, as she sat quiet, panting.

"*You're* a great sportsman," she gasped, when she had breath enough.

Feeling all the weight off the rope of a sudden, the man above shouted down thickly, "Sure you have got her, sir?"

"Right as rain," she called up from her perch.

Bell added: "Leave the rope slack, and dig in. We'll come up when you're comfy."

The man gave a tuneless yodel of joy and was plying his ax the same instant; chips and wedges of ice came pelting down from the great step that he must be cutting, from which to make the whole caravan fast. In five minutes he ceased hacking, braced himself, drew in the slack of the rope and announced that now he could hold up a cow for a day.

Bell let the woman cannily down till her feet found a trim ledge that he had managed to scratch out while holding her up. But some four or five feet of smooth ledgeless ice intervened between this and the lowest step the woman had cut, coming down, before she slipped off. Some new ones had to be made. "Care to cut 'em?" Bell asked. "Or shall I?"

She ruefully opened the hands in which no ax was now held. "I dropped it," she said, "like a mug. I feel sick with shame."

"Have mine," he said, holding it out.

Her open boy face shone with joyous relief, as if at a gift of free absolution from sin. Even now their lives hung on this ax that he was entrusting to her, the convicted ax dropper. She took it. "You are a very generous person," she said. "Now I'll unrope, and go up by myself, and you shall tie on."

He shook his head firmly. "You mustn't unrope."

Her eyes broke out in a quick sparkle of anger. "You've *got* to rope up," she said, flushing. "I know that I've done a dud thing and can't preach. But what about you? Climbing alone! coming up out of nowhere, almost at night. Up a worse slope than this beast! Think it bears looking into? Eh? Well, do you mean to rope up, or shall both of us climb in this way that you seem to think right?"

Bell fairly funked the scrutiny of the young woman's spirited simplicity. When once simplicity sets out to inquire, what else is so penetrating? "Well, you tie on in the middle," he said, "and I at the end."

"That's fair," she agreed. A few feet of spare rope were let down by her husband. In two or three minutes, at most, the man who would have shuffled off the mortal coil was securely girt with the most delectable of its loops, the cheerfullest symbol of human determination not to withdraw from the banquet of life—only to salt a dish now and then with a few little hazards.

XI

The last daylight was gone when the three stood safe on the level roof of the ridge, scrunching its gritty granular snow somewhat shyly, though partly kept in countenance by the dark, which is itself a shy, friendly thing. Bell, now a mere dual creature again, had been wondering, all the way up the last flight of ice stairs, how he should give these married lovers a chance to reassert their lately threatened right to possession of each other's lips. Best, he thought, just to turn his back on them when he got up, and try to look busy, coiling the rope.

But they also seemed to have some sort of plan. The man was waiting above the last step, to shake Bell by the hand—really to shake him—and mumbling something which Bell did not desire to make out more clearly. The cup of his consternation was filled when the lady

raised his disengaged hand to her lips, a gesture for which he had
not been prepared by her vivacity lower down.

Then, with one silent consent, they all stampeded away from the key
of emotion. "You travel light, sir," said Bell, just to say something
trivial. The other two seemed to carry not so much as a prune or a
biscuit between them.

"Well——" said the man, and then Bell imagined the man must be
having a quiet laugh in the dark.

"Oh! I know I can't talk," Bell admitted. "The fact is I didn't expect
to be coming right over the Pass."

"Same here," said the man. "We just walked up from Randa—
meant to go only as far as the hut for the Weisshorn, eat our sand-
wiches there, and go back to dinner. Then—it *was* rather mad, but the
snow was so toppingly good—we thought we might just rush the
Schallijoch before dark, sleep at Zinal, and come back tomorrow."

"Gosh, it was rash!" exclaimed Bell, off his guard. He felt sure, the
next instant, the man was quite seeing the humour of such a rebuke
from such a sinner. Hastily trying to cover the slip, Bell made another.
He asked, "How on earth did you miss the way down?"

The man didn't exactly say, "How did *you* miss the way up?" but he
did say, "Yes, it was stupid, but—well, you know how it isn't so easy to
see a way down from above as it is from below?"

"Hadn't we better push off?" said Bell rather hurriedly. "We'll be
getting friz, up here." But it was not the cold that he minded. It was
the heat. It felt as if he couldn't move his tongue without burning his
fingers.

The three truants had luck. Just such a full moon as they needed,
not having a lantern, was on the point of rising from behind the snowy
mass of the Mischabel, beyond the forest glen of the Visp. The mounting light could no longer contain itself. Its bright animation was
pulsing up the dark violet of the sky in tremulous waves. It would
be easy, by such a light as was coming, to follow the downward track
left by the couple, on their way up, almost to the door of the old
Weisshorn hut, a refuge squat, squalid, flea-haunted and cramped, but
divinely rich in raw materials for manufacturing heat, against a long
night of hard frost.

At any time it is rather exciting to walk in the dark, and in silence,
with anyone whom you like but don't yet know very well. What is he
thinking about? You? And, if so, in what way? Barring you? Liking
you? Wanting to throw down the conventional fence and talk frankly?
An hour or two of this blindfold contact between mind and mind may so

work on them both that when their eyes meet under a lamp at the end of the walk it may feel as if they had had a long and intimate conversation, leaving each of them just slightly anxious to know that the other has taken nothing amiss. Even thus, with friendly and deprecatory looks, did Bell and the strangers regard each other by candlelight two hours later, among the strong shadows and smells of the hut.

In ten minutes more the man's wife, who had walked like a true Joan of Arc, was exercising the blessed privilege of healthy and tired young people of thirty or so. While she slept like a prosperous babe, her man and Bell smoked as they lay in the hay at the big sleeping shelf's other end. Smoking helps to keep talk good. A man can puff at his pipe between each thing he really wants to say and the next. No gap-filling rubble is required.

Bell ascertained first that the man's name was Gollen and that he was a doctor—the Harley Street species of doctor. Bell gave in return his own name and description. Then they enjoyed one of those unembarrassing pauses. Then Bell said, somewhat brusquely, "There's one thing we have to get straight."

"Go it," said Gollen.

"You seem to imagine you're under some sort of obligation to me."

"Well, you see, we're alive. And, before you appeared, our number was up."

"So was mine."

"Oh! everyone's is, in a sense. 'All condemned to death,' doesn't somebody say, 'with an indefinite reprieve.' But ours wasn't indefinite. We were booked to go West in five minutes."

"I was to do it in one. In less. I should have dropped off my holds in ten seconds if you people hadn't blown in."

"Hullo?"

"Sure thing. I was done. I had never known until then how far doneness could go. That's how it felt, anyhow. Then your wife's ax came along. That by itself held me on for a jiffy or two. And then you hollered—gad! you *can* holler—and everything changed. There was something new in me, or round me, at work on me somehow. Every bit of soreness and worry and funk was taken right off me—nothing was left in the world but one energy—just an enveloping, mastering sort of a push. It went up like a flame and it took me along—it made everything easy and light. And it wasn't only a thing in the mind. Old brother body himself was roped into the movement: some of the waft of this impulse seemed to get itself into my muscles. D'you follow these ravings?"

"Rather. Physicians aren't the fools that they were. We don't go on missing out what the mind—or the soul, if you like—has to say to all the dynamic affairs of the body."

Bell puffed his pipe for a while. Then he said "See? That's how you two preserved me. So if thanking is what we're about, thanky kindly."

Gollen, too, smoked in silence for the next minute or two, before asking, "The ice overhung where you were when I first caterwauled?"

"Can't tell you the angle. Hadn't got a clinometer thing. Of course it wasn't a motoring road."

Gollen laughed. Bell liked Gollen's face when he laughed, so far as it could be seen among the tangle of wry shadows thrown about the hut by a small flame that still leapt in the stove. Gollen's face made Bell think of a trade term—"good ordinary." He had blunt goodish features, strong and good-tempered. A straight, friendly man, you would say, and easily amused; a good man to be in a hole with. Bell enjoyed such men. They made the world go round. As he was thinking so, Gollen suddenly asked, "I say—why did you do it?"

As Bell did not answer at once, Gollen added, "Of course, it's cheek —asking. Tell me to go to hell, if you like, and I'll warmly approve. Only, well—I'm a doctor."

Bell cut the thing short. He answered at once what Gollen might go on to ask in another few minutes. "Yes—the spring's running dry. The salt losing its savour, you know—the wine going flat. And worse coming."

Again Gollen did the bold thing. "Any particular evil?" he said.

Bell liked the man. And when two men would both have been dead a few hours ago if either had failed at a pinch, they may soon get on terms. Bell avowed the whole business—his symptoms, his surmises and disgusts, and his specious experiment.

Gollen listened, as wise doctors do. "Did that numbness cramp you to-day?" he asked at the end.

"No. But it was there all the day—except just the time—ten minutes or so, I suppose—when——" Bell hesitated for a moment.

"When you were in action?" said Gollen.

"Action?"

"Oh! I don't mean just doing violent things out of doors—pressing triggers or lassoing cows. I mean getting every Jack fibre there is in your nature alive and utterly turned on to something outside you—

absorbed in it, lost in it—every bit of your consciousness taken up into some ecstasy of endeavour that's passion and peace."

Bell nodded, and Gollen went on: "I guess the great artists—all sorts of 'em—know how to bring the fit on, or it comes when they're at the top of their form—they seem to get further and further above 'emselves —hold the note out in a way that we can't—bring every tissue they have in their being to bear on the effort to get a wee touch to come right. Saints, too, I suppose—the pukka ones, like Francis, the man at Assisi: they have the knack too: they can get more alive; they've found how to exist at a sort of top pressure. I fancy all of us get just a glimpse of the thing now and then—of what living might be, you know—at a great turn in a game, or when we're in love, or if some beautiful thing in a book bowls us over. Only, we can't hold the note, or we can't do it yet: the pitch is too high for our reach; so we flop back into flatness. But we shall get there. I do believe that. What we've done since we started as jellyfish is to get more and more of ourselves into action, and we shall go on until we are as much more in action—real true action— than now, as we are now than when we were jellyfish. Why, in a few thousand years we may all be able to live half our time as you lived to-day for ten minutes."

"Something in that," Bell assented.

Gollen apologized meekly. "Sorry to verge upon 'uplift.' Still, one can't always bother about the convention that talk has got to be pessi- mist piffle."

Bell nodded. Reigning conventions had few less dutiful followers than he.

They smoked again for a while. Presently Gollen said, "How goes the weather?" He rose and opened the door of the hut very quietly. Bell followed him out to the hut's tiny terrace.

Nothing at all was wrong with that night. Beyond the queenly white shape of Mont Rose the moon rode gloriously high, burnished and flashing with frost, above sleeping Lombardy. Gowned in new snow and bejewelled with sparkles of light, the Weisshorn, the greatest great lady in nature, looked as lovely to Bell as when the first sight of that pale supreme grace had taken his breath away in his youth. At the height where they stood the frost had silenced every trickle of water, leaving all space to be filled with subtler challenges to the ear. The air almost crackled with crispness: it was alive with the massed animation of millions of infinitesimal crystallizations. The Schalliberg Glacier, a little away to their right, had its own living whisper, the sum of the innumerable tiny creaks and fractures of its jostling molecules of ice. Up here, where the quiet of night was suffused with this audible stir of the forces fashioning the earth, it felt as if some murmurous joint voice of all existence were abroad and life itself were trying to make its high urgency felt.

"Pretty good!" Gollen said presently.

"Yes, it's all right," answered Bell.

Gollen waited a minute or two. Then he asked, "Is it all right—enough?"

"Oh! yes," said Bell. "I'm sticking on."

Commentary

It is appropriate that the content of a story named "Action" should be presented in a form that so vividly depicts action. The action of the story is developed in eleven clearly marked episodes or incidents. The initial episode is the simple wakening of the central character one morning and the beginning of his day's action. In this very short opening section, we learn that Christopher Bell is fifty-two, that his body is waging a battle against nature because he seems to have had a stroke. We learn that it is September, the autumn of his life as well as nature's. The story, we observe, is to be told from the third-person-central point of view (see p. 35): everything we learn is to come through the thoughts, feelings, and actions of the central character. The theme is suggested in this first episode as the conflict, both external and internal (see p. 25), is presented: numbness versus action—man versus physical nature (external) and man versus his human nature (internal). By the end of the short initial episode, we have been promised fictional content whose character, action, and theme are harmoniously interrelated.

The second section is less an episode than a passage of exposition (see p. 26). We learn some of the background of the central character, what has happened to him, what kind of person he has been, why the action of the story has started with the conflict it has: Christopher Bell's body is fighting nature, but his soul is also fighting human nature; he has lost his wife and, for all practical purposes, his children, too; he is a man alone and loveless, wrapped up in self.

The third section continues the exposition, further develops the characterization, and also presents an episode that makes the action progress. Bell goes on the tram to work and by mistake offers the conductor a button instead of a coin for his fare: additional evidence that he is losing his battle against nature. Is he losing his sight? his senses? His social vision, too, is going, for he scarcely notices the conductor's tact and sympathy. Bell is still very much wrapped up in himself. In the fourth section, while exposition and characterization continue, the action finds Bell at work in his Manchester firm, which is not doing very well. Momentarily forgetting his numbness—both of body and soul—he works hard, demonstrating social concern and responsibility. But at lunch, he is alone and free to worry again. Then he observes the good-mannered deference to him of some young people, but his reaction is not that of a warm, outgoing human response; he sees what happens only as further evidence of nature's old theme of youth versus age.

Home again that night, Bell permits numbness of soul and body to take over. He reads some of his Alpine books and dreams of an autumn during the war, a foreshadowing of the crucial mountain climb later in the story. Bell decides not to commit suicide but rather to seek painless forgetfulness in "an unforeseen accident" before it is too late for him to take action. He chooses to risk dying through action rather than to live in numbness. But he is still alone and wrapped up in self.

In the sixth episode, Bell is in Switzerland at the Zinal hotel. He still cannot find himself by forgetting himself. The elderly woman in the dining room is kindly toward him, but he "could face her no longer. It was too treacherous." Once again he has rejected his human natural drive to reach out to another human being. By now we can see that the conflict of this story is not only the external one of man against physical nature but also the internal one between man and his own human nature.

The seventh episode finds Bell choosing the west side of the Schallijoch for his mountain ascent the next day; it is the kind of climb "avoided by climbers happily wedded to life." But progressions toward a change in his attitude (now that he is about to take further action) occur when he determines to fight nature honestly—he will do his best to prove man can do more than he knows. A positive ending for the story is hereby foreshadowed.

At eight the next morning, Bell's numbness of body is not apparent as he starts his climb; he is an outward figure of health. A poetic, detailed description of the ice, rock, and snow is an affirmation of nature's beauty and order which enable the man to "cut every step as if he defied the whole solar system to say that it was not the work of a good craftsman bent upon keeping alive." Bell skillfully carves "letter box" holds for his feet and hands as he scales the Weisshorn through strong agonizing action, "fierce physical effort." But as the climb becomes steeper, his efforts begin to flag. "I'm done," he says and ceases to struggle upwards. Suspense for the reader is heightened: perhaps nature will win out over man after all. Suddenly, chips of ice fall on Bell, then an ax falls, and a human yell—the Alpine distress signal—brings him as well as the action of the story to the point of highest tension between the opposing external forces of man and nature; on the one hand, and the opposing forces of man and his human nature, on the other hand.

The tenth is the climactic episode for both external and internal conflicts. Later on, we learn from Bell as he is talking to the doctor and his wife, that the doctor's second yell had changed everything for Bell. That yell is the point of climax in the story when a man wins his battle against nature and against the selfish side of his human nature. Bell conquers body and mountain as he physically rescues the woman, but he is able to do so because he has forgotten himself for the sake of another human being. He finds both physical strength and strength of soul, through almost superhuman action—"the cheerfullest symbol of human determination not to withdraw from the banquet of life—only to salt a dish now and then with a few little hazards."

The eleventh and last episode is the denouement of the action. Bell and the doctor and his wife take refuge in the old Weisshorn hut and become acquainted. Nature seems to acknowledge the victory of human action. "How goes the weather?" asks Dr. Gollen. The answer is "Nothing at all was wrong with that night." The moon shines over "queenly" Mont Rosa and the Weisshorn, "the greatest great lady in nature." Bell thinks how "the forces fashioning the earth" join human life, making its "high urgency felt." The story and action end on a high note of human affirmation: "Oh! yes," said Bell. "I'm sticking on."

Questions

1. C. E. Montague has created a remarkable characterization in Christopher Bell. The biographical details of Bell's life as told in the second section of "Action" parallel some of Montague's own life: he, too, was a man of action, a sportsman, an Alpine climber, a soldier at the age of forty, and a victim of poor health. During the course of the story, we learn many other details about Bell that substantiate the general statements about him in the second section.

For example, how do we know that Bell has been a traveler? What places in the world do his thoughts indicate he has visited? What are his attitudes toward some of these places? What do these attitudes suggest about his character?

2. How do we know that Bell is a man who "values the arts and sciences"? How does this valuing motivate his triumphant action over nature and self?

3. The story abounds with literary allusions that show the kind of reader Bell has been and what books have meant to him. What attitudes toward life are reflected in some of the books he has read? In *Bartlett's Familiar Quotations,* find the sources for the following literary allusions: "*the silver cord* going loose and the *golden bowl* cracking"; "the man who would have *shuffled off the mortal coil* was securely girt with the most delectable of its loops. . . ."; "Bare ruined choirs where late the sweet birds sang"; "*Mene, mene,* etc.—every wall seemed to be covered with sinister shreds of writing." In Sir James George Frazer's *The Golden Bough,* look up the myth of Daphne, to whom Bell alludes when he thinks of the "tip of some spire of granite and ice that had all but turned you back in despair by the *Daphnean rigour* of its resistance."

4. What does Bell mean when he thinks: "There, uplifted on the swell of the round earth, you could see how men had come to dream Gardens of Eden and Ages of Gold"? What does this thought suggest of the effect nature has on man? on man's artistic impulse?

5. When an author selects details that are not essential to the reader's understanding of the content of a story, the author has what we call "a free choice." He may choose any such details he wishes as long as they do not detract from or contradict his theme. The careful, skilled writer, however, when he has such a free choice, will select details that are not only relevant to the content but also make an enriching contribution to our understanding of the meaning of the story. For example, in the Inn's tiny library the books that Bell examines are not just *any* books. They are Goldsmith's *The Vicar of Wakefield,* a book by Nat Gould, one by William James, and "the common aphrodisiac novel of commerce." What are Bell's knowledge of and attitude toward these particular books, and how does reference to them imply more about him as well as about the theme of "Action"?

6. During his climb of the Weisshorn, Bell becomes aware of the sunset's "sabbatical calm" and of "the majesty and mystery of mountains." He remembers as a boy liking the verse:

> And here indeed might death be fair
> If death be dying into air
> And souls evanished mix with the
> Illumined sky, eternal sea.

Why does this particular verse come into Bell's head at just the time it does? How does it relate to the Man and Nature theme of the story?

7. There are many poetic passages in "Action," reflecting not only Bell's familiarity with the poetry he has read but also his own poetic vision. For example, after the sudden sunset, he observes: "A cold, sharp-edged shadow raced up from the valley, chasing the sunlight before it. Pursuer and fugitive scudded up over the tops of the firs and across the bright green of the Alp Bell had passed, and then up the ice fall and on up the wall till the shadow came down like a great frigid hand on the sweaty back of his neck." Not only is this passage a poetic expression of the image described, but it is also a metaphorical comment on how Bell is feeling and acting at this point in the story. How *is* he feeling and acting? Find other poetic passages in the story that show a man's appreciation of and kinship with nature.

8. The final section of the story recapitulates the theme. It is actually stated by Dr. Gollen. Find his statement and, on the basis of the characterization of Dr. and Mrs. Gollen, determine why it is significant that it is he who states the theme of "Action."

Man and Nature: General Questions

1. In "The Fair Young Willowy· Tree" and "To Build a Fire" the third-person narrators create attitudes toward their respective characters (see p. 34). Find examples of editorializing—expressions of judgment—by the respective narrators. How do these comments contribute to or detract from the total effect of each story? What relationship between human beings and nature is thereby implied?

2. Note the imagery of landscapes in "To Build a Fire," "Action," "Autumn Mountain," and "The Fair Young Willowy Tree." In each case, how does the imagery suggest the interdependence of man and nature and the ambivalence of man's attitude toward nature?

3. How are nature and human nature depicted as different and

as similar in the four stories? To what extent is man depicted as a part of nature?

4. How important to the meaning of the experience of each story is the setting? (See p. 27.)

5. Drawing upon the four stories to illustrate your thesis, demonstrate whether nature is beautiful, ugly, benign, hostile, or indifferent to man.

MORE STORIES ABOUT MAN AND NATURE

"A Bear Hunt" and "A Race at Morning" by William Faulkner

"A Passion in the Desert" by Honoré de Balzac

"My Apples" by Robert Granat

"Old Red" and "The Last Day in the Field" by Caroline Gordon

"Tabusse and His Dogs" by André Chamson

"The Big Bear of Arkansas" by T. B. Thorpe

"The Chrysanthemums" by John Steinbeck

"The Open Boat" by Stephen Crane

"Winter" in Cress Delahanty by Jessamyn West

Man Alone

Introduction

Man's need to be a unique individual in his own right and his equally strong need to identify with society create a duality in his nature. Sometimes the two impulses are in conflict and establish an intolerable situation for him. He must be different from other men and assert his individuality. But conversely, he must submerge his individuality in order to conform to the conventions of his society. When to conform and when not to, then, becomes one of the most serious questions of the humanities, a question that has grown in importance with the growth of modern industrialized society and the shrinking of the world in relation to its increased population.

When man's individuality and social identification are at odds with each other, the polarity of love and hate is accentuated. If man withdraws from society, refusing to conform, he may be foolish or he may be wise. But no matter how right or wrong he may be, the price he pays for nonconformity is loneliness. Sometimes it is his own fault; at other times it is because he is a helpless victim of circumstances beyond his control. Whether internally or externally caused, man's loneliness and how he ultimately copes with it are among the most profound of the themes of the humanities.

Herman Melville's "Bartleby" is about a man who chose a living death, building a wall around himself, rather than compromise his attitude toward the behavior of those whose actions he disapproved. But the lesson he unconsciously taught his employer made the employer understand humanity.

Kafka's "The Burrow" is an allegory that also probes the problem of man's loneliness and the horrors he can create for himself if he withdraws from society instead of facing up to life. In "The Guest" Nobel prize winner Albert Camus explores the isolation that two men experience, an isolation that might have been alleviated for both of them had not social forces beyond them prevented their mutual friendship and support.

An irresponsible social attitude and the extreme egotism and selfish-

ness of a man are the result of fear akin to hate in student James
Renthal's short story "What Mistake?" in the last section of this
book.   But the violation of a moral code in "So Much Unfairness
of Things" results not only in remorse and punishment for a schoolboy,
but also in the promise of love and release from the loneliness he had
suffered.

Man Alone is a theme that recurs in many other stories that also
illustrate different universal themes.   The dual nature of man—he is
both an individual and a social being—is apparent in all the stories
in the Love and Hate and Youth and Age sections; in "To Build a Fire"
and "Action" in the Man and Nature section; in "The Sisters," "The
Man of Adamant," and "Holiday" in the Mortality and Imagination
section; and in the student story "Checking-Out."

Bartleby the Scrivener

A STORY OF WALL STREET

Herman Melville

I am a rather elderly man. The nature of my avocations, for the last thirty years, has brought me into more than ordinary contact with what would seem an interesting and somewhat singular set of men, of whom, as yet, nothing, that I know of, has ever been written—I mean, the law-copyists, or scriveners. I have known very many of them, professionally and privately, and, if I pleased, could relate divers histories, at which good-natured gentlemen might smile, and senti-mental souls might weep. But I waive the biographies of all other scriveners, for a few passages in the life of Bartleby, who was a scrivener, the strangest I ever saw, or heard of. While, of other law-copyists, I might write the complete life, of Bartleby nothing of that sort can be done. I believe that no materials exist for a full and satis-factory biography of this man. It is an irreparable loss to literature. Bartleby was one of those beings of whom nothing is ascertainable, except from the original sources, and, in his case, those are very small. What my own astonished eyes saw of Bartleby, *that* is all I know of him, except, indeed, one vague report, which will appear in the sequel.

Ere introducing the scrivener, as he first appeared to me, it is fit I make some mention of myself, my *employés,* my business, my cham-bers, and general surroundings; because some such description is in-dispensable to an adequate understanding of the chief character about to be presented. Imprimis: I am a man who, from his youth upwards, has been filled with a profound conviction that the easiest way of life is the best. Hence, though I belong to a profession proverbially energetic and nervous, even to turbulence, at times, yet nothing of that sort have I ever suffered to invade my peace. I am one of those unambitious lawyers who never addresses a jury, or in any way draws down public applause; but, in the cool tranquillity of a snug retreat, do a snug busi-ness among rich men's bonds, and mortgages, and title-deeds. All who know me, consider me an eminently *safe* man. The late John Jacob Astor, a personage little given to poetic enthusiasm, had no hesitation in pronouncing my first grand point to be prudence; my next, method. I do not speak it in vanity, but simply record the fact, that I was not unemployed in my profession by the late John Jacob Astor: a name which, I admit, I love to repeat; for it hath a rounded and orbicular sound to it, and rings like unto bullion. I will freely add, that I was not insensible to the late John Jacob Astor's good opinion.

Some time prior to the period at which this little history begins, my avocations had been largely increased. The good old office, now extinct in the State of New York, of a Master in Chancery, had been conferred upon me. It was not a very arduous office, but very pleasantly remunerative. I seldom lose my temper; much more seldom indulge in dangerous indignation at wrongs and outrages; but, I must be permitted to be rash here, and declare, that I consider the sudden and violent abrogation of the office of Master in Chancery, by the new Constitution, as a —— premature act; inasmuch as I had counted upon a life-lease of the profits, whereas I only received those of a few short years. But this is by the way.

My chambers were up stairs, at No. — Wall street. At one end, they looked upon the white wall of the interior of a spacious sky-light shaft, penetrating the building from top to bottom.

This view might have been considered rather tame than otherwise, deficient in what landscape painters call "life." But, if so, the view from the other end of my chambers offered, at least, a contrast, if nothing more. In that direction, my windows commanded an unobstructed view of a lofty brick wall, black by age and everlasting shade; which wall required no spy-glass to bring out its lurking beauties, but, for the benefit of all near-sighted spectators, was pushed up to within ten feet of my window panes. Owing to the great height of the surrounding buildings, and my chambers being on the second floor, the interval between this wall and mine not a little resembled a huge square cistern.

At the period just preceding the advent of Bartleby, I had two persons as copyists in my employment, and a promising lad as an office-boy. First, Turkey; second, Nippers; third, Ginger Nut. These may seem names, the like of which are not usually found in the Directory. In truth, they were nicknames, mutually conferred upon each other by my three clerks, and were deemed expressive of their respective persons or characters. Turkey was a short, pursy Englishman, of about my own age—that is, somewhere not far from sixty. In the morning, one might say, his face was of a fine florid hue, but after twelve o'clock, meridian—his dinner hour—it blazed like a grate full of Christmas coals; and continued blazing—but, as it were, with a gradual wane—till six o'clock, P.M., or thereabouts; after which, I saw no more of the proprietor of the face, which, gaining its meridian with the sun, seemed to set with it, to rise, culminate, and decline the following day, with the like regularity and undiminished glory.   There are many singular coincidences I have known in the course of my life, not the least among which was the fact, that, exactly when Turkey displayed his fullest beams from his red and radiant countenance, just then, too, at that critical moment, began the daily period when I considered his business capacities as seriously disturbed for the remainder of the twenty-four hours.   Not that he was absolutely idle, or averse to business, then; far from it.   The difficulty was, he was apt to be altogether too energetic. There was a strange, inflamed, flurried, flighty recklessness of activity about him.   He would be incautious in dipping his pen into his inkstand.   All his blots upon my documents were dropped there after twelve o'clock, meridian.   Indeed, not only would he be reckless, and sadly given to making blots in the afternoon, but, some days, he went further, and was rather noisy.   At such times, too, his face flamed with augmented blazonry, as if cannel coal had been heaped on anthracite. He made an unpleasant racket with his chair; spilled his sand-box; in mending his pens, impatiently split them all to pieces, and threw them on the floor in a sudden passion; stood up, and leaned over his table, boxing his papers about in a most indecorous manner, very sad to behold in an elderly man like him.   Nevertheless, as he was in many ways a most valuable person to me, and all the time before twelve o'clock, meridian, was the quickest, steadiest creature, too, accomplishing a great deal of work in a style not easily to be matched—for these reasons, I was willing to overlook his eccentricities, though, indeed, occasionally, I remonstrated with him.   I did this very gently, however, because, though the civilest, nay, the blandest and most reverential of men in the morning, yet, in the afternoon, he was disposed, upon provocation, to be slightly rash with his tongue—in fact, insolent.   Now, valuing his morning services as I did, and resolved not to lose them—yet, at the same time, made uncomfortable by his inflamed ways after twelve o'clock—and being a man of peace, unwilling by my admonitions to call forth unseemly retorts from him, I took upon me, one Saturday noon (he was always worse on Saturdays) to hint to him, very kindly, that, perhaps, now that he was growing old, it might be well to abridge his labors; in short, he need not come to my chambers after twelve o'clock, but, dinner over, had best go home to his lodgings, and

rest himself till tea-time. But no; he insisted upon his afternoon devo-
tions. His countenance became intolerably fervid, as he oratorically
assured me—gesticulating with a long ruler at the other end of the room
—that if his services in the morning were useful, how indispensable,
then, in the afternoon?

"With submission, sir," said Turkey, on this occasion, "I consider myself your right-hand man. In the morning I but marshal and deploy
my columns; but in the afternoon I put myself at their head, and gal-
lantly charge the foe, thus"—and he made a violent thrust with the
ruler.

"But the blots, Turkey," intimated I.

"True; but, with submission, sir, behold these hairs! I am getting
old. Surely, sir, a blot or two of a warm afternoon is not to be severely
urged against gray hairs. Old age—even if it blot the page—is honor-
able. With submission, sir, we *both* are getting old."

This appeal to my fellow-feeling was hardly to be resisted. At all
events, I saw that go he would not. So, I made up my mind to let him
stay, resolving, nevertheless, to see to it that, during the afternoon, he
had to do with my less important papers.

Nippers, the second on my list, was a whiskered, sallow, and, upon
the whole, rather piratical-looking young man, of about five and twenty.
I always deemed him the victim of two evil powers—ambition and indigestion. The ambition was evinced by a certain impatience of the
duties of a mere copyist, an unwarrantable usurpation of strictly professional affairs, such as the original drawing up of legal documents.
The indigestion seemed betokened in an occasional nervous testiness
and grinning irritability, causing the teeth to audibly grind together
over mistakes committed in copying; unnecessary maledictions, hissed,
rather than spoken, in the heat of business; and especially by a continual discontent with the height of the table where he worked. Though
of a very ingenious mechanical turn, Nippers could never get this table
to suit him. He put chips under it, blocks of various sorts, bits of
pasteboard, and at last went so far as to attempt an exquisite adjustment, by final pieces of folded blotting-paper. But no invention would
answer. If, for the sake of easing his back, he brought the table lid at a
sharp angle well up towards his chin, and wrote there like a man using
the steep roof of a Dutch house for his desk, then he declared that it
stopped the circulation in his arms. If now he lowered the table to his
waistbands, and stooped over it in writing, then there was a sore aching
in his back. In short, the truth of the matter was, Nippers knew not
what he wanted. Or, if he wanted anything, it was to be rid of a

scrivener's table altogether. Among the manifestations of his diseased ambition was a fondness he had for receiving visits from certain ambiguous-looking fellows in seedy coats, whom he called his clients. Indeed, I was aware that not only was he, at times, considerable of a ward-politician, but he occasionally did a little business at the Justices' courts, and was not unknown on the steps of the Tombs. I have good reason to believe, however, that one individual who called upon him at my chambers, and who, with a grand air, he insisted was his client, was no other than a dun, and the alleged title-deed, a bill. But, with all his failings, and the annoyances he caused me, Nippers, like his compatriot Turkey, was a very useful man to me; wrote a neat, swift hand; and, when he chose, was not deficient in a gentlemanly sort of deportment. Added to this, he always dressed in a gentlemanly sort of way; and so, incidentally, reflected credit upon my chambers. Whereas, with respect to Turkey, I had much ado to keep him from being a reproach to me. His clothes were apt to look oily, and smell of eating-houses. He wore his pantaloons very loose and baggy in summer. His coats were execrable; his hat not to be handled. But while the hat was a thing of indifference to me, inasmuch as his natural civility and deference, as a dependent Englishman, always led him to doff it the moment he entered the room, yet his coat was another matter. Concerning his coats, I reasoned with him; but with no effect. The truth was, I suppose, that a man with so small an income could not afford to sport such a lustrous face and lustrous coat at one and the same time. As Nippers once observed, Turkey's money went chiefly for red ink. One winter day, I presented Turkey witth a highly respectable-looking coat of my own—a padded gray coat, of a most comfortable warmth, and which buttoned straight up from the knee to the neck. I thought Turkey would appreciate the favor, and abate his rashness and obstreperousness of afternoons. But no; I verily believe that buttoning himself up in so downy and blanket-like a coat had a pernicious effect upon him—upon the same principle that too much oats are bad for horses. In fact, precisely as a rash, restive horse is said to feel his oats, so Turkey felt his coat. It made him insolent. He was a man whom prosperity harmed.

Though, concerning the self-indulgent habits of Turkey, I had my own private surmises, yet, touching Nippers, I was well persuaded that, whatever might be his faults in other respects, he was, at least, a temperate young man. But, indeed, nature herself seemed to have been his vintner, and, at his birth, charged him so thoroughly with an irritable, brandy-like disposition, that all subsequent potations were needless.

When I consider how, amid the stillness of my chambers, Nippers would sometimes impatiently rise from his seat, and stooping over his table, spread his arms wide apart, seize the whole desk, and move it, and jerk it, with a grim, grinding motion on the floor, as if the table were a perverse voluntary agent, intent on thwarting and vexing him, I plainly perceive that, for Nippers, brandy-and-water were altogether superfluous.

It was fortunate for me that, owing to its peculiar cause—indigestion —the irritability and consequent nervousness of Nippers were mainly observable in the morning, while in the afternoon he was comparatively mild. So that, Turkey's paroxysms only coming on about twelve o'clock, I never had to do with their eccentricities at one time. Their fits relieved each other, like guards. When Nippers's was on, Turkey's was off; and *vice versa*. This was a good natural arrangement, under the circumstances.

Ginger Nut, the third on my list, was a lad, some twelve years old. His father was a carman, ambitious of seeing his son on the bench instead of a cart, before he died. So he sent him to my office, as student at law, errand-boy, cleaner and sweeper, at the rate of one dollar a week. He had a little desk to himself, but he did not use it much. Upon inspection, the drawer exhibited a great array of the shells of various sorts of nuts. Indeed, to this quick-witted youth, the whole noble science of the law was contained in a nut-shell. Not the least among the employments of Ginger Nut, as well as one which he discharged with the most alacrity, was his duty as cake and apple purveyor for Turkey and Nippers. Copying law-papers being proverbially a dry, husky sort of business, my two scriveners were fain to moisten their mouths very often with Spitzenbergs, to be had at the numerous stalls nigh the Custom House and Post Office. Also, they sent Ginger Nut very frequently for that peculiar cake—small, flat, round, and very spicy —after which he had been named by them. Of a cold morning, when business was but dull, Turkey would gobble up scores of these cakes, as if they were mere wafers—indeed, they sell them at the rate of six or eight for a penny—the scrape of his pen blending with the crunching of the crisp particles in his mouth. Of all the fiery afternoon blunders and flurried rashnesses of Turkey, was his once moistening a ginger-cake between his lips, and clapping it on to a mortgage, for a seal. I came within an ace of dismissing him then. But he mollified me by making an oriental bow, and saying—

"With submission, sir, it was generous of me to find you in stationery on my own account."

Now my original business—that of a conveyancer and title hunter, and draw-up of recondite documents of all sorts—was considerably increased by receiving the master's office. There was now great work for scriveners. Not only must I push the clerks already with me, but I must have additional help.

In answer to my advertisement, a motionless young man one morning stood upon my office threshold, the door being open, for it was summer. I can see that figure now—pallidly neat, pitiably respectable, incurably forlorn! It was Bartleby.

After a few words touching his qualifications, I engaged him, glad to have among my corps of copyists a man of so singularly sedate an aspect, which I thought might operate beneficially upon the flighty temper of Turkey, and the fiery one of Nippers.

I should have stated before that ground glass folding-doors divided my premises into two parts, one of which was occupied by my scriveners, the other by myself. According to my humor, I threw open these doors, or closed them. I resolved to assign Bartleby a corner by the folding-doors, but on my side of them, so as to have this quiet man within easy call, in case any trifling thing was to be done. I placed his desk close up to a small side-window in that part of the room, a window which originally had afforded a lateral view of certain grimy back-yards and bricks, but which, owing to subsequent erections, commanded at present no view at all, though it gave some light. Within three feet of the panes was a wall, and the light came down from far above, between two lofty buildings, as from a very small opening in a dome. Still further to a satisfactory arrangement, I procured a high green folding screen, which might entirely isolate Bartleby from my sight, though not remove him from my voice. And thus, in a manner, privacy and society were conjoined.

At first, Bartleby did an extraordinary quantity of writing. As if long famishing for something to copy, he seemed to gorge himself on my documents. There was no pause for digestion. He ran a day and night line, copying by sun-light and by candle-light. I should have been quite delighted with his application, had he been cheerfully industrious. But he wrote on silently, palely, mechanically.

It is, of course, an indispensable part of a scrivener's business to verify the accuracy of his copy, word by word. Where there are two or more scriveners in an office, they assist each other in this examination, one reading from the copy, the other holding the original. It is a very dull, wearisome, and lethargic affair. I can readily imagine that, to some sanguine temperaments, it would be altogether intolerable. For example, I cannot credit that the mettlesome poet, Byron, would have contentedly sat down with Bartleby to examine a law document of, say five hundred pages, closely written in a crimpy hand.

Now and then, in the haste of business, it had been my habit to assist in comparing some brief document myself, calling Turkey or Nippers for this purpose. One object I had, in placing Bartleby so handy to me behind the screen, was, to avail myself of his services on such trivial occasions. It was on the third day, I think, of his being with me, and before any necessity had arisen for having his own writing examined, that, being much hurried to complete a small affair I had in hand, I abruptly called to Bartleby. In my haste and natural expectancy of instant compliance, I sat with my head bent over the original on my desk, and my right hand sideways, and somewhat nervously extended with the copy, so that, immediately upon emerging from his retreat, Bartleby might snatch it and proceed to business without the least delay.

In this very attitude did I sit when I called to him, rapidly stating what it was I wanted him to do—namely, to examine a small paper with me. Imagine my surprise, nay, my consternation, when, without moving from his privacy, Bartleby, in a singularly mild, firm voice, replied, "I would prefer not to."

I sat awhile in perfect silence, rallying my stunned faculties. Immediately it occurred to me that my ears had deceived me, or Bartleby had entirely misunderstood my meaning. I repeated my request in the clearest tone I could assume; but in quite as clear a one came the previous reply, "I would prefer not to."

"Prefer not to," echoed I, rising in high excitement, and crossing the room with a stride. "What do you mean? Are you moon-struck? I want you to help me compare this sheet here—take it," and I thrust it towards him.

"I would prefer not to," said he.

I looked at him steadfastly. His face was leanly composed; his gray eye dimly calm. Not a wrinkle of agitation rippled him. Had there been the least uneasiness, anger, impatience or impertinence in his manner; in other words, had there been any thing ordinarily human about him, doubtless I should have violently dismissed him from the premises. But as it was, I should have as soon thought of turning my pale plaster-of-paris bust of Cicero out of doors. I stood gazing at him awhile, as he went on with his own writing, and then reseated myself at my desk. This is very strange, thought I. What had one best do? But my business hurried me. I concluded to forget the matter for the present, reserving it for my future leisure. So calling Nippers from the other room, the paper was speedily examined.

A few days after this, Bartleby concluded four lengthy documents, being quadruplicates of a week's testimony taken before me in my High Court of Chancery. It became necessary to examine them. It was an important suit, and great accuracy was imperative. Having all things arranged, I called Turkey, Nippers and Ginger Nut, from the next room, meaning to place the four copies in the hands of my four clerks, while I should read from the original. Accordingly, Turkey, Nippers, and Ginger Nut had taken their seats in a row, each with his document in his hand, when I called to Bartleby to join this interesting group.

"Bartleby! quick, I am waiting."

I heard a slow scrape of his chair legs on the uncarpeted floor, and soon he appeared standing at the entrance of his hermitage.

"What is wanted?" said he, mildly.

"The copies, the copies," said I, hurriedly. "We are going to examine them. There"—and I held towards him the fourth quadruplicate.

"I would prefer not to," he said, and gently disappeared behind the screen.

For a few moments I was turned into a pillar of salt, standing at the head of my seated column of clerks. Recovering myself, I advanced towards the screen, and demanded the reason for such extraordinary conduct.

"*Why* do you refuse?"

"I would prefer not to."

With any other man I should have flown outright into a dreadful passion, scorned all further words, and thrust him ignominiously from my presence. But there was something about Bartleby that not only strangely disarmed me, but, in a wonderful manner, touched and disconcerted me. I began to reason with him.

"These are your own copies we are about to examine. It is labor saving to you, because one examination will answer for your four papers. It is common usage. Every copyist is bound to help examine his copy. Is it not so? Will you not speak? Answer!"

"I prefer not to," he replied in a flutelike tone. It seemed to me that, while I had been addressing him, he carefully revolved every statement that I made; fully comprehended the meaning; could not gainsay the irresistible conclusion; but, at the same time, some paramount consideration prevailed with him to reply as he did.

"You are decided, then, not to comply with my request—a request made according to common usage and common sense?"

He briefly gave me to understand, that on that point my judgment
was sound. Yes: his decision was irreversible.

It is not seldom the case that, when a man is browbeaten in some
unprecedented and violently unreasonable way, he begins to stagger
in his own plainest faith. He begins, as it were, vaguely to surmise
that, wonderful as it may be, all the justice and all the reason is on the
other side. Accordingly, if any disinterested persons are present, he
turns to them for some reinforcement for his own faltering mind.

"Turkey," said I, "what do you think of this? Am I not right?"

"With submission, sir," said Turkey, in his blandest tone, "I think
that you are."

"Nippers," said I, "what do *you* think of it?"

"I think I should kick him out of the office."

(The reader, of nice perceptions, will here perceive that, it being
morning, Turkey's answer is couched in polite and tranquil terms, but
Nippers replies in ill-tempered ones. Or, to repeat a previous sentence,
Nippers's ugly mood was on duty, and Turkey's off.)

"Ginger Nut," said I, willing to enlist the smallest suffrage in my be-
half, "what do *you* think of it?"

"I think, sir, he's a little *luny*," replied Ginger Nut, with a grin.

"You hear what they say," said I, turning towards the screen, "come
forth and do your duty."

But he vouchsafed no reply. I pondered a moment in sore perplexity. But once more business hurried me. I determined again to
postpone the consideration of this dilemma to my future leisure. With
a little trouble we made out to examine the papers without Bartleby,
though at every page or two Turkey deferentially dropped his opinion,
that this proceeding was quite out of the common; while Nippers,
twitching in his chair with a dyspeptic nervousness, ground out, between his set teeth, occasional hissing maledictions against the stubborn
oaf behind the screen. And for his (Nippers's) part, this was the first
and the last time he would do another man's business without pay.

Meanwhile Bartleby sat in his hermitage, oblivious to everything but
his own peculiar business there.

Some days passed, the scrivener being employed upon another
lengthy work. His late remarkable conduct led me to regard his ways
narrowly. I observed that he never went to dinner; indeed, that he
never went anywhere. As yet I had never, of my personal knowledge,
known him to be outside of my office. He was a perpetual sentry in
the corner. At about eleven o'clock though, in the morning, I noticed
that Ginger Nut would advance toward the opening in Bartleby's

screen, as if silently beckoned thither by a gesture invisible to me where I sat. The boy would then leave the office, jingling a few pence, and reappear with a handful of ginger-nuts, which he delivered in the hermitage, receiving two of the cakes for his trouble.

He lives, then, on ginger-nuts, thought I; never eats a dinner, properly speaking; he must be a vegetarian, then; but no; he never eats even vegetables, he eats nothing but ginger-nuts. My mind then ran on in reveries concerning the probable effects upon the human constitution of living entirely on ginger-nuts. Ginger-nuts are so called, because they contain ginger as one of their peculiar constituents, and the final flavoring one. Now, what was ginger? A hot, spicy thing. Was Bartleby hot and spicy? Not at all. Ginger, then, had no effect upon Bartleby. Probably he preferred it should have none.

Nothing so aggravates an earnest person as a passive resistance. If the individual so resisted be of a not inhumane temper, and the resisting one perfectly harmless in his passivity, then, in the better moods of the former, he will endeavor charitably to construe to his imagination what proves impossible to be solved by his judgment. Even so, for the most part, I regarded Bartleby and his ways. Poor fellow! thought I, he means no mischief; it is plain he intends no insolence; his aspect sufficiently evinces that his eccentricities are involuntary. He is useful to me. I can get along with him. If I turn him away, the chances are he will fall in with some less-indulgent employer, and then he will be rudely treated, and perhaps driven forth miserably to starve. Yes. Here I can cheaply purchase a delicious self-approval. To befriend Bartleby; to humor him in his strange willfulness, will cost me little or nothing, while I lay up in my soul what will eventually prove a sweet morsel for my conscience. But this mood was not invariable with me. The passiveness of Bartleby sometimes irritated me. I felt strangely goaded on to encounter him in new opposition—to elicit some angry spark from him answerable to my own. But, indeed, I might as well have essayed to strike fire with my knuckles against a bit of Windsor soap. But one afternoon the evil impulse in me mastered me, and the following little scene ensued:

"Bartleby," said I, "when those papers are all copied, I will compare them with you."

"I would prefer not to."

"How? Surely you do not mean to persist in that mulish vagary?"

No answer.

I threw open the folding-doors near by, and, turning upon Turkey and Nippers, exclaimed:

"Bartleby a second time says, he won't examine his papers. What do you think of it, Turkey?"

It was afternoon, be it remembered. Turkey sat glowing like a brass boiler; his bald head steaming; his hands reeling among his blotted papers.

"Think of it?" roared Turkey; "I think I'll just step behind his screen, and black his eyes for him!"

So saying, Turkey rose to his feet and threw his arms into a pugilistic position. He was hurrying away to make good his promise, when I detained him, alarmed at the effect of incautiously rousing Turkey's combativeness after dinner.

"Sit down, Turkey," said I, "and hear what Nippers has to say. What do you think of it, Nippers? Would I not be justified in immediately dismissing Bartleby?"

"Excuse me, that is for you to decide, sir. I think his conduct quite unusual, and, indeed, unjust, as regards Turkey and myself. But it may only be a passing whim."

"Ah," exclaimed I, "you have strangely changed your mind, then— you speak very gently of him now."

"All beer," cried Turkey; "gentleness is effects of beer—Nippers and I dined together to-day. You see how gentle *I* am, sir. Shall I go and black his eyes?"

"You refer to Bartleby, I suppose. No, not to-day, Turkey," I replied; "pray, put up your fists."

I closed the doors, and again advanced towards Bartleby. I felt additional incentives tempting me to my fate. I burned to be rebelled against again. I remembered that Bartleby never left the office.

"Bartleby," said I, "Ginger Nut is away; just step around to the Post Office, won't you? (it was but a three minutes' walk), and see if there is anything for me."

"I would prefer not to."

"You *will* not?"

"I *prefer* not."

I staggered to my desk, and sat there in a deep study. My blind inveteracy returned. Was there any other thing in which I could procure myself to be ignominiously repulsed by this lean, penniless wight?—my hired clerk? What added thing is there, perfectly reasonable, that he will be sure to refuse to do?

"Bartleby!"

No answer.

"Bartleby," in a louder tone.

No answer.

"Bartleby," I roared.

Like a very ghost, agreeably to the laws of magical invocation, at the third summons, he appeared at the entrance of his hermitage.

"Go to the next room, and tell Nippers to come to me."

"I prefer not to," he respectfully and slowly said, and mildly disappeared.

"Very good, Bartleby," said I, in a quiet sort of serenely-severe self-possessed tone, intimating the unalterable purpose of some terrible retribution very close at hand. At the moment I half intended something of the kind. But upon the whole, as it was drawing towards my dinner-hour, I thought it best to put on my hat and walk home for the day, suffering much from perplexity and distress of mind.

Shall I acknowledge it? The conclusion of this whole business was, that it soon became a fixed fact of my chambers, that a pale young scrivener, by the name of Bartleby, had a desk there; that he copied for me at the usual rate of four cents a folio (one hundred words); but he was permanently exempt from examining the work done by him, that duty being transferred to Turkey and Nippers, out of compliment, doubtless, to their superior acuteness; moreover, said Bartleby was never, on any account, to be dispatched on the most trivial errand of any sort; and that even if entreated to take upon him such a matter, it was generally understood that he would "prefer not to"—in other words, that he would refuse point-blank.

As days passed on, I became considerably reconciled to Bartleby. His steadiness, his freedom from all dissipation, his incessant industry (except when he chose to throw himself into a standing revery behind his screen), his great stillness, his unalterableness of demeanor under all circumstances, made him a valuable acquisition. One prime thing was this—*he was always there*—first in the morning, continually through the day, and the last at night. I had a singular confidence in his honesty. I felt my most precious papers perfectly safe in his hands. Sometimes, to be sure, I could not, for the very soul of me, avoid falling into sudden spasmodic passions with him. For it was exceeding difficult to bear in mind all the time those strange peculiarities, privileges, and unheard of exemptions, forming the tacit stipulations on Bartleby's part under which he remained in my office. Now and then, in the eagerness of dispatching pressing business, I would inadvertently summon Bartleby, in a short, rapid tone, to put his finger, say, on the incipient tie of a bit of red tape with which I was about compressing some papers. Of course, from behind the screen the usual answer, "I prefer not to," was sure to come; and then, how could a human creature, with the common infirmities of our nature, refrain from bitterly exclaiming upon such perverseness—such unreasonableness. However, every added repulse of this sort which I received only tended to lessen the probability of my repeating the inadvertence.

Here it must be said, that according to the custom of most legal gentlemen occupying chambers in densely-populated law buildings, there were several keys to my door. One was kept by a woman residing in the attic, which person weekly scrubbed and daily swept and dusted my apartments. Another was kept by Turkey for convenience sake. The third I sometimes carried in my own pocket. The fourth I knew not who had.

Now, one Sunday morning I happened to go to Trinity Church, to hear a celebrated preacher, and finding myself rather early on the ground I thought I would walk round to my chambers for a while. Luckily I had my key with me; but upon applying it to the lock, I found it resisted by something inserted from the inside. Quite surprised, I called out; when to my consternation a key was turned from within; and thrusting his lean visage at me, and holding the door ajar, the apparition of Bartleby appeared, in his shirt sleeves, and otherwise in a strangely tattered deshabille, saying quietly that he was sorry, but he was deeply engaged just then, and—preferred not admitting me at present. In a brief word or two, he moreover added, that perhaps I had better walk round the block two or three times, and by that time he would probably have concluded his affairs.

Now, the utterly unsurmised appearance of Bartleby, tenanting my law-chambers of a Sunday morning, with his cadaverously gentlemanly *nonchalance*, yet withal firm and self-possessed, had such a strange effect upon me, that incontinently I slunk away from my own door, and did as desired. But not without sundry twinges of impotent rebellion against the mild effrontery of this unaccountable scrivener. Indeed, it was his wonderful mildness chiefly, which not only disarmed me, but unmanned me as it were. For I consider that one, for the time, is a sort of unmanned when he tranquilly permits his hired clerk to dictate to him, and order him away from his own premises. Furthermore, I was full of uneasiness as to what Bartleby could possibly be doing in my office in his shirt sleeves, and in an otherwise dismantled condition of a Sunday morning. Was anything amiss going on? Nay, that was out of the question. It was not to be thought of for a moment that Bartleby was an immoral person. But what could he be doing there?— copying? Nay again, whatever might be his eccentricities, Bartleby was an eminently decorous person. He would be the last man to sit down to his desk in any state approaching to nudity. Besides, it was Sunday; and there was something about Bartleby that forbade the supposition that he would by any secular occupation violate the proprieties of the day.

Nevertheless, my mind was not pacified; and full of a restless curiosity, at last I returned to the door. Without hindrance I inserted my key, opened it, and entered. Bartleby was not to be seen. I looked round anxiously, peeped behind his screen; but it was very plain that he was gone. Upon more closely examining the place, I surmised that for an indefinite period Bartleby must have ate, dressed, and slept in my office, and that, too without plate, mirror, or bed. The cushioned seat of a ricketty old sofa in one corner bore the faint impress of a lean, reclining form. Rolled away under his desk, I found a blanket; under the empty grate, a blacking box and brush; on a chair, a tin basin, with soap and a ragged towel; in a newspaper a few crumbs of ginger-nuts and a morsel of cheese. Yes, thought I, it is evident enough that Bartleby has been making his home here, keeping bachelor's hall all by himself. Immediately then the thought came sweeping across me, what miserable friendlessness and loneliness are here revealed! His poverty is great; but his solitude, how horrible! Think of it. Of a Sunday, Wall-street is deserted as Petra; and every night of every day it is an emptiness. This building, too, which of week-days hums with industry and life, at nightfall echoes with sheer vacancy, and all through Sunday is forlorn. And here Bartleby makes his home; sole spectator of a solitude which he has seen all populous—a sort of innocent and transformed Marius brooding among the ruins of Carthage!

For the first time in my life a feeling of overpowering stinging melancholy seized me. Before, I had never experienced aught but a not unpleasing sadness. The bond of a common humanity now drew me irresistibly to gloom. A fraternal melancholy! For both I and Bartleby were sons of Adam. I remembered the bright silks and sparkling faces I had seen that day, in gala trim, swan-like sailing down the Mississippi of Broadway; and I contrasted them with the pallid copyist, and thought to myself, Ah, happiness courts the light, so we deem the world is gay; but misery hides aloof, so we deem that misery there is none. These sad fancyings—chimeras, doubtless, of a sick and silly brain—led on to other and more special thoughts, concerning the eccentricities of Bartleby. Presentiments of strange discoveries hovered round me. The scrivener's pale form appeared to me laid out, among uncaring strangers, in its shivering winding sheet.

Suddenly I was attracted by Bartleby's closed desk, the key in open sight left in the lock.

I mean no mischief, seek the gratification of no heartless curiosity, thought I; besides, the desk is mine, and its contents, too, so I will make bold to look within. Everything was methodically arranged, the papers smoothly placed. The pigeon holes were deep, and removing the files of documents, I groped into their recesses. Presently I felt something there, and dragged it out. It was an old bandanna handkerchief, heavy and knotted. I opened it, and saw it was a savings bank.

I now recalled all the quiet mysteries which I had noted in the man. I remembered that he never spoke but to answer; that, though at intervals he had considerable time to himself, yet I had never seen him reading—no, not even a newspaper; that for long periods he would stand looking out, at his pale window behind the screen, upon the dead brick wall; I was quite sure he never visited any refectory or eating house; while his pale face clearly indicated that he never drank beer like Turkey, or tea and coffee even, like other men; that he never went anywhere in particular that I could learn; never went out for a walk, unless, indeed, that was the case at present; that he had declined telling who he was, or whence he came, or whether he had any relatives in the world; that though so thin and pale, he never complained of ill health. And more than all, I remembered a certain unconscious air of pallid—how shall I call it?—of pallid haughtiness, say, or rather an austere reserve about him, which had positively awed me into my tame compliance with his eccentricities, when I had feared· to ask him to do the slightest incidental thing for me, even though I might know, from his long-continued motionlessness, that behind his screen he must be standing in one of those dead-wall reveries of his.

Revolving all these things, and coupling them with the recently discovered fact, that he made my office his constant abiding place and home, and not forgetful of his morbid moodiness; revolving all these things, a prudential feeling began to steal over me. My first emotions had been those of pure melancholy and sincerest pity; but just in proportion as the forlornness of Bartleby grew and grew to my imagination, did that same melancholy merge into fear, that pity into repulsion. So true it is, and so terrible, too, that up to a certain point the thought or sight of misery enlists our best affections; but, in certain special cases, beyond that point it does not. They err who would assert that invariably this is owing to the inherent selfishness of the human heart. It rather proceeds from a certain hopelessness of remedying excessive and organic ill. To a sensitive being, pity is not seldom pain. And

when at last it is perceived that such pity cannot lead to effectual suc-
cor, common sense bids the soul be rid of it.   What I saw that morning
persuaded me that the scrivener was the victim of innate and incurable
disorder.   I might give alms to his body; but his body did not pain him;
it was his soul that suffered, and his soul I could not reach.

I did not accomplish the purpose of going to Trinity Church that
morning.   Somehow, the things I had seen disqualified me for the time
from church-going.   I walked homeward, thinking what I would do
with Bartleby.   Finally, I resolved upon this—I would put certain calm
questions to him the next morning, touching his history, etc., and if he
declined to answer them openly and unreservedly (and I supposed he
would prefer not), then to give him a twenty dollar bill over and above
whatever I might owe him, and tell him his services were no longer
required; but that if in any other way I could assist him, I would be
happy to do so, especially if he desired to return to his native place,
wherever that might be, I would willingly help to defray the expenses.
Moreover, if, after reaching home, he found himself at any time in want
of aid, a letter from him would be sure of a reply.

The next morning came.

"Bartleby," said I, gently calling to him behind his screen.

No reply.

"Bartleby," said I, in a still gentler tone, "come here; I am not going
to ask you to do anything you would prefer not to do—I simply wish to
speak to you."

Upon this he noiselessly slid into view.

"Will you tell me, Bartleby, where you were born?"

"I would prefer not to."

"Will you tell me *anything* about yourself?"

"I would prefer not to."

"But what reasonable objection can you have to speak to me?   I feel
friendly towards you."

He did not look at me while I spoke, but kept his glance fixed upon
my bust of Cicero, which, as I then sat, was directly behind me, some
six inches above my head.

"What is your answer, Bartleby?" said I, after waiting a considerable
time for a reply, during which his countenance remained immovable,
only there was the faintest conceivable tremor of the white attenuated
mouth.

"At present I prefer to give no answer," he said, and retired into his
hermitage.

It was rather weak in me I confess, but his manner, on this occasion, nettled me. Not only did there seem to lurk in it a certain calm disdain, but his perverseness seemed ungrateful, considering the undeniable good usage and indulgence he had received from me.

Again I sat ruminating what I should do. Mortified as I was at his behavior, and resolved as I had been to dismiss him when I entered my office, nevertheless I strangely felt something superstitious knocking at my heart, and forbidding me to carry out my purpose, and denouncing me for a villain if I dared to breathe one bitter word against this forlornest of mankind. At last, familiarly drawing my chair behind his screen, I sat down and said: "Bartleby, never mind, then, about revealing your history; but let me entreat you, as a friend, to comply as far as may be with the usages of this office. Say now, you will help to examine papers to-morrow or next day: in short, say now, that in a day or two you will begin to be a little reasonable:—say so, Bartleby."

"At present I would prefer not to be a little reasonable," was his mildly cadaverous reply.

Just then the folding-doors opened, and Nippers approached. He seemed suffering from an unusually bad night's rest, induced by severer indigestion than common. He overheard those final words of Bartleby.

"*Prefer not*, eh?" gritted Nippers—"I'd *prefer* him, if I were you, sir," addressing me—"I'd *prefer* him; I'd give him preferences, the stubborn mule! What is it, sir, pray, that he *prefers* not to do now?"

Bartleby moved not a limb.

"Mr. Nippers," said I, "I'd prefer that you would withdraw for the present."

Somehow, of late, I had got into the way of involuntarily using this word "prefer" upon all sorts of not exactly suitable occasions. And I trembled to think that my contact with the scrivener had already and seriously affected me in a mental way. And what further and deeper aberration might it not yet produce? This apprehension had not been without efficacy in determining me to summary measures.

As Nippers, looking very sour and sulky, was departing, Turkey blandly and deferentially approached.

"With submission, sir," said he, "yesterday I was thinking about Bartleby here, and I think that if he would but prefer to take a quart of good ale every day, it would do much towards mending him, and enabling him to assist in examining his papers."

"So you have got the word, too," said I, slightly excited.

"With submission, what word, sir," asked Turkey, respectfully crowding himself into the contracted space behind the screen, and by so doing, making me jostle the scrivener. "What word, sir?"

"I would prefer to be left alone here," said Bartleby, as if offended at being mobbed in his privacy.

"*That's* the word, Turkey," said I—"*that's* it."

"Oh, *prefer?* oh yes—queer word. I never use it myself. But, sir, as I was saying, if he would but prefer—"

"Turkey," interrupted I, "you will please withdraw."

"Oh certainly, sir, if you prefer that I should."

As he opened the folding-door to retire, Nipper at his desk caught a glimpse of me, and asked whether I would prefer to have a certain paper copied on blue paper or white. He did not in the least roguishly accent the word prefer. It was plain that it involuntarily rolled from his tongue. I thought to myself, surely I must get rid of a demented man, who already has in some degree turned the tongues, if not the heads of myself and clerks. But I thought it prudent not to break the dismission at once.

The next day I noticed that Bartleby did nothing but stand at his window in his dead-wall revery. Upon asking him why he did not write, he said that he had decided upon doing no more writing.

"Why, how now? what next?" exclaimed I, "do no more writing?"

"No more."

"And what is the reason?"

"Do you not see the reason for yourself," he indifferently replied.

I looked steadfastly at him, and perceived that his eyes looked dull and glazed. Instantly it occurred to me, that his unexampled diligence in copying by his dim window for the first few weeks of his stay with me might have temporarily impared his vision.

I was touched. I said something in condolence with him. I hinted that of course he did wisely in abstaining from writing for a while; and urged him to embrace that opportunity of taking wholesome exercise in the open air. This, however, he did not do. A few days after this, my other clerks being absent, and being in a great hurry to dispatch certain letters by the mail, I thought that, having nothing else earthly to do, Bartleby would surely be less inflexible than usual, and carry these letters to the post-office. But he blankly declined. So, much to my inconvenience, I went myself.

Still added days went by. Whether Bartleby's eyes improved or not, I could not say. To all appearance I thought they did. But when I asked him if they did, he vouchsafed no answer. At all events, he would do no copying. At last, in reply to my urgings, he informed me that he had permanently given up copying.

"What!" exclaimed I, "suppose your eyes should get entirely well—better than ever before—would you not copy then?"

"I have given up copying," he answered, and slid aside.

He remained as ever, a fixture in my chamber. Nay—if that were possible—he became still more of a fixture than before. What was to be done? He would do nothing in the office; why should he stay there? In plain fact, he had now become a millstone to me, not only useless as a necklace, but afflictive to bear. Yet I was sorry for him. I speak less than truth when I say that, on his own account, he occasioned me uneasiness. If he would but have named a single relative or friend, I would instantly have written, and urged their taking the poor fellow away to some convenient retreat. But he seemed alone, absolutely alone in the universe. A bit of wreck in the mid Atlantic. At length necessities connected with my business tyrannized over all other considerations. Decently as I could, I told Bartleby that in six days' time he must unconditionally leave the office. I warned him to take measures, in the interval, for procuring some other abode. I offered to assist him in this endeavor, if he himself would but take the first step towards a removal. "And when you finally quit me, Bartleby," added I, "I shall see that you go not away entirely unprovided. Six days from this hour, remember."

At the expiration of that period, I peeped behind the screen, and lo! Bartleby was there.

I buttoned up my coat, balanced myself, advanced slowly towards him, touched his shoulder, and said, "The time has come; you must quit this place; I am sorry for you; here is money; but you must go."

"I would prefer not," he replied, with his back still towards me.

"You *must.*"

He remained silent.

Now I had an unbounded confidence in this man's common honesty. He had frequently restored to me sixpences and shillings carelessly dropped upon the floor, for I am apt to be very reckless in such shirt-button affairs. The proceeding, then, which followed will not be deemed extraordinary.

"Bartleby," said I, "I owe you twelve dollars on account; here are thirty-two; the odd twenty are yours—Will you take it?" and I handed the bills towards him.

But he made no motion.

"I will leave them here, then," putting them under a weight on the table. Then taking my hat and cane and going to the door, I tranquilly turned and added—"After you have removed your things from these offices, Bartleby, you will of course lock the door—since every one is now gone for the day but you—and if you please, slip your key underneath the mat, so that I may have it in the morning. I shall not see you again; so good-by to you. If, hereafter, in your new place of abode, I can be of any service to you, do not fail to advise me by letter. Good-by, Bartleby, and fare you well."

But he answered not a word; like the last column of some ruined temple, he remained standing mute and solitary in the middle of the otherwise deserted room.

As I walked home in a pensive mood, my vanity got the better of my pity. I could not but highly plume myself on my masterly management in getting rid of Bartleby. Masterly I call it, and such it must appear to any dispassionate thinker. The beauty of my procedure seemed to consist in its perfect quietness. There was no vulgar bullying, no bravado of any sort, no choleric hectoring, and striding to and fro across the apartment, jerking out vehement commands for Bartleby to bundle himself off with his beggarly traps. Nothing of the kind. Without loudly bidding Bartleby depart—as an inferior genius might have done—I *assumed* the ground that depart he must; and upon that assumption built all I had to say. The more I thought over my procedure, the more I was charmed with it. Nevertheless, next morning, upon awakening, I had my doubts—I had somehow slept off the fumes of vanity. One of the coolest and wisest hours a man has, is just after he awakes in the morning. My procedure seemed as sagacious as ever —but only in theory. How it would prove in practice—there was the rub. It was truly a beautiful thought to have assumed Bartleby's departure; but, after all, that assumption was simply my own, and none of Bartleby's. The great point was, not whether I had assumed that he would quit me, but whether he would prefer so to do. He was more a man of preferences than assumptions.

After breakfast, I walked down town, arguing the probabilities *pro* and *con*. One moment I thought it would prove a miserable failure, and Bartleby would be found all alive at my office as usual; the next moment it seemed certain that I should find his chair empty. And so I kept veering about. At the corner of Broadway and Canal street, I saw quite an excited group of people standing in earnest conversation.

"I'll take odds he doesn't," said a voice as I passed.

"Doesn't go?—done!" said I, "put up your money."

I was instinctively putting my hand in my pocket to produce my own, when I remembered that this was an election day. The words I had

overheard bore no reference to Bartleby, but to the success or non-
success of some candidate for the mayoralty. In my intent frame of
mind, I had, as it were, imagined that all Broadway shared in my excitement, and were debating the same question with me. I passed on,
very thankful that the uproar of the street screened my momentary
absent-mindedness.

As I had intended, I was earlier than usual at my office door. I stood
listening for a moment. All was still. He must be gone. I tried the
knob. The door was locked. Yes, my procedure had worked to a
charm; he indeed must be vanished. Yet a certain melancholy mixed
with this: I was almost sorry for my brilliant success. I was fumbling
under the door mat for the key, which Bartleby was to have left there
for me, when accidentally my knee knocked against a panel, producing
a summoning sound, and in response a voice came to me from within—
"Not yet; I am occupied."

It was Bartleby.

I was thunderstruck. For an instant I stood like the man who, pipe
in mouth, was killed one cloudless afternoon long ago in Virginia, by
summer lightning; at his own warm open window he was killed, and
remained leaning out there upon the dreamy afternoon, till some one
touched him, when he fell.

"Not gone!" I murmured at last. But again obeying that wondrous
ascendancy which the inscrutable scrivener had over me, and from
which ascendancy, for all my chafing, I could not completely escape, I
slowly went down stairs and out into the street, and while walking
round the block, considered what I should next do in this unheard-of
perplexity. Turn the man out by an actual thrusting I could not; to
drive him away by calling him hard names would not do; calling in the
police was an unpleasant idea; and yet, permit him to enjoy his cadaverous triumph over me—this, too, I could not think of. What was to
be done? or, if nothing could be done, was there anything further that
I could *assume* in the matter? Yes, as before I had prospectively assumed that Bartleby would depart, so now I might retrospectively assume that departed he was. In the legitimate carrying out of this
assumption, I might enter my office in a great hurry, and pretending not
to see Bartleby at all, walk straight against him as if he were air. Such
a proceeding would in a singular degree have the appearance of a
home-thrust. It was hardly possible that Bartleby could withstand
such an application of the doctrine of assumptions. But upon second
thoughts the success of the plan seemed rather dubious. I resolved to
argue the matter over with him again.

"Bartleby," said I, entering the office, with a quietly severe expression, "I am seriously displeased. I am pained, Bartleby. I had thought better of you. I had imagined you of such a gentlemanly organization, that in any delicate dilemma a slight hint would suffice—in short, an assumption. But it appears I am deceived. Why," I added, unaffectedly starting, "you have not even touched that money yet," pointing to it, just where I had left it the evening previous.

He answered nothing.

"Will you, or will you not, quit me?" I now demanded in a sudden passion, advancing close to him.

"I would prefer *not* to quit you," he replied gently emphasizing the *not*.

"What earthly right have you to stay here? Do you pay any rent? Do you pay my taxes? Or is this property yours?"

He answered nothing.

"Are you ready to go on and write now? Are your eyes recovered? Could you copy a small paper for me this morning? or help examine a few lines? or step round to the post-office? In a word, will you do anything at all, to give a coloring to your refusal to depart the premises?"

He silently retired into his hermitage.

I was now in such a state of nervous resentment that I thought it but prudent to check myself at present from further demonstrations. Bartleby and I were alone. I remembered the tragedy of the unfortunate Adams and the still more unfortunate Colt in the solitary office of the latter; and how poor Colt, being dreadfully incensed by Adams, and imprudently permitting himself to get wildly excited, was at unawares hurried into his fatal act—an act which certainly no man could possibly deplore more than the actor himself. Often it had occurred to me in my ponderings upon the subject, that had that altercation taken place in the public street, or at a private residence, it would not have terminated as it did. It was the circumstance of being alone in a solitary office, up stairs, of a building entirely unhallowed by humanizing domestic associations—an uncarpeted office, doubtless, of a dusty, haggard sort of appearance—this it must have been, which greatly helped to enhance the irritable desperation of the hapless Colt.

But when this old Adam of resentment rose in me and tempted me concerning Bartleby, I grappled him and threw him. How? Why, simply by recalling the divine injunction: "A new commandment give I unto you, that ye love one another." Yes, this it was that saved me. Aside from higher considerations, charity often operates as a vastly wise and prudent principle—a great safeguard to its possessor. Men have committed murder for jealousy's sake, and anger's sake, and hatred's sake, and selfishness' sake, and spiritual pride's sake; but no man, that ever I heard of, ever committted a diabolical murder for sweet charity's sake. Mere self-interest, then, if no better motive can be enlisted, should, especially with high-tempered men, prompt all beings to charity and philanthropy. At any rate, upon the occasion in question, I strove to drown my exasperated feelings towards the scrivener by benevolently construing his conduct. Poor fellow, poor fellow! thought I, he don't mean anything; and besides, he has seen hard times, and ought to be indulged.

I endeavored, also, immediately to occupy myself, and at the same time to comfort my despondency. I tried to fancy, that in the course of the morning, at such time as might prove agreeable to him, Bartleby, of his own free accord, would emerge from his hermitage and take up some decided line of march in the direction of the door. But no. Half-past twelve o'clock came; Turkey began to glow in the face, overturn his inkstand, and become generally obstreperous; Nippers abated down into quietude and courtesy; Ginger Nut munched his noon apple; and Bartleby remained standing at his window in one of his profoundest dead-wall reveries. Will it be credited? Ought I to acknowledge it? That afternoon I left the office without saying one further word to him.

Some days now passed, during which, at leisure intervals I looked a little into "Edwards on the Will," and "Priestley on Necessity." Under the circumstances, those books induced a salutary feeling. Gradually I slid into the persuasion that these troubles of mine, touching the scrivener, had been all predestinated from eternity, and Bartleby was billeted upon me for some mysterious purpose of an allwise Providence, which it was not for a mere mortal like me to fathom. Yes, Bartleby, stay there behind your screen, thought I; I shall persecute you no more; you are harmless and noiseless as any of these old chairs; in short, I never feel so private as when I know you are here. At last I see it, I feel it; I penetrate to the predestinated purpose of my life. I am content. Others may have loftier parts to enact; but my mission in this world, Bartleby, is to furnish you with office-room for such period as you may see fit to remain.

I believe that this wise and blessed frame of mind would have continued with me, had it not been for the unsolicited and uncharitable remarks obtruded upon me by my professional friends who visited the rooms. But thus it often is, that the constant friction of illiberal minds wears out at last the best resolves of the more generous. Though to be sure, when I reflected upon it, it was not strange that people entering my office should be struck by the peculiar aspect of the unaccountable Bartleby, and so be tempted to throw out some sinister observations concerning him. Sometimes an attorney, having business with me, and calling at my office, and finding no one but the scrivener there, would undertake to obtain some sort of precise information from him touching my whereabouts; but without heeding his idle talk, Bartleby would remain standing immovable in the middle of the room. So after contemplating him in that position for a time, the attorney would depart, no wiser than he came.

Also, when a reference was going on, and the room full of lawyers and witnesses, and business driving fast, some deeply-occupied legal gentleman present, seeing Bartleby wholly unemployed, would request him to run round to his (the legal gentleman's) office and fetch some papers for him. Thereupon, Bartleby would tranquilly decline, and yet remain idle as before. Then the lawyer would give a great stare, and turn to me. And what could I say? At last I was made aware that all through the circle of my professional acquaintance, a whisper of wonder was running round, having reference to the strange creature I kept at my office. This worried me very much. And as the idea came upon me of his possibly turning out a long-lived man, and keep occupying my chambers, and denying my authority; and perplexing my visitors; and scandalizing my professional reputation; and casting a general gloom over the premises; keeping soul and body together to the last upon his savings (for doubtless he spent but half a dime a day), and in the end perhaps outlive me, and claim possession of my office by right of his perpetual occupancy: as all these dark anticipations crowded upon me more and more, and my friends continually intruded their relentless remarks upon the apparition in my room; a great change was wrought in me. I resolved to gather all my faculties together, and forever rid me of this intolerable incubus.

Ere revolving any complicated project, however, adapted to this end, I first simply suggested to Bartleby the propriety of his permanent departure. In a calm and serious tone, I commended the idea to his careful and mature consideration. But, having taken three days to meditate upon it, he apprised me, that his original determination remained the same; in short, that he still preferred to abide with me.

What shall I do? I now said to myself, buttoning up my coat to the last button. What shall I do? what ought I to do? what does conscience say I *should* do with this man, or, rather, ghost. Rid myself of him, I must; go, he shall. But how? You will not thrust him, the poor, pale, passive mortal—you will not thrust such a helpless creature out of your door? you will not dishonor yourself by such cruelty? No, I will not, I cannot do that. Rather would I let him live and die here, and then mason up his remains in the wall. What, then, will you do? For all your coaxing, he will not budge. Bribes he leaves under your own paper-weight on your table; in short, it is quite plain that he prefers to cling to you.

Then something severe, something unusual must be done. What! surely you will not have him collared by a constable, and commit his innocent pallor to the common jail? And upon what ground could you procure such a thing to be done?—a vagrant, is he? What! he a vagrant, a wanderer, who refuses to budge? It is because he will *not* be a vagrant, then, that you seek to count him *as* a vagrant. That is too absurd. No visible means of support: there I have him. Wrong again: for indubitably he *does* support himself, and that is the only unanswerable proof that any man can show of his possessing the means so to do. No more, then. Since he will not quit me, I must quit him. I will change my offices; I will move elsewhere, and give him fair notice, that if I find him on my new premises I will then proceed against him as a common trespasser.

Acting accordingly, next day I thus addressed him: "I find these chambers too far from the City Hall; the air is unwholesome. In a word, I propose to remove my offices next week, and shall no longer require your services. I tell you this now, in order that you may seek another place."

He made no reply, and nothing more was said.

On the appointed day I engaged carts and men, proceeded to my chambers, and, having but little furniture, everything was removed in a few hours. Throughout, the scrivener remained standing behind the screen, which I directed to be removed the last thing. It was withdrawn; and, being folded up like a huge folio, left him the motionless occupant of a naked room. I stood in the entry watching him a moment, while something from within me upbraided me.

I re-entered, with my hand in my pocket—and—and my heart in my mouth.

"Good-by, Bartleby; I am going—good-by, and God some way bless you; and take that," slipping something in his hand. But it dropped upon the floor, and then—strange to say—I tore myself from him whom I had so longed to be rid of.

Established in my new quarters, for a day or two I kept the door locked, and started at every footfall in the passages. When I returned to my rooms, after any little absence, I would pause at the threshold for an instant, and attentively listen, ere applying my key. But these fears were needless. Bartleby never came nigh me.

I thought all was going well, when a perturbed-looking stranger visited me, inquiring whether I was the person who had recently occupied rooms at No. — Wall street.

Full of forebodings, I replied that I was.

"Then, sir," said the stranger, who proved a lawyer, "you are responsible for the man you left there. He refuses to do any copying; he refuses to do anything; he says he prefers not to; and he refuses to quit the premises."

"I am very sorry, sir," said I, with assumed tranquillity, but an inward tremor, "but, really, the man you allude to is nothing to me—he is no relation or apprentice of mine, that you should hold me responsible for him."

"In mercy's name, who is he?"

"I certainly cannot inform you. I know nothing about him. Formerly I employed him as a copyist; but he has done nothing for me now for some time past."

"I shall settle him, then—good morning, sir."

Several days passed, and I heard nothing more; and, though I often felt a charitable prompting to call at the place and see poor Bartleby, yet a certain squeamishness, of I know not what, withheld me.

All is over with him, by this time, thought I, at last, when, through another week, no further intelligence reached me. But, coming to my room the day after, I found several persons waiting at my door in a high state of nervous excitement.

"That's the man—here he comes," cried the foremost one, whom I recognized as the lawyer who had previously called upon me alone.

"You must take him away, sir, at once," cried a portly person among them, advancing upon me, and whom I knew to be the landlord of No. — Wall street. "These gentlemen, my tenants, cannot stand it any longer; Mr. B——," pointing to the lawyer, "has turned him out of his room, and he now persists in haunting the building generally, sitting upon the banisters of the stairs by day, and sleeping in the entry by night. Everybody is concerned; clients are leaving the offices; some fears are entertained of a mob; something you must do, and that without delay."

Aghast at this torrent, I fell back before it, and would fain have locked myself in my new quarters. In vain I persisted that Bartleby was nothing to me—no more than to any one else. In vain—I was the last person known to have anything to do with him, and they held me to the terrible account. Fearful, then, of being exposed in the papers (as one person present obscurely threatened), I considered the matter, and, at length, said, that if the lawyer would give me a confidential interview with the scrivener, in his (the lawyer's) own room, I would, that afternoon, strive my best to rid them of the nuisance they complained of.

Going up stairs to my old haunt, there was Bartleby silently sitting upon the banister at the landing.

"What are you doing here, Bartleby?" said I.

"Sitting upon the banister," he mildly replied.

I motioned him into the lawyer's room, who then left us.

"Bartleby," said I, "are you aware that you are the cause of great tribulation to me, by persisting in occupying the entry after being dismissed from the office?"

No answer.

"Now one of two things must take place. Either you must do something, or something must be done to you. Now what sort of business would you like to engage in? Would you like to re-engage in copying for some one?"

"No; I would prefer not to make any change."

"Would you like a clerkship in a dry-goods store?"

"There is too much confinement about that. No, I would not like a clerkship; but I am not particular."

"Too much confinement," I cried, "why you keep yourself confined all the time!"

"I would prefer not to take a clerkship," he rejoined, as if to settle that little item at once.

"How would a bar-tender's business suit you? There is no trying of the eye-sight in that."

"I would not like it at all; though, as I said before, I am not particular."

His unwonted wordiness inspirited me. I returned to the charge.

"Well, then, would you like to travel through the country collecting bills for the merchants? That would improve your health."

"No, I would prefer to be doing something else."

"How, then, would going as a companion to Europe, to entertain some young gentleman with your conversation—how would that suit you?"

"Not at all. It does not strike me that there is anything definite about that. I like to be stationary. But I am not particular."

"Stationary you shall be, then," I cried, now losing all patience, and, for the first time in all my exasperating connection with him, fairly flying into a passion. "If you do not go away from these premises before night, I shall feel bound—indeed, I *am* bound—to—to—to quit the premises myself!" I rather absurdly concluded, knowing not with what possible threat to try to frighten his immobility into compliance. Despairing of all further efforts, I was precipitately leaving him, when a final thought occurred to me—one which had not been wholly unindulged before.

"Bartleby," said I, in the kindest tone I could assume under such exciting circumstances, "will you go home with me now—not to my office, but my dwelling—and remain there till we can conclude upon some convenient arrangement for you at our leisure? Come, let us start now, right away."

"No: at present I would prefer not to make any change at all."

I answered nothing; but, effectually dodging every one by the suddenness and rapidity of my flight, rushed from the building, ran up Wall street towards Broadway, and, jumping into the first omnibus, was soon removed from pursuit. As soon as tranquillity returned, I distinctly perceived that I had now done all that I possibly could, both in respect to the demands of the landlord and his tenants, and with regard to my own desire and sense of duty, to benefit Bartleby, and shield him from rude persecution. I now strove to be entirely care-free and quiescent; and my conscience justified me in the attempt; though, indeed, it was not so successful as I could have wished. So fearful was I of being again hunted out by the incensed landlord and his exasperated tenants, that, surrendering my business to Nippers, for a few days, I drove about the upper part of the town and through the suburbs, in my rockaway; crossed over to Jersey City and Hoboken, and paid fugitive visits to Manhattanville and Astoria. In fact, I almost lived in my rockaway for the time.

When again I entered my office, lo, a note from the landlord lay upon the desk. I opened it with trembling hands. It informed me that the writer had sent to the police, and had Bartleby removed to the Tombs as a vagrant. Moreover, since I knew more about him than any one else, he wished me to appear at that place, and make a suitable statement of the facts. These tidings had a conflicting effect upon me. At first I was indignant; but, at last, almost approved. The landlord's energetic, summary disposition, had led him to adopt a procedure which I do not think I would have decided upon myself; and yet, as a last resort, under such peculiar circumstances, it seemed the only plan.

As I afterwards learned, the poor scrivener, when told that he must be conducted to the Tombs, offered not the slightest obstacle, but, in his pale, unmoving way, silently acquiesced.

Some of the compassionate and curious bystanders joined the party; and headed by one of the constables arm in arm with Bartleby, the silent procession filed its way through all the noise, and heat, and joy of the roaring thoroughfares at noon.

The same day I received the note, I went to the Tombs, or, to speak more properly, the Halls of Justice. Seeking the right officer, I stated the purpose of my call, and was informed that the individual I described was, indeed, within. I then assured the functionary that Bartleby was a perfectly honest man, and greatly to be compassionated, however unaccountably eccentric. I narrated all I knew, and closed by suggesting the idea of letting him remain in as indulgent confinement as possible, till something less harsh might be done—though, indeed, I hardly knew what. At all events, if nothing else could be decided upon, the alms-house must receive him. I then begged to have an interview.

Being under no disgraceful charge, and quite serene and harmless in all his ways, they had permitted him freely to wander about the prison, and, especially, in the inclosed grass-platted yards thereof. And so I found him there, standing all alone in the quietest of the yards, his face towards a high wall, while all around, from the narrow slits of the jail windows, I thought I saw peering out upon him the eyes of murderers and thieves.

"Bartleby!"

"I know you," he said, without looking round—"and I want nothing to say to you."

"It was not I that brought you here, Bartleby," said I, keenly pained at his implied suspicion. "And to you, this should not be so vile a place. Nothing reproachful attaches to you by being here. And see, it is not so sad a place as one might think. Look, there is the sky, and here is the grass."

"I know where I am," he replied, but would say nothing more, and so I left him.

As I entered the corridor again, a broad meat-like man, in an apron, accosted me, and, jerking his thumb over his shoulder, said—"Is that your friend?"

"Yes."

"Does he want to starve? If he does, let him live on the prison fare, that's all."

"Who are you?" asked I, not knowing what to make of such an unoffi-cially speaking person in such a place.

"I am the grub-man. Such gentlemen as have friends here, hire me to provide them with something good to eat."

"Is this so?" said I, turning to the turnkey.

He said it was.

"Well, then," said I, slipping some silver into the grub-man's hands (for so they called him), "I want you to give particular attention to my friend there; let him have the best dinner you can get. And you must be as polite to him as possible."

"Introduce me, will you?" said the grub-man, looking at me with an expression which seemed to say he was all impatience for an oppor-tunity to give a specimen of his breeding.

Thinking it would prove of benefit to the scrivener, I acquiesced; and, asking the grub-man his name, went up with him to Bartleby.

"Bartleby, this is a friend; you will find him very useful to you."

"Your sarvant, sir, your sarvant," said the grub-man, making a low salutation behind his apron. "Hope you find it pleasant here, sir; nice grounds—cool apartments—hope you'll stay with us some time—try to make it agreeable. What will you have for dinner to-day?"

"I prefer not to dine to-day," said Bartleby, turning away. "It would disagree with me; I am unused to dinners." So saying, he slowly moved to the other side of the inclosure, and took up a position front-ing the dead-wall.

"How's this?" said the grub-man, addressing me with a stare of as-tonishment. "He's odd, ain't he?"

"I think he is a little deranged," said I, sadly.

"Deranged? deranged is it? Well, now, upon my word, I thought that friend of yourn was a gentleman forger; they are always pale and genteel-like, them forgers. I can't help pity 'em—can't help it, sir. Did you know Monroe Edwards?" he added, touchingly, and paused. Then, laying his hand piteously on my shoulder, sighed, "he died of consump-tion at Sing-Sing. So you weren't acquainted with Monroe?"

"No, I was never socially acquainted with any forgers. But I cannot stop longer. Look to my friend yonder. You will not lose by it. I will see you again."

Some few days after this, I again obtained admission to the Tombs, and went through the corridors in quest of Bartleby; but without find-ing him.

"I saw him coming from his cell not long ago," said a turnkey, "may be he's gone to loiter in the yards."

So I went in that direction.

"Are you looking for the silent man?" said another turnkey, passing me. "Yonder he lies—sleeping in the yard there. 'Tis not twenty minutes since I saw him lie down."

The yard was entirely quiet. It was not accessible to the common prisoners. The surrounding walls, of amazing thickness, kept off all sounds behind them. The Egyptian character of the masonry weighed upon me with its gloom. But a soft imprisoned turf grew under foot. The heart of the eternal pyramids, it seemed, wherein, by some strange magic, through the clefts, grass-seed, dropped by birds, had sprung.

Strangely huddled at the base of the wall, his knees drawn up, and lying on his side, his head touching the cold stones, I saw the wasted Bartleby. But nothing stirred. I paused; then went close up to him; stooped over, and saw that his dim eyes were open; otherwise he seemed profoundly sleeping. Something prompted me to touch him. I felt his hand, when a tingling shiver ran up my arm and down my spine to my feet.

The round face of the grub-man peered upon me now. "His dinner is ready. Won't he dine to-day, either? Or does he live without dining?"

"Lives without dining," said I, and closed the eyes.

"Eh!—He's asleep, ain't he?"

"With kings and counselors," murmured I.

* * * * * *

There would seem little need for proceeding further in this history. Imagination will readily supply the meagre recital of poor Bartleby's interment. But, ere parting with the reader, let me say, that if this little narrative has sufficiently interested him, to awaken curiosity as to who Bartleby was, and what manner of life he led prior to the present narrator's making his acquaintance, I can only reply, that in such curiosity I fully share, but am wholly unable to gratify it. Yet here I hardly know whether I should divulge one little item of rumor, which came to my ear a few months after the scrivener's decease. Upon what basis it rested, I could never ascertain; and hence, how true it is I cannot now tell. But, inasmuch as this vague report has not been without a certain suggestive interest to me, however sad, it may prove the same with some others; and so I will briefly mention it. The report was this: that Bartleby had been a subordinate clerk in the Dead Letter Office at Washington, from which he had been suddenly removed by a change in the administration. When I think over this rumor, hardly can I express the emotions which seize me. Dead letters! does it not sound like dead men? Conceive a man by nature and misfortune prone to a pallid hopelessness, can any business seem more fitted to heighten it than that of continually handling these dead letters, and assorting them for the flames? For by the cart-load they are annually burned. Sometimes from out the folded paper the pale clerk takes a ring—the finger it was meant for, perhaps, moulders in the grave; a bank-note sent in swiftest charity—he whom it would relieve, nor eats nor hungers any more; pardon for those who died despairing; hope for those who died unhoping; good tidings for those who died stifled by unrelieved calamities. On errands of life, these letters speed to death.

Ah, Bartleby! Ah, humanity!

Commentary

The title of this story and the first person point of view (see p. 31) from which it is told might lead the reader into believing that Bartleby is the central character. Indeed, the narrator tells us in the second paragraph that the title character is the "chief character about to be presented." The narration thus focuses on Bartleby; however, by the time we meet him he has withdrawn from conflict and is no longer central to the action. Keeping in mind the unity achieved through skillful interrelationship of character, action, and theme, the wary reader soon realizes that the lawyer who tells the story is the central character.

It is what happens to the narrator as a result of his association with Bartleby that constitutes the central action and its projection of the theme. It is the lawyer who finds himself in conflict over dealing with Bartleby, and, as a result of the conflict, has an insight not only into Bartleby, but also into society, himself, and man. "Ah, Bartleby! Ah, humanity!" is his closing statement.

The first and last lines of a story are conspicuous ones, and a skillful author will employ them to communicate his total meaning. "I am a rather elderly man," begins the narrator, subjectively. The statement is a clue to the fact that the story is primarily about him. The concluding sentence indicates the change from subjective observation to objective sympathy: "Ah, Bartleby! Ah, humanity!" The story is about man.

The narrator has changed during the course of the action from a self-centered, "eminently *safe* man"—a methodical, successful Wall Street lawyer—into a compassionate human being. He has become an individual who recognizes the chief dilemma of man, whose mortality challenges him to cope with his dual needs to be a unique individual yet to identify responsibly with society. The lawyer understands the lonely, even courageous individuality of Bartleby and in so doing has taken a social responsibility for him. The narrator is nameless, yet he emerges as a believable, unforgettable character. Bartleby is equally unforgettable; few of us have ever known anyone like him. We sympathize with him, even admire him, but it is with the narrator that we can identify.

The title certainly would indicate that Bartleby is important to the story, and he is, but as the character who affects the central character. In the light of the theme, the subtitle becomes more important: "A Story of Wall Street." It is a metaphysical pun if we consider how character in action produces theme. The ambiguity or multi-level meaning of the subtitle enriches the story through the literary device of symbolism which the subtitle suggests. On the literal level, the story is about Wall Street and how the physical walls of the law office and, later, of the Tombs limit physical vision. But there are levels of meaning other than the literal. Psychologically, Wall Street and the walls, now becoming considered as a symbol as well as concrete images (see p. 40), have an emotional, mentally deranging effect. Socially and economically, too, the walls represent the shutting off of all other human pursuits for the sake of financial success—not co-operation with others, but competition for personal gain. Philosophically, the walls become the symbol of the barrier between the individual and society and between the individual and his personal goals. And what, if not death itself, can be more of a barrier between the individual and society and between the individual and his personal achievement?

Considered thus, the walls become a symbol of death, and Bartleby gives up the human effort to cope with the limiting power of the wall of death which he could do were he to compromise between the demands of society and those of his individual integrity. He simply "prefers not to" make such a compromise. Knowing life to be such a compromise, the lawyer discovers through Bartleby the insight that furnishes the theme of the story: refusal to make a compromise.

Being a scrivener, a copyist, the uncompromising Bartleby is not engaged in a creative act, such as art, whose composition for many people has become the means by which they communicate with society at the same time that they fulfill their individual goal of self-expression. Bartleby's work became intolerable to him in its frustration of his self-expression. Rejecting those he feels have imposed the frustration upon him, he withdraws from society as well as from individual action. He cannot be saved by the interest, concern—the love—which the lawyer eventually shows for him. Bartleby has become a silent contemplator of walls.

What Bartleby failed to see and what we may infer the lawyer learned is that walls need not be barriers, or that mortality need not be a barrier between an individual and society and between an individual and his own fulfillment.

In *Death of a Salesman,* a modern tragic drama by Arthur Miller, which is also about a man who is at once the victim and the cause of his social isolation, the stage setting depicts a house without walls. Walls can be barriers that both separate the members of the family and enclose them, protecting them from outside forces. The house that has no walls fails to protect the harmony of the family or to insure the privacy of the individual. On the other hand, the house that has walls would be equally negative in that the walls would be barriers between the members of the family and between the family and the larger society outside. But at least the house that has walls can have doors in those walls. There can be no doorways if there are no walls. Walls that have doors are penetrable.

The narrator in "Bartleby" understands this matter of walls, how they are protective yet penetrable, safe yet risky, like being mortal. The green screen the lawyer puts between his desk and Bartleby's and the ground glass folding-doors in the office are protective yet penetrable. The lawyer has learned that man can achieve privacy by closing the man-made door in the wall. He knows, too, that he may be able to overcome his loneliness by opening the door and coming out. As he contemplates death, however, the only thing he knows is that he may achieve privacy only in the tomb, whose walls have no doors that man can control.

Questions

1. Bartleby's origin is mysterious. Why does the narrator pique the reader's curiosity by postscripting the report that Bartleby had been a subordinate clerk in the Dead Letter Office?
2. What emotional effect does the repetition of Bartleby's "I would prefer not to" have on the reader and the narrator?
3. How does the story achieve an impact that balances the comic and the tragic? the ridiculous and the pathetic?

4. The narrator gives detailed descriptions not only of himself and Bartleby, but also of the minor characters Turkey, Nippers, and Ginger Nut. What is their function in the story? Why do they have those nicknames?

5. How do you explain the unusual nature of Bartleby's diet? How does it relate to the narrator's statement to the grub-man that Bartleby "Lives without dining"?

6. In his essay "On the Duty of Civil Disobedience," Henry David Thoreau, a contemporary of Herman Melville, stated, "I simply wish to refuse allegiance to the State, to withdraw and stand aloof from it effectually." In the same essay, Thoreau, who had been jailed for refusal to pay a poll tax, said, "I declined to pay." "I can afford to refuse allegiance." Bartleby also "would prefer not to" fulfill social obligations. How absolute a stand against social conformity can any individual *afford* to take?

7. When the grub-man asks the lawyer, "He's asleep, ain't he?" the narrator murmurs, "With kings and counselors." What insight into the common bond of all men is he implying here?

8. How does the *green* screen that the lawyer sets up around Bartleby relate to the grass in the prison yard?

9. The story is designed so that the action has a definite progression. Identify the three "scenes" or movements of the action and show how they determine the development of character and illumination of theme to make the story an affirmation rather than a negation of life.

10. How do the lawyer's attempts to deal with Bartleby reveal the change in the lawyer's character?

The Burrow

Franz Kafka

I have completed the construction of my burrow and it seems to be successful. All that can be seen from outside is a big hole; that, however, really leads nowhere; if you take a few steps you strike against natural firm rock. I can make no boast of having contrived this ruse intentionally; it is simply the remains of one of my many abortive building attempts, but finally it seemed to me advisable to leave this one hole without filling it in. True, some ruses are so subtle that they defeat themselves, I know that better than any one, and it is certainly a risk to draw attention by this hole to the fact that there may be something in the vicinity worth enquiring into. But you do not know me if you think I am afraid, or that I built my burrow simply out of fear. At a distance of some thousand paces from this hole lies, covered by a movable layer of moss, the real entrance to the burrow; it is secured as safely as anything in this world can be secured; yet some one could step on the moss or break through it, and then my burrow would lie open, and anybody who liked—please note, however, that quite uncommon abilities would also be required—could make his way in and destroy everything for good. I know that very well, and even now that I am better off than ever before I can scarcely pass an hour in complete tranquillity; at that one point in the dark moss I am vulnerable, and in my dreams I often see a greedy muzzle sniffing round it persistently. It will be objected that I could quite well have filled in the entrance too, with a thin layer of hard earth on top and with loose soil further down, so that it would not cost me much trouble to dig my way out again whenever I liked. But that plan is impossible; prudence itself demands that I should have a way of leaving at a moment's notice if necessary, prudence itself demands, as alas! so often, the element of risk in life. All this involves very laborious calculation, and the sheer pleasure of the mind in its own keenness is often the sole reason why one keeps it up. I must have a way of leaving at a moment's notice, for, despite all my vigilance, may I not be attacked from some quite unexpected quarter? I live in peace in the inmost chamber of my house, and meanwhile the enemy may be burrowing his way slowly and stealthily straight towards me. I do not say that he has a better scent than I; probably he knows as little about me as I of him. But there are insatiable robbers who burrow blindly through the ground, and to whom the very size of my house gives the hope of hitting by chance on some of its far-flung passages. I certainly have the advantage of being in my own house and knowing all the passages and how they run. A robber may very easily become my victim and a succulent one too. But I am growing old; I am not as strong as many others, and my enemies are countless; it could well happen that in flying from one enemy I might run into the jaws of another. Anything might happen! In any case I must have the confident knowledge that somewhere there is an exit easy to reach and quite free, where I have to do nothing whatever to get out, so that I might never—Heaven shield us!—suddenly feel the teeth of the pursuer in my flank while I am desperately burrowing away, even if it is at loose easy soil. And it is not only by external enemies that I am threatened. There are also enemies in the bowels of the earth. I have never seen them, but legend tells of them and I firmly believe in them. They are creatures of the inner earth; not even legend can describe them. Their very victims can scarcely have seen them; they come, you hear the scratching of their claws just under you in the ground, which is their element, and already you are lost. Here it is of no avail to console yourself with the thought that you are in your own house; far rather are you in theirs. Not even my exit could save me from them; indeed in all probability it would not save me in any case, but rather betray me; yet it is a hope, and I cannot live without it. Apart from this main exit I am also connected with the outer world by quite narrow, tolerably safe passages which provide me with good fresh air to breathe. They are the work of the field mice. I have made judicious use of them, transforming them into an organic part of my burrow. They also give me the possibility of scenting things from afar, and thus serve as a protection. All sorts of small fry, too, come running through them, and I devour these; so I can have a certain amount of subterranean hunting, sufficient for a modest way of life, without leaving my burrow at all; and that is naturally a great advantage.

But the most beautiful thing about my burrow is the stillness. Of course, that is deceitful. At any moment it may be shattered and then all will be over. For the time being, however, the silence is still with

me. For hours I can stroll through my passages and hear nothing
except the rustling of some little creature, which I immediately reduce
to silence between my jaws, or the pattering of soil, which draws my
attention to the need for repair; otherwise all is still. The fragrance
of the woods floats in; the place feels both warm and cool. Sometimes
I lie down and roll about in the passage with pure joy. When autumn
sets in to possess a burrow like mine, and a roof over your head, is
great good fortune for any one getting on in years. Every hundred
yards I have widened the passages into little round cells; there I can
curl myself up in comfort and lie warm. There I sleep the sweet sleep
of tranquillity, of satisfied desire, of achieved ambition; for I possess a
house. I do not know whether it is a habit that still persists from
former days, or whether the perils even of this house of mine are great
enough to awaken me; but invariably every now and then I start up
out of profound sleep and listen, listen into the stillness which reigns
here unchanged day and night, smile contentedly and then sink with
loosened limbs into still profounder sleep. Poor homeless wanderers
in the roads and woods, creeping for warmth into a heap of leaves or a
herd of their comrades, delivered to all the perils of heaven and earth!
I lie here in a room secured on every side—there are more than fifty
such rooms in my burrow—and pass as much of my time as I choose
between dozing and unconscious sleep.

Not quite in the centre of the burrow, carefully chosen to serve as
a refuge in case of extreme danger from siege if not from immediate
pursuit, lies the chief cell. While all the rest of the burrow is the outcome rather of intense intellectual than of physical labour, this Castle
Keep was fashioned by the most arduous labour of my whole body.
Several times, in the despair brought on by physical exhaustion, I was
on the point of giving up the whole business, flung myself down panting and cursed the burrow, dragged myself outside and left the place
lying open to all the world. I could afford to do that, for I had no
longer any wish to return to it, until at last, after four hours or days,
back I went repentantly, and when I saw that the burrow was un-
harmed I could almost have raised a hymn of thanksgiving, and in
sincere gladness of heart started on the work anew. My labours on the
Castle Keep were also made harder, and unnecessarily so (unnecessarily
in that the burrow derived no real benefit from those labours) by the
fact that just at the place where, according to my calculations, the
Castle Keep should be, the soil was very loose and sandy and had
literally to be hammered and pounded into a firm state to serve as
a wall for the beautifully vaulted chamber. But for such tasks the

only tool I possess is my forehead. So I had to run with my forehead thousands and thousands of times, for whole days and nights, against the ground, and I was glad when the blood came, for that was a proof that the walls were beginning to harden; and in that way, as everybody must admit, I richly paid for my Castle Keep.

In the Castle Keep I assemble my stores; everything over and above my daily wants that I capture inside the burrow, and everything I bring back with me from my hunting expeditions outside, I pile up here. The place is so spacious that food for half a year scarcely fills it. Consequently I can divide up my stores, walk about among them, play with them, enjoy their plenty and their various smells, and reckon up exactly how much they represent. That done, I can always arrange accordingly, and make my calculations and hunting plans for the future, taking into account the season of the year. There are times when I am so well provided for that in my indifference to food I never even touch the smaller fry that scuttle about the burrow, which, however, is probably imprudent of me. My constant preoccupation with defensive measures involves a frequent alteration or modification, though within narrow limits, of my views on how the building can best be organized for that end. Then it sometimes seems risky to make the Castle Keep the basis of defence; the ramifications of the burrow present me with manifold possibilities, and it seems more in accordance with prudence to divide up my stores somewhat, and put part of them in certain of the smaller rooms; thereupon I mark off every third room, let us say, as a reserve store-room, or every fourth room as a main and every second as an auxiliary store-room, and so forth. Or I ignore certain passages altogether and store no food in them, so as to throw any enemy off the scent, or I choose quite at random a very few rooms according to their distance from the main exit. Each of these new plans involves of course heavy work; I have to make my calculations and then carry my stores to their new places. True, I can do that at my leisure and without any hurry, and it is not all unpleasant to carry such good food in your jaws, to lie down and rest whenever you like, and, which is an actual pleasure, to have an occasional nibble. But it is not so pleasant when, as sometimes happens, you suddenly fancy, starting up from your sleep, that the present distribution of your stores is completely and totally wrong, capable of leading to great dangers, and must be set right at once, no matter how tired or sleepy you may be; then I rush, then I fly, then I have no time for calculation; as I am burning to execute my perfectly new, perfectly satisfactory plan, I seize whatever my teeth hit upon and drag it or carry it away, sighing, groaning, stumbling, and nothing will content me but some radical alteration of the present state of things, which seems imminently dangerous. Until little by little full wakefulness sobers me, and I can hardly understand my panic haste, breathe in deeply the tranquillity of my house, which I myself have disturbed, return to my resting-place, fall asleep at once in a new-won exhaustion, and on awakening find hanging from my jaws, say, a rat, as indubitable proof of night labours which already seem almost unreal. Then again there are times when the storing of all my food in one place seems the best plan of all. Of what use to me could my stores in the smaller rooms be, how much could I store there in any case? And whatever I put there would block the passage, and be a greater hindrance than help to me if I were pursued and had to fly. Besides. it is stupid but true that one's self-conceit suffers if one cannot see all one's stores together, and so at one glance know how much one possesses. And in dividing up my food in those various ways might not a great deal get lost? I can't be always scouring through all my passages and cross-passages so as to make sure that everything is in order. The idea of dividing up my stores is of course a good one, but only if one had several rooms similar to my Castle Keep. Several such rooms! Indeed! And who is to build them? In any case they could not be worked into the general plan of my burrow at this late stage. But I will admit that that is a fault in my burrow; it is always a fault to have only one copy of anything. And I confess too that during the whole time I was constructing the burrow a vague divination that I should have more such cells stirred in my mind, vaguely, yet clearly enough if I had only welcomed it; I did not yield to it, I felt too feeble for the enormous labour it would involve, more, I felt too feeble even to admit to myself the necessity for that labour, and comforted myself as best I could with the vague hope that a building which in any other case would clearly be inadequate, would in my own unique, exceptional, favoured case suffice, presumably, because providence was interested in the preservation of my forehead, that unique instrument. So I have only one Castle Keep, but my dark premonitions that one would not suffice have faded. However that may be I must content myself with the one big chamber, the smaller ones are simply no substitute for it, and so, when this conviction has grown on me, I begin once more to haul all my stores back from them to the Castle Keep. For some time afterwards I find a certain comfort in having all the passages and rooms free, in seeing my stores growing in the Castle Keep and emitting their variegated and mingled smells, each of which delights me in its own fashion, and every one of which I can distinguish even at a distance, as far as the very remotest passages. Then I usually enjoy periods of particular tranquillity, in which I change my sleeping-place by stages, always working in towards the centre of the burrow, always steeping myself more profoundly in the mingled smells, until at last I can no longer restrain myself and one night rush into the Castle Keep, mightily fling myself upon my stores, and glut myself with the best that I can seize until I am completely gorged. Happy, but dangerous hours; any one who knew how to exploit them could destroy me with ease and without any risk. Here too the absence of a second or third large store-room works to my detriment; for it is the single huge accumulated mass of food that seduces me. I try to guard myself in various ways against this danger; the distribution of my stores in the smaller rooms is really one of these expedients; but unfortunately, like other such expedients, it leads through renunciation to still greater greed, which, overruling my intelligence, makes me arbitrarily alter my plans of defence to suit its ends.

To regain my composure after such lapses I make a practice of reviewing the burrow, and after the necessary improvements have been carried out, frequently leave it, though only for a short spell. At such moments the hardship of renouncing it for a long time seems too punitive, even to myself, yet I recognize clearly the need for my occasional short excursions. It is always with a certain solemnity that I approach the exit again. During my spells of home life I avoid it, steer clear even of the outer windings of the corridor that leads to it; besides, it is no easy job to wander about there, for I have contrived there a whole little maze of passages; it was there that I began my burrow, at a time when I had no hope of ever completing it according to my plans; I began, half in play, at that corner, and so my first joy in labour found riotous satisfaction there in a labyrinthine burrow which at the time seemed to me the crown of all burrows, but which I judge to-day, perhaps with more justice, to be too much of an idle *tour de force*, not really worthy of the rest of the burrow, and though perhaps theoretically brilliant—here is my main entrance, I said in those days, ironically addressing my invisible enemies and seeing them all already caught and stifled in the outer labyrinth—is in reality a flimsy piece of jugglery that would hardly withstand a serious attack or the struggles of an enemy fighting for his life. Should I reconstruct this part of my burrow? I keep on postponing the decision, and the labyrinth will probably remain as it is. Apart from the sheer hard work that I should have to face, the task would also be the most dangerous imaginable. When I began the burrow I could work away at it in comparative peace of

mind, the risk wasn't much greater than any other risk; but to attempt
that to-day would be to draw the whole world's attention, and gratui-
tously, to my burrow; to-day the whole thing is impossible. I am almost glad of that, for I still have a certain sentiment about this first
achievement of mine. And if a serious attack were attempted, what
pattern of entrance at all would be likely to save me? An entrance can
deceive, can lead astray, can give the attacker no end of worry, and the
present one too can do that at a pinch. But a really serious attack has
to be met by an instantaneous mobilisation of all the resources in the
burrow and all the forces of my body and soul—that, of course, is self-
evident. So this entrance can very well remain where it is. The burrow has so many unavoidable defects imposed by natural causes that it
can surely stand this one defect for which I am responsible, and which
I recognize as a defect, even if only after the event. In spite of that,
however, I do not deny that this fault worries me from time to time,
indeed always. If on my customary rounds I avoid this part of the burrow, the fundamental reason is because the sight of it is painful to me,
because I don't want to be perpetually reminded of a defect in my
house, even if that defect is only too disturbingly present in my mind.
Let it continue to exist ineradicably at the entrance; I can at least refuse to look at it as long as that is possible. If I merely walk in the direction of the entrance, even though I may be separated from it by
several passages and rooms, I find myself sensing an atmosphere of
great danger, actually as if my hair were growing thin and in a moment
might fly off and leave me bare and shivering, exposed to the howls of
my enemies. Yes, the mere thought of the door itself brings such feelings with it, yet it is the labyrinth leading up to it that torments me
most of all. Sometimes I dream that I have reconstructed it, transformed it completely, quickly, in a night, with a giant's strength, nobody having noticed, and now it is impregnable; the nights in which
such dreams come to me are the sweetest I know, tears of joy and deliv-
erance still glisten on my beard when I awaken.

So I must thread the tormenting complications of this labyrinth
physically as well as mentally whenever I go out, and I am both exasperated and touched when, as sometimes happens, I lose myself for a
moment in my own maze, and the work of my hands seems to be still
doing its best to prove its sufficiency to me, its maker, whose final judgment has long since been passed on it. But then I find myself beneath
the mossy covering, which has been left untouched for so long—for I
stay for long spells in my house—that it has grown fast to the soil round
it, and now only a little push with my head is needed and I am in the

upper world. For a long time I do not dare to make that little movement, and if it were not that I would have to traverse the labyrinth
once more, I would certainly leave the matter for the time being and
turn back again. Just think. Your house is protected and self-suffi-
cient. You live in peace, warm, well-nourished, master, sole master of
all your manifold passages and rooms, and all this you are prepared, it
appears, not merely to give up, but actually to abandon; you nurse the
confident hope, certainly, that you will regain it; yet is it not a dangerous, a far too dangerous stake that you are playing for? Can there be
any reasonable grounds for such a step? No, for such acts as these
there can be no reasonable grounds. But all the same I then cautiously raise the trap-door and slip outside, let it softly fall back again,
and fly as fast as I can from the treacherous spot.

Yet I am not really free. True, I am no longer confined by narrow
passages, but rush through the open woods, and feel new powers awakening in my body for which there was no room, as it were, in the burrow, not even in the Castle Keep, though it had been ten times as big.
The food too is better up here; though hunting is more difficult, success
more rare, the results are more valuable from every point of view; I do
not deny all this; I appreciate it and take advantage of it as fully as
most animals, and probably more fully, for I do not hunt like a vagrant
out of mere idleness or desperation, but calmly and methodically. Also
I am not permanently doomed to this free life, for I know that my term
is measured, that I do not have to hunt here for ever, and that, whenever I am weary of this life and wish to leave it, Someone, whose invita-
tion I shall not be able to withstand, will, so to speak, summon me to
him. And so I can pass my time here quite without care and in complete enjoyment, or rather I could, and yet I cannot. My burrow takes
up too much of my thoughts. I fled from the entrance fast enough,
but soon I am back at it again. I seek out a good hiding-place and
keep watch on the entrance of my house—this time from outside—for
whole days and nights. Call it foolish if you like; it gives me infinite
pleasure and reassures me. At such times it is as if I were not so much
looking at my house as at myself sleeping, and had the joy of being in
a profound slumber and simultaneously of keeping vigilant guard over
myself. I am privileged, as it were, not only to dream about the
spectres of the night in all the helplessness and blind trust of sleep, but
also at the same time to confront them in actuality with the calm judgment of the fully awake. And strangely enough I discover that my
situation is not so bad as I had often thought, and will probably think
again when I return to my house. In this connection—it may be in

others too, but in this one especially—these excursions of mine are truly indispensable. Carefully as I have chosen an out-of-the-way place for my door, the traffic that passes it is nevertheless, if one takes a week's observation, very great; but so it is, no doubt, in all inhabited regions, and probably it is actually better to hazard the risks of dense traffic, whose very impetus carries it past, than to be delivered in complete solitude to the first persistently searching intruder. Here enemies are numerous and their allies and accomplices still more numerous, but they fight one another, and while thus employed rush past my burrow without noticing it. In all my time I have never seen any one investigating the actual door of my house, which is fortunate both for me and for him, for I would certainly have launched myself at his throat, forgetting everything else in my anxiety for the burrow. True, intruders come in whose neighbourhood I dare not remain, and from whom I have to fly as soon as I scent them in the distance; on their attitude to the burrow I really can't pronounce with certainty, but it is at least a reassurance that when I presently return I never find any of them there, and the entrance is undamaged. There have been happy periods in which I could almost assure myself that the enmity of the world towards me had ceased or been assuaged, or that the strength of the burrow had raised me above the destructive struggle of former times. The burrow has probably protected me in more ways than I thought or dared think while I was inside it. This fancy used to have such a hold over me that sometimes I have been seized by the childish desire never to return to the burrow again, but to settle down somewhere close to the entrance, to pass my life watching the entrance, and gloat perpetually upon the reflection—and in that find my happiness—how steadfast a protection my burrow would be if I were inside it. Well, one is soon roughly awakened from childish dreams. What does this protection which I am looking at here from the outside amount to after all? Dare I estimate the danger which I run inside the burrow from observations which I make when outside? Can my enemies, to begin with, have any proper awareness of me if I am not in my burrow? A certain awareness of me they certainly have, but not full awareness. And is not that full awareness the real definition of a state of danger? So the experiments I attempt here are only half-experiments or even less, calculated merely to reassure my fears and by giving me false reassurance to lay me open to great perils. No, I do not watch over my own sleep, as I imagined; rather it is I who sleep, while the destroyer watches. Perhaps he is one of those who pass the entrance without seeming to notice it, concerned merely to ascertain, just like myself, that the door is

still untouched and waits for their attack, and only pass because they
know that the master of the house is out, or because they are quite
aware that he is guilelessly lying on the watch in the bushes close by.
And I leave my post of observation and find I have had enough of this
outside life; I feel that there is nothing more that I can learn here,
either now or at any time. And I long to say a last goodbye to everything up here, to go down into my burrow never to return again, let
things take their course, and not try to retard them with my profitless
vigils. But spoilt by seeing for such a long time everything that happened round the entrance, I find great difficulty in summoning the
resolution to carry out the actual descent, which might easily draw any
one's attention, and without knowing what is happening behind my
back and behind the door after it is fastened. I take advantage of
stormy nights to get over the necessary preliminaries, and quickly
bundle in my spoil; that seems to have come off, but whether it has
really come off will only be known when I myself have made the
descent; it will be known, but not by me, or by me, but too late. So I
give up the attempt and do not make the descent. I dig an experimental burrow, naturally at a good distance from the real entrance, a
burrow just as long as myself, and seal it also with a covering of moss.
I creep into my hole, close it after me, wait patiently, keep vigil for
long or short spells, and at various hours of the day, then fling off the
moss, issue from my hole, and summarise my observations. These are
extremely heterogeneous, and both good and bad; but I have never
been able to discover a universal principle or an infallible method of
descent. In consequence of all this I have not yet summoned the resolution to make my actual descent, and am thrown into despair at the
necessity of doing it soon. I almost screw myself to the point of deciding to emigrate to distant parts and take up my old comfortless life
again, which had no security whatever, but was one indiscriminate succession of perils, yet in consequence prevented one from perceiving
and fearing particular perils, as I am constantly reminded by comparing my secure burrow with ordinary life. Certainly such a decision
would be an arrant piece of folly, produced simply by living too long in
senseless freedom; the burrow is still mine, I have only to take a single
step and I am safe. And I tear myself free from all my doubts and by
broad daylight rush to the door, quite resolved to raise it now; but I
cannot, I rush past it and fling myself into a thorn bush, deliberately, as
a punishment, a punishment for some sin I do not know of. Then, at
the last moment, I am forced to admit to myself that I was right after
all, and that it was really impossible to go down into the burrow with-

out leaving the thing I love best, for a little while at least, at the disposal of all my enemies, on the ground, in the trees, in the air. And the danger is by no means a fanciful one, but very real. It need not be any particular enemy that is provoked to pursue me, it may very well be some chance innocent little creature, some disgusting little beast which follows me out of curiosity, and thus, without knowing it, becomes the leader of all the world against me; nor need it be even that, it may be—and that would be just as bad, indeed in some respects worse—it may be some one of my own kind, a connoisseur and prizer of burrows, a hermit, a lover of peace, but all the same a filthy scoundrel who wishes to be housed where he has not built. If he were actually to arrive now, if in his obscene lust he were to discover the entrance and set about working at it, lifting the moss; if he were actually to succeed, if he were actually to wriggle his way in in my stead, until only his hindquarters still showed; if all this were actually to happen, so that at last, casting all prudence to the winds, I might in my blind rage leap on him, maul him, tear the flesh from his bones, destroy him, drink his blood and fling his corpse among the rest of my spoil, but above all—that is the main thing—were at last back in my burrow once more, I would have it in my heart to greet the labyrinth itself with rapture; but first I would draw the moss covering over me, and I would want to rest, it seems to me, for all the remainder of my life. But nobody comes and I am left to my own resources. Perpetually obsessed by the sheer difficulty of the attempt, I lose much of my timidity, I no longer attempt even to appear to avoid the entrance, but make a hobby of prowling round it; by now it is almost as if I were the enemy spying out a suitable opportunity for successfully breaking in. If I only had some one I could trust to keep watch at my post of observation; then of course I could descend in perfect peace of mind. I would make an agreement with this trusty confederate of mine that he would keep a careful note of the state of things during my descent and for quite a long time afterwards, and if he saw any sign of danger knock on the moss covering, and if he saw nothing do nothing. With that a clean sweep would be made of all my fears, no residue would be left, or at most my confidant. For would he not demand some counter-service from me; would he not at last want to see the burrow? That in itself, to let any one freely into my burrow, would be exquisitely painful to me. I built it for myself, not for visitors, and I think I would refuse to admit him; not even though he alone made it possible for me to get into the burrow would I let him in. But I simply could not admit him, for either I must let him go in first by himself, which is simply unimaginable, or we must both descend at the same time, in which case the advantage I am supposed to derive from him, that of being kept watch over, would be lost. And what trust can I really put in him? Can I trust one whom I have had under my eyes just as fully when I can't see him, and the moss covering separates us? It is comparatively easy to trust any one if you are supervising him or at least can supervise him; perhaps it is possible even to trust some one at a distance; but completely to trust some one outside the burrow when you are inside the burrow, that is, in a different world, that, it seems to me, is impossible. But such considerations are not in the least necessary; the mere reflection is enough that during or after my descent one of the countless accidents of existence might prevent my confidant from fulfilling his duty, and what incalculable results might not the smallest accident of that kind have for me? No, if one takes it by and large, I have no right to complain that I am alone and have nobody that I can trust. I certainly lose nothing by that and probably spare myself trouble. I can only trust myself and my burrow. I should have thought of that before and taken measures to meet the difficulty that worries me so much now. When I began the burrow it would at least have been partly possible. I should have so constructed the first passage that it had two entrances at a moderate distance from each other, so that after descending through the one entrance with that slowness which is unavoidable, I might rush at once through the passage to the second entrance, slightly raise the moss covering, which would be so arranged as to make that easy, and from there keep watch on the position for several days and nights. That would have been the only right way of doing it. True, the two entrances would double the risk, but that consideration need not delay me, for one of the entrances, serving merely as a post of observation, could be quite narrow. And with that I lose myself in a maze of technical speculations, I begin once more to dream my dream of a completely perfect burrow, and that somewhat calms me; with closed eyes I behold with delight perfect or almost perfect structural devices for enabling me to slip out and in unobserved. While I lie there thinking such things I admire these devices very greatly, but only as technical achievements, not as real advantages; for this freedom to slip out and in at will, what does it amount to? It is the mark of a restless nature, of inner uncertainty, disreputable desires, evil propensities that seem still worse when one thinks of the burrow, which is there at one's hand and can flood one with peace if one only remains quite open and receptive to it. For the present, however, I am outside it seeking some possibility of returning, and for that the necessary technical devices would be very desirable. But perhaps not so very desirable after all. Is it not a very grave injustice to the burrow to regard it in moments of nervous panic as a mere hole into which one can creep and be safe? Certainly it is a hole among other things, and a safe one, or should be, and when I picture myself in the midst of danger, then I insist with clenched teeth and all my will that the burrow should be nothing but a hole set apart to save me, and that it should fulfil that clearly defined function with the greatest possible efficiency, and I am ready to absolve it from every other duty. Now the truth of the matter—and one has no eye for that in times of great peril, and only by a great effort even in times when danger is threatening—is that in reality the burrow does provide a considerable degree of security, but by no means enough, for is one ever free from anxieties inside it? These anxieties are different from ordinary ones, prouder, richer in content, often long repressed, but in their destructive effects they are perhaps much the same as the anxieties that existence in the outer world gives rise to. Had I constructed the burrow exclusively to assure my safety I would not have been disappointed, it is true; nevertheless the relation between the enormous labour involved and the actual security it would provide, at least in so far as I could feel it and profit by it, would not have been in my favour. It is extremely painful to have to admit such things to oneself, but one is forced to do it, confronted by that entrance over there which now literally locks and bars itself against me, the builder and possessor. Yet the burrow is not a mere hole for taking refuge in. When I stand in the Castle Keep surrounded by my piled-up stores, surveying the ten passages which begin there, raised and sunken passages, vertical and rounded passages, wide and narrow passages, as the general plan dictates, and all alike still and empty, ready by their various routes to conduct me to all the other rooms, which are also still and empty—then all thought of mere safety is far from my mind, then I know that here is my castle, which I have wrested from the refractory soil with tooth and claw, with pounding and hammering blows, my castle which can never belong to any one else, and is so essentially mine that I can calmly accept in it even my enemy's mortal stroke at the final hour, for my blood will ebb away here in my own soil and not be lost. And what but that is the meaning of the blissful hours which I pass, now peacefully slumbering, now happily keeping watch, in these passages, these passages which suit me so well, where one can stretch oneself out in comfort, roll about in childish delight, lie and dream, or sink into blissful sleep. And the smaller rooms, each familiar to me, so familiar that in spite of their complete similarity I can clearly distinguish one from the other with my eyes shut by the mere feel of the wall: they enclose me more peacefully and warmly than a bird is enclosed in its nest. And all, all still and empty.

But if that is the case, why do I hang back? why do I dread the thought of the intruding enemy more than the possibility of never seeing my burrow again? Well, the latter alternative is fortunately an impossibility; there is no need for me even to take thought to know what the burrow means to me; I and the burrow belong so indissolubly together that in spite of all my fears I could make myself quite comfortable out here, and not even need to overcome my repugnance and open the door; I could be quite content to wait here passively, for nothing can part us for long, and somehow or other I shall quite certainly find myself in my burrow again. But on the other hand how much time may pass before then, and how many things may happen in that time, up here no less than down there? And it lies with me solely to curtail that interval and to do what is necessary at once.

And then, too exhausted to be any longer capable of thought, my head hanging, my legs trembling with fatigue, half-asleep, feeling my way rather than walking, I approach the entrance, slowly raise the moss covering, slowly descend, leaving the door open in my distraction for a needlessly long time, and presently remember my omission, and get out again to make it good—but what need was there to get out for that? All that was needed was to draw to the moss covering; right; so I creep in again and now at last draw to the moss covering. Only in this state, and in this state alone, can I achieve my descent.—So at last I lie down beneath the moss on the top of my bloodstained spoil and can now enjoy my longed-for sleep. Nothing disturbs me, no one has tracked me down, above the moss everything seems to be quiet thus far at least, but even if all were not quiet I question whether I could stop to keep watch now; I have changed my place, I have left the upper world and am in my burrow, and I feel its effect at once. It is a new world, endowing me with new powers, and what I felt as fatigue up there is no longer that here. I have returned from a journey, dog-tired with my wanderings, but the sight of the old house, the thought of all the things that are waiting to be done, the necessity at least to cast a glance at all the rooms, but above all to make my way immediately to the Castle Keep; all this transforms my fatigue into ardent zeal; it is as though at the moment when I set foot in the burrow I had wakened from a long and profound sleep. My first task is a very laborious one and requires all my attention; I mean getting my spoil through the

narrow and thin-walled passages of the labyrinth. I shove with all my
might, and the work gets done too, but far too slowly for me; to hasten
it I drag part of my flesh supply back again and push my way over it
and through it; now I have only a portion of my spoil before me and it
is easier to make progress; but my road is so blocked by all this flesh
in these narrow passages, through which it is not always easy for me to
make my way when I am alone, that I could quite easily smother
among my own stores; sometimes I can only rescue myself from their
pressure by eating and drinking a clear space for myself. But the work
of transport is successful, I finish it in quite a reasonable time, the labyrinth is behind me, I reach an ordinary passage and breathe freely,
push my spoil through a communication passage into a main passage
expressly designed for the purpose, a passage sloping down steeply to
the Castle Keep. What is left to be done is not really work at all; my
whole load rolls and flows down the passage almost of itself. The
Castle Keep at last. At last I can dare to rest. Everything is unchanged, no great mishap seems to have occurred, the few little defects that I note at a first glance can soon be repaired; first, however, I
must go my long round of all the passages, but that is no hardship, that
is merely to commune again with friends, as I often did in the old days
or—I am not so very old yet, but my memory of many things is already
quite confused—as I often did, or as I have often imagined I did. I begin with the second passage, but break off in the middle and turn into
the third passage and let it take me back again to the Castle Keep, and
now of course I have to begin at the second passage once more, and so
I play with my task and lengthen it out and smile to myself and con-
gratulate myself and become quite dazed with all the work in front of
me, but never think of turning aside from it. It is for your sake, ye passages and rooms, and you, Castle Keep, above all, that I have come
back, counting my own life as nothing in the balance, after stupidly
trembling for it for so long, and postponing my return to you. What
do I care for danger now that I am with you? You belong to me, I to
you, we are united; what can harm us? What if my foes should be
assembling even now up above there and their muzzles be preparing
to break through the moss? And with its silence and emptiness the
burrow answers me, confirming my words.—But now a feeling of lassi-
tude overcomes me and in some favourite room I curl myself up tentatively, I have not yet surveyed everything by a long way, though still
resolved to examine everything to the very end; I have no intention of
sleeping here, I have merely yielded to the temptation of making myself
comfortable and pretending I want to sleep, I merely wish to find out

if this is as good a place for sleeping in as it used to be. It is, but it is a better place for sleep than for wakening, and I remain lying where I am in deep slumber.

I must have slept for a long time. I was only wakened when I had reached the last light sleep which dissolves of itself, and it must have been very light, for it was an almost inaudible whistling noise that wakened me. I recognised what it was immediately; the smaller fry, whom I had allowed far too much latitude, had burrowed a new channel somewhere during my absence, this channel must have chanced to intersect an older one, the air was caught there, and that produced the whistling noise. What an indefatigably busy lot these smaller fry are, and what a nuisance their diligence can be! First I shall have to listen at the walls of my passages and locate the place of disturbance by experimental excavations, and only then will I be able to get rid of the noise. However, this new channel may be quite welcome as a further means of ventilation, if it can be fitted into the plan of the burrow. But after this I shall keep a much sharper eye on the small fry than I used to; I shall spare none of them.

As I have a good deal of experience in investigations of this kind the work probably will not take me long and I can start upon it at once; there are other jobs awaiting me, it is true, but this is the most urgent. I must have silence in my passages. This noise, however, is a comparatively innocent one; I did not hear it at all when I first arrived, although it must certainly have been there; I must first feel quite at home before I could hear it; it is, so to speak, audible only to the ear of the householder. And it is not even constant, as such noises usually are; there are long pauses, obviously caused by stoppages of the current of air. I start on my investigations, but I can't find the right place to begin at, and though I cut a few trenches I do it at random; naturally that has no effect, and the hard work of digging and the still harder work of filling the trenches up again and beating the earth firm is so much labour lost. I don't seem to be getting any nearer to the place where the noise is, it goes on always on the same thin note, with regular pauses, now a sort of whistling, but again like a kind of piping. Now I could leave it to itself for the time being; it is very disturbing, certainly, but there can hardly be any doubt that its origin is what I took it to be at first; so it can scarcely become louder, on the contrary such noises may quite well—though until now I have never had to wait so long for that to happen—may quite well vanish of themselves in the course of time through the continued labours of these little burrowers; and apart from that often chance itself puts one on the track of the disturbance, where systematic investigation has failed for a long time. In such ways I comfort myself, and resolve simply to continue my tour of the passages, and visit the rooms, many of which I have not even seen yet since my return, and enjoy myself contemplating the Castle Keep now and then between times; but my anxiety will not let me, and I must go on with my search. These little creatures take up much, far too much, time that could be better employed. In such cases as the present it is usually the technical problem that attracts me; for example, from the noise, which my ear can distinguish in all its finest shades, so that it has a perfectly clear outline to me, I deduce its cause, and now I am on fire to discover whether my conclusion is valid. And with good reason, for as long as that is not established I cannot feel safe, even if it were merely a matter of discovering where a grain of sand that had fallen from one of the walls had rolled to. And even a noise such as this is by no means a trifling matter, regarded from that angle. But whether trifling or important, I can find nothing, no matter how hard I search, or it may be that I find too much. This had to happen just in my favourite room, I think to myself, and I walk a fair good distance away from it, almost half-way along the passage leading to the next room; but I do this merely as a joke, pretending to myself that my favourite room is not alone to blame, but that there are disturbances elsewhere as well, and with a smile on my face I begin to listen; but soon I stop smiling, for, right enough, the same whistling meets me here too. It is really nothing to worry about; sometimes I think that nobody but myself would hear it; it is true, I hear it now more and more distinctly, for my ear has grown keener through practice; though in reality it is exactly the same noise wherever I may hear it, as I have convinced myself by comparing· my impressions. Nor is it growing louder; I recognise this when I listen in the middle of the passage instead of pressing my ear against the wall. Then it is only by straining my ears, indeed by lowering my head as well, that I can more guess at than hear the merest trace of a noise now and then. But it is this very uniformity of the noise everywhere that disturbs me most, for it cannot be made to agree with my original assumption. Had I rightly divined the cause of the noise, then it must have issued with greatest force from some given place, which it would be my task to discover, and after that have grown fainter and fainter. But if my hypothesis does not meet the case, what can the explanation be? There still remains the possibility that there are two noises, that up to now I have been listening at a good distance from the two centres, and that while its noise increases, when I draw near to one of them, the total result remains approxi-

mately the same for the ear in consequence of the lessening volume of
sound from the other centre. Already I have almost fancied sometimes,
when I have listened carefully, that I could distinguish, if very indis-
tinctly, differences of tone which support this new assumption. In any
case I must extend my sphere of investigation far farther than I have
done. Accordingly I descend the passage to the Castle Keep and begin
to listen there. Strange, the same noise there too. Now it is a noise
produced by the burrowing of some species of small fry who have
infamously exploited my absence; in any case they have no intention of
doing me harm, they are simply busied with their own work, and so
long as no obstacle comes in their way they will keep on in the direction
they have taken: I know all this, yet that they should have dared to
approach the very Castle Keep itself is incomprehensible to me and
fills me with agitation, and confuses the faculties which I need so urgently for the work before me. Here I have no wish to discover whether
it is the unusual depth at which the Castle Keep lies, or its great extent
and correspondingly powerful air suction, calculated to scare burrowing creatures away, or the mere fact that it is the Castle Keep, that by
some channel or other has penetrated to their dull minds. In any case I
have never noticed any sign of burrowing in the walls of the Castle
Keep until now. Crowds of little beasts have come here, it is true, attracted by the powerful smells; here I have had a constant hunting-
ground, but my quarry has always burrowed a way through in the
upper passages, and come running down here, somewhat fearfully, but
unable to withstand such a temptation. But now, it seems, they are
burrowing in all the passages. If I had only carried out the best of the
grand plans I thought out in my youth and early manhood, or rather, if
I had only had the strength to carry them out, for there would have
been no lack of will. One of these favourite plans of mine was to isolate
the Castle Keep from its surroundings, that is to say, to restrict the
thickness of its wall to about my own height, and leave a free space of
about the same width all round the Castle Keep, except for a narrow
foundation, which unfortunately would have to be left to bear up the
whole. I had always pictured this free space, and not without reason,
as the loveliest imaginable haunt. What a joy to lie pressed against the
rounded outer wall, pull oneself up, let oneself slide down again, miss
one's footing and find oneself on firm earth, and play all those games
literally upon the Castle Keep and not inside it; to avoid the Castle
Keep, to rest one's eyes from it whenever one wanted, to postpone the
joy of seeing it until later and yet not have to do without it, but literally
hold it safe between one's claws, a thing that is impossible if you have

only an ordinary open entrance to it; but above all to be able to stand guard over it, and in that way to be so completely compensated for renouncing the actual sight of it that, if one had to choose between staying all one's life in the Castle Keep or in the free space outside it, one would choose the latter, content to wander up and down there all one's days and keep guard over the Castle Keep. Then there would be no noises in the walls, no insolent burrowing up to the very Keep itself; then peace would be assured there and I would be its guardian; then I would not have to listen with loathing to the burrowing of the small fry, but with delight to something that I cannot hear now at all: the murmurous silence of the Castle Keep.

But that beautiful dream is past and I must set to work, almost glad that now my work has a direct connection with the Castle Keep, for that wings it. Certainly, as I can see more and more clearly, I need all my energies for this task, which at first seemed quite a trifling one. I listen now at the walls of the Castle Keep, and wherever I listen, high or low, at the roof or the floor, at the entrance or in the corners, everywhere, everywhere, I hear the same noise. And how much time, how much care must be wasted in listening to that noise, with its regular pauses. One can, if one wishes, find a tiny deceitful comfort in the fact that here in the Castle Keep, because of its vastness, one hears nothing at all, as distinguished from the passages, when one stands back from the walls. Simply as a rest and a means to regain my composure I often make this experiment, listen intently and am overjoyed when I hear nothing. But the question still remains, what can have happened? Confronted with this phenomenon my original explanation completely falls to the ground. But I must also reject other explanations which present themselves to me. One· could assume, for instance, that the noise I hear is simply that of the small fry themselves at their work. But all my experience contradicts this; I cannot suddenly begin to hear now a thing that I have never heard before though it was always there. My sensitiveness to disturbances in the burrow has perhaps become greater with the years, yet my hearing has by no means grown keener. It is of the very nature of small fry not to be heard. Would I have tolerated them otherwise? Even at the risk of starvation I would have exterminated them. But perhaps—this idea now insinuates itself—I am concerned here with some animal unknown to me. That is possible. True, I have observed the life down here long and carefully enough, but the world is full of diversity and is never wanting in painful surprises. Yet it cannot be a single animal, it must be a whole swarm that has suddenly fallen upon my domain, a huge swarm of little creatures, which as they are audible, must certainly be bigger than the small fry, but yet cannot be very much bigger, for the sound of their labours is itself very faint. It may be, then, a swarm of unknown creatures on their wanderings, who happen to be passing by my way, who disturb me, but will presently cease to do so. So I could really wait for them to pass, and need not put myself to the trouble of work that will be needless in the end. Yet if these creatures are strangers, why is it that I never see any of them? I have already dug a host of trenches, hoping to catch one of them, but I can find not a single one. Then it occurs to me that they may be quite tiny creatures, far tinier than any I am acquainted with, and that it is only the noise they make that is greater. Accordingly I investigate the soil I have dug up, I cast the lumps into the air so that they break into quite small particles, but the noisemakers are not among them. Slowly I come to realize that by digging such small fortuitous trenches I achieve nothing; in doing that I merely disfigure the walls of my burrow, scratching hastily here and there without taking time to fill up the holes again; at many places already there are heaps of earth which block my way and my view. Still, that is only a secondary worry; for now I can neither wander about my house, nor review it, nor rest; often already I have fallen asleep at my work in some hole or other, with one paw clutching the soil above me, from which in a semi-stupor I have been trying to tear a lump. I intend now to alter my methods. I shall dig a wide and carefully constructed trench in the direction of the noise and not cease from digging until, independent of all theories, I find the real cause of the noise. Then I shall eradicate it, if that is within my power, and if it is not, at least I shall know the truth. That truth will bring me either peace or despair, but whether the one or the other, it will be beyond doubt or question. This decision strengthens me. All that I have done till now seems to me far too hasty; in the excitement of my return, while I had not yet shaken myself free from the cares of the upper world, and was not yet completely penetrated by the peace of the burrow, but rather hypersensitive at having had to renounce it for such a long time, I was thrown into complete confusion of mind by an unfamiliar noise. And what was it? A faint whistling, audible only at long intervals, a mere nothing to which I don't say that one could actually get used, for no one could get used to it, but which one could, without actually doing anything about it at once, observe for a while; that is, listen every two hours, let us say, and patiently register the results, instead of, as I had done, keeping one's ear fixed to the wall and at every hint of noise tearing out a lump of earth, not really hoping to find anything, but simply so as to do something to give expression to one's inward agitation. All that will be changed now, I hope. And then, with furious shut eyes, I have to admit to myself that I hope nothing of the kind, for I am still trembling with agitation just as I was hours ago, and if my reason did not restrain me I would probably like nothing better than to start stubbornly and defiantly digging, simply for the sake of digging, at some place or other, whether I heard anything there or not; almost like the small fry, who burrow either without any object at all or simply because they eat the soil. My new and reasonable plan both tempts me and leaves me cold. There is nothing in it to object to, I at least know of no objection; it is bound, so far as I can see, to achieve my aim. And yet at bottom I do not believe in it; I believe in it so little that I do not even fear the terrors which its success may well bring, I do not believe even in a dreadful denouément; indeed it seems to me that I have been thinking ever since the first appearance of the noise of such a methodical trench, and have not begun upon it until now simply because I put no trust in it. In spite of that I shall of course start on the trench; I have no other alternative; but I shall not start at once, but postpone the task for a little while. If reason is to be reinstated on the throne again, it must be completely reinstated; I shall not rush blindly into my task. In any case I shall first repair the damage that I have done to the burrow with my wild digging; that will take a good long time, but it is necessary; if the new trench is really to reach its goal it will probably be long, and if it should lead to nothing at all it will be endless; in any case this task means a longish absence from the burrow, though an absence by no means so painful as an absence in the upper world, for I can interrupt my work whenever I like and pay a visit to my house; and even if I should not do that the air of the Castle Keep will be wafted to me and surround me while I work; nevertheless it means leaving the burrow and surrendering myself to an uncertain fate, and consequently I want to leave the burrow in good order behind me; it shall not be said that I, who am fighting for its peace, have myself destroyed that peace without reinstating it at once. So I begin by shovelling the soil back into the holes from which it was taken, a kind of work I am familiar with, that I have done countless times almost without regarding it as work, and at which, particularly as regards the final pressing and smoothing down—and this is no empty boast, but the simple truth—I am unbeatable. But this time everything seems difficult, I am too distracted, every now and then, in the middle of my work, I press my ear to the wall and listen, and without taking any notice let the soil that I have just lifted trickle back into the passage again. The final embellishments, which demand a stricter attention, I can hardly achieve at all. Hideous protuberances, disturbing cracks remain, not to speak of the fact that the old buoyancy simply cannot be restored again to a wall patched up in such a way. I try to comfort myself with the reflection that my present work is only temporary. When I return after peace has been restored I shall repair everything properly: work will be mere play to me then. Oh yes, work is mere play in fairy tales, and this comfort of mine belongs to the realm of fairy tales too. It would be far better to do the work thoroughly now, at once, far more reasonable than perpetually to interrupt it and wander off through the passages to discover new sources of noise, which is easy enough, all that is needed being to stop at any point one likes and listen. And that is not the end of my useless discoveries. Sometimes I fancy that the noise has stopped, for it makes long pauses; sometimes such a faint whistling escapes one, one's own blood is pounding all too loudly in one's ears; then two pauses come one after another, and for a while one thinks that the whistling has stopped for ever. I listen no longer, I jump up, all life is transfigured; it is as if the fountains from which flows the silence of the burrow were unsealed. I refrain from verifying my discovery at once, I want first to find some one to whom in all good faith I can confide it, so I rush to the Castle Keep, I remember, for I and everything in me has awakened to new life, that I have eaten nothing for a long time, I snatch something or other from among my store of food half buried under debris and hurriedly begin to swallow it while I hurry back to the place where I made my incredible discovery, I only want to assure myself about it incidentally, perfunctorily, while I am eating; I listen, but the most perfunctory listening shows at once that I was shamefully deceived: away there in the distance the whistling still remains unshaken. And I spit out my food, and would like to trample it underfoot, and go back to my task, not caring which I take up; any place where it seems to be needed, and there are enough places like that, I mechanically start on something or other, just as if the overseer had appeared and I must make a pretence of working for his benefit. But hardly have I well begun in this fashion when it may happen that I make a new discovery. The noise seems to have become louder, not much louder, of course—here it is always a matter of the subtlest shades —but all the same sufficiently louder for the ear to recognise it clearly. And his growing-louder is like a coming-nearer; still more distinctly than you hear the increasing loudness of the noise, you can literally see the step that brings it closer to you. You leap back from the wall, you try to grasp at once all the possible consequences that this discovery

will bring with it. You feel as if you had never really organised the
burrow for defence against attack; you had intended to do so, but despite all your experience of life the danger of an attack, and consequently the need to organise the place for defence, seemed remote—or
rather not remote (how could it possibly be!)—but infinitely less important than the need to put it in a state where one could live peacefully;
and so that consideration was given priority in everything relating to
the burrow. Many things in this direction might have been done without affecting the plan of the whole; most incomprehensibly they have
been neglected. I have had a great deal of luck all of those years, luck
has spoilt me; I have had anxieties, but anxiety leads to nothing when
you have luck to back you.

The thing to do, really to do now, would be to go carefully over the
burrow and consider every possible means of defending it, work out a
plan of defense and a corresponding plan of construction, and then
start on the work at once with the vigour of youth. This is the work
that would really be needed, for which, I need not say, it is now far too
late in the day; yet that is what would really be needed, and not the
digging of a grand experimental trench, whose only real result would
be to deliver me hand and foot to the search for danger, out of the foolish fear that it will not arrive quickly enough of itself. Suddenly I cannot comprehend my former plan. I can find no slightest trace of reason
in what had seemed so reasonable; once more I lay aside my work and
even my listening; I have no wish to discover any further signs that the
noise is growing louder; I have had enough of discoveries; I let everything slide; I would be quite content if I could only still the conflict going on within me. Once more I let my passages lead me where they
will, I come to more and more remote ones that I have not yet seen
since my return, and that are quite unsullied by my scratching paws,
and whose silence rises up to meet me and sinks into me. I do not surrender to it, I hurry on, I do not know what I want, probably simply to
put off the hour. I stray so far that I find myself at the labyrinth; the
idea of listening beneath the moss covering tempts me; such distant
things, distant for the moment, chain my interest. I push my way up
and listen. Deep stillness; how lovely it is here, outside there nobody
troubles about my burrow, everybody has his own affairs, which have
no connection with me; how have I managed to achieve this state of
things with all my calculations? Here under the moss covering is perhaps the only place in my burrow now where I can listen for hours and
hear nothing. A complete reversal of things in the burrow; what was
once the place of danger has become a place of tranquillity, while the

Castle Keep has been plunged into the mêlée of the world and all its perils. Still worse, even here there is no peace in reality, here nothing has changed; silent or vociferous, danger lies in ambush as before above the moss, but I have grown insensitive to it, my mind is far too much taken up with the whistling in my walls. Is my mind really taken up with it? It grows louder, it comes nearer, but I wriggle my way through the labyrinth and make a couch for myself up here under the moss; it is almost as I were already leaving the house to the whistler, content if I can only have a little peace up here. To the whistler? Have I come, then, to a new conclusion concerning the cause of the noise? But surely the noise is caused by the channels bored by the small fry? Is not that my considered opinion? It seems to me that I have not retreated from it thus far. And if the noise is not caused directly by these channels, it is indirectly. And even if it should have no connection with them whatever, one is not at liberty to make *a priori* assumptions, but must wait until one finds the cause, or it reveals itself. One could play with hypotheses, of course, even at this stage; for instance it is possible that there has been a water burst at some distance away, and that what seems a piping or whistling to me is in reality a gurgling. But apart from the fact that I have no experience in that sphere—the groundwater that I found at the start I drained away at once, and in this sandy soil it has never returned—apart from this fact the noise is undeniably a whistling and simply not to be translated into a gurgling. But what avail all exhortations to be calm; my imagination will not rest, and I have actually come to believe—it is useless to deny it to myself—that the whistling is made by some beast, and moreover not by a great many small ones, but by a single great one. Many signs contradict this. The noise can be heard everywhere and always at the same strength, and moreover uniformly, both by day and night. At first, therefore, one cannot but incline to the hypothesis of a great number of little animals; but as I must have found some of them during my digging and I have found nothing, it only remains for me to assume the existence of a great beast, especially as the things that seem to contradict the hypothesis are merely things which make the beast, not so much impossible, as merely dangerous beyond all one's powers of conception. For that reason alone have I stuck out against this hypothesis. I shall cease from this self-deception. For a long time already I have played with the idea that the beast can be heard at such a great distance because it works so furiously; it burrows as fast through the ground as another animal can walk on the open road; the ground still trembles at its burrowing when it has ceased; this reverberation and the noise of the boring itself unite into one sound at such a great distance, and I, as I hear only the last dying ebb of that sound, hear it always at the same uniform strength. It follows from this also that the beast is not making for me, seeing that the noise never changes; more likely it has a plan in view whose purpose I cannot decipher; I merely assume that the beast—and I make no claim whatever that it knows of my existence—is encircling me; it has probably made several circles round my burrow already since I began to observe it. The nature of the noise, the piping or whistling, gives me much food for thought. When I scratch and scrape in the soil in my own fashion the sound is quite different. I can explain the whistling only in this way: that the beast's chief means of burrowing is not its claws, which it probably employs merely as a secondary resource, but its snout or its muzzle, which, of course, apart from its enormous strength, must also be fairly sharp at the point. It probably bores its snout into the earth with one mighty push and tears out a great lump; while it is doing that I hear nothing; that is the pause; but then it draws in the air for a new push. This indrawal of its breath, which must be an earth-shaking noise, not only because of the beast's strength, but of its haste, its furious lust for work as well: this noise I hear then as a faint whistling. But quite incomprehensible remains the beast's capacity to work without stopping; perhaps the short pauses provide also the opportunity of snatching a moment's rest; but apparently the beast has never yet allowed itself a really long rest, day and night it goes on burrowing, always with the same freshness and vigour, always thinking of its object, which must be achieved with the utmost expedition, and which it has the ability to achieve with ease. Now I could not have foreseen such an opponent. But apart altogether from the beast's peculiar characteristics, what is happening now is only something which I should really have feared all the time, something against which I should have been constantly prepared: the fact that some one would come. By what chance can everything have flowed on so quietly and happily for such a long time? Who can have diverted my enemies from their path, and forced them to make a wide detour round my property? Why have I been spared for so long, only to be delivered to such terrors now? Compared with this, what are all the petty dangers in brooding over which I have spent my life! As owner of the burrow I had hoped to be in a stronger position than any enemy who might chance to appear. But simply by virtue of being owner of this great vulnerable edifice I am obviously defenceless against any serious attack. The joy of possessing it has spoilt me, the vulnerability of the burrow has made me vulnerable; any wound to it hurts me as if I my-self were hit. It is precisely this that I should have foreseen; instead of thinking only of my own defence—and how perfunctorily and vainly I have done even that—I should have thought of the defence of the bur-row. Above all, provision should have been made for cutting off sec-tions of the burrow, and as many as possible of them, from the endan-gered sections when they are attacked; this should have been done by means of improvised land-slides, calculated to operate at a moment's notice; moreover these should have been so thick, and have provided such an effectual barrier, that the attacker would not even guess that the real burrow only began at the other side. More, these land-slides should have been so devised that they not only concealed the burrow, but also entombed the attacker. Not the slightest attempt have I made to carry out such a plan, nothing at all has been done in this direction, I have been as thoughtless as a child, I have passed my manhood's years in childish games, I have done nothing but play even with the thought of danger, I have shirked really taking thought for actual dan-ger. And there has been no lack of warning.

Nothing, of course, approaching the present situation has happened before; nevertheless there was an incident not unlike it when the bur-row was only beginning. The main difference between that time and this is simply that the burrow was only beginning then. . . . In those days I was literally nothing more than a humble apprentice in his first year, the labyrinth was only sketched out in rough outline, I had al-ready dug a little room, but the proportions and the execution of the walls were sadly bungled; in short everything was so tentative that it could only be regarded as an experiment, as something which, if one lost patience some day, one could leave lying as was without much re-gret. Then one day as I lay on a heap of earth resting from my la-bours—I have rested far too often from my labours all my life—suddenly I heard a noise in the distance. Being young at the time, I was less frightened than curious. I left my work to look after itself and set my-self to listen; I listened and listened, and had no wish to fly up to my moss covering and stretch myself out there so that I might not hear. I did listen, at least. I could clearly recognize that the noise came from some kind of burrowing similar to my own; it was somewhat fainter, of course, but how much of that might be put down to the distance one could not tell. I was intensely interested, but otherwise calm and cool. Perhaps I am in somebody else's burrow, I thought to myself, and now the owner is boring his way towards me. If that assumption had proved to be correct I would have gone away, for I have never had any desire for conquest or bloodshed, and begun building somewhere else. But after all I was still young and still without a burrow, so I could remain quite cool. Besides, the further course of the noise brought no real cause for apprehension, except that it was not easy to explain. If whoever was boring there was really making for me, because he had heard me boring, then if he changed his direction, as now actually happened, it could not be told whether he did this because my pause for rest had deprived him of any definite point to make towards, or because—which was more plausible—he had himself changed his plans. But perhaps I had been deceived altogether, and he had never been actually making in my direction; at any rate the noise grew louder for a while as if he were drawing nearer, and being young at that time I probably would not have been displeased to see the burrower suddenly rising from the ground; but nothing of that kind happened, at a certain point the sound of boring began to weaken, it grew fainter and fainter, as if the burrower were gradually diverging from his first route, and suddenly it broke off altogether, as if he had decided now to take the diametrically opposite direction and were making straight away from me into the distance. For a long time I still went on listening for him in the silence, before I returned once more to my work. Now that warning was definite enough, but I soon forgot it, and it scarcely influenced my building plans.

Between that day and this lie my years of maturity, but is it not as if there were no interval at all between them? I still take long rests from my labours and listen at the wall, and the burrower has changed his intention anew, he has turned back, he is returning from his journey, thinking he has given me ample time in the interval to prepare for his reception. But on my side everything is worse prepared for than it was then; the great burrow stands defenceless, and I am no longer a young apprentice, but an old architect and the powers I still have fail me when the decisive hour comes; yet old as I am it seems to me that I would gladly be still older, so old that I should never be able to rise again from my resting-place under the moss. For to be honest I cannot endure the place, I rise up and rush, as if I had filled myself up there with new anxieties instead of peace, down into the house again.—What was the state of things the last time I was here? Had the whistling grown fainter? No, it had grown louder. I listen at ten places chosen at random and definitely note my own disappointment; the whistling is just the same as ever, nothing has altered. Up there under the moss no change touches one, there one is at peace, uplifted above time; but here every instant frets and gnaws at the listener. I go once more the long road to the Castle Keep, all my surroundings seem filled with agitation, seem to be looking at me, and then look away again so as not to annoy me, yet cannot refrain the very next moment from trying to read the saving solution from my expression. I shake my head, I have not yet found any solution. Nor do I go to the Castle Keep in pursuance of any plan. I pass the spot where I had intended to begin the experimental trench, I look it over once more, it would have been an admirable place to begin at, the trench's course would have been in the direction where lay the majority of the tiny ventilation holes, which would have greatly lightened my labours; perhaps I should not have had to dig very far, should not even have had to dig to the source of the noise; perhaps if I had listened at the ventilation holes it would have been enough. But no consideration is potent enough to animate me to this labour of digging. This trench will bring me certainty, you say? I have reached the stage where I no longer wish to have certainty. In the Castle Keep I choose a lovely piece of flayed red flesh and creep with it into one of the heaps of earth; there I shall have silence at least, such silence, at any rate, as still can be said to exist here. I munch and nibble at the flesh, think of the strange beast going its own road in the distance, and then again that I should enjoy my store of food as fully as possible, while I still have the chance. This last is probably the sole plan I have left that I can carry out. For the rest I try to unriddle the beast's plans. Is it on its wanderings, or is it working on its own burrow? If it is on its wanderings then perhaps an understanding with it might be possible. If it should really break through to the burrow I shall give it some of my store and it will go on its way again. It will go its way again, a fine story! Lying on my heap of earth I can naturally dream of all sorts of things, even of an understanding with the beast, though I know well enough that no such thing can happen, and that at the instant when we see each other, more, at the moment when we merely guess at each other's presence, we shall both blindly bare our claws and teeth, neither of us a second before or after the other, both of us filled with a new and different hunger, even if we should already be gorged to bursting. And with entire justice, for who, even if he were merely on his wanderings, would not change his itinerary and his plans for the future on catching sight of the burrow? But perhaps the beast is digging in its own burrow, in which case I cannot even dream of an understanding. Even if it should be such a peculiar beast as to be able to tolerate a neighbour near its burrow, it could not tolerate my burrow, it would not tolerate in any case a neighbour who could be clearly heard. Now actually the beast seems to be a great distance away; if it would only withdraw a little farther the noise too would probably disappear; perhaps in that case everything would be peaceful again as in the old days; all this would then become a painful but salutary lesson, spurring me on to make the most diverse improvements on the burrow; if I have peace, and danger does not immediately threaten me, I am still quite fit for all sorts of hard work; perhaps, considering the enormous possibilities which its powers of work open before it, the beast has given up the idea of extending its burrow in my direction, and is compensating itself for that in some other one. That consummation also cannot, of course, be brought about by negotiation, but only by the beast itself, or by some compulsion exercised from my side. In both cases the decisive factor will be whether the beast knows about me, and if so what it knows. The more I reflect upon it the more improbable does it seem to me that the beast has even heard of me; it is possible, though unimaginable, that it can have received news of me through some other channel, but it has certainly never heard me. So long as I still knew nothing about it, it simply cannot have heard me, for at that time I kept quiet, nothing could be more quiet than my return to the burrow; afterwards, when I dug the experimental trenches, perhaps it could have heard me, though my style of digging makes very little noise; but if it had heard me I must have noticed some sign of it, the beast must at least have stopped its work every now and then to listen. But all remained unchanged.—

Commentary

Like Melville's "Bartleby," Kafka's "The Burrow" is a story of withdrawal and isolation, a retreat from life. But whereas "Bartleby" provides a character with whom the reader can identify (the lawyer) and another character for whom he can feel sympathy (Bartleby), "The Burrow" has only a single character, with whom the reader does not want to identify and for whom he can feel only revulsion.

This single character does not have a name. We do not even learn its biological species. Its story is told from the first person point of view (see p. 31). It does not emerge as a full, developed being, for it lacks the dimension of identity with anything else (except the burrow of its own creation) or with anybody else (except the fearsome figments of its imagination). The creature has blood, jaws, teeth, and a forehead. It breathes, digs, sleeps, wakens, reasons, listens, smiles, kills "the small fry"—and it fears. Or so it tells us. But its animation is only that of a half-life; its total isolation makes it a living death.

It is enveloped in itself despite its intense fear of "the enemy."
The creature is incapable of recognizing itself as an entity apart
from the existence of anything else. It is its own mind; its only
reality is its own rationality. It is a completely subjective thing.
The burrow is a construction of this subjective mind, which, in turn,
is one and the same with the burrow; "What do I care for danger now
that I am with you?" it asks the burrow. "You belong to me, I to
you, we are united; what can harm us?"

The construction of the burrow is as elaborate as that of the brain.
The burrow's labyrinthine channels and cells reflect the whorls and
passages of its creator's reasoning. The burrow, "this house of mine,"
is described in detail. It has a single entrance with "a moss covering,"
though the creature debates frequently the advisability of having
a second door as an avenue of escape from the anonymous enemy
the creature fears. Every hundred yards the passages of the burrow
widen into a little round cell. Fifty such cells are for sleeping purposes. In the center of the burrow is the chief cell, the Castle Keep,
where the creature hoards its store of food, including the small fry,
some of which he devours while enjoying their smells. He also
keeps stores in every third room as a reserve store-room, every fourth
room as a main store-room, and every second room as an auxiliary
warehouse, using his teeth to carry the food about from room to
room. Eventually, though, as a safeguard, he hauls all the food into
the Castle Keep.

Once, thinking his labors of building the burrow and safely hoarding
food are over, he emerges through the moss covering to keep guard
over the burrow, enjoying yet fearing his freedom from it. Reasoning
that the burrow is less dangerous than the world outside, however, he
returns to the burrow—but he finds it less and less perfect. He
discovers he cannot always find in it "the peace" for which he built
it.

Peace—or silence—and noise become the primary motif of the
story. "The most beautiful thing about my burrow is the stillness."
Yet the creature cannot find peace, for "Of course, that is deceitful.
At any moment it [the stillness] may be shattered. . . ." Every now
and then he wakens from a sound sleep and listens "into the stillness
which reigns here unchanged day and night," smiles contentedly, and
then sinks "with loosened limbs into still profounder sleep."

Then, after one long nap, he wakens and hears a noise, which he
at first attributes to the small fry scampering, perhaps digging burrows
of their own. "I must have silence in my passages," he declares and

starts digging again, boring the soil, tamping it with his forehead, reinforcing the walls of the burrow, while trying to find the source of "this very *uniformity* of noise."

But he cannot find the source of the noise, so regular in its starts and pauses. Perhaps it is not the small fry making the noise but rather some unknown animal. As the creature's agitation grows, his panic rises, his sentences grow swifter, longer, more convoluted. "That noise with its regular pauses" continues. It sounds like a kind of whistling. Perhaps it is the gurgling from a burst water pipe. But he had drained all ground water away and in that sandy soil the water has never returned. No, the uniform sounds must be those of some beast, not a great many small ones, but a single great one. The regularity of the pauses and whistles, silence and noise, must be the boring of a great beast's snout and its intermittent intakes of breath.

The frightened creature seems cleverly analytical in its continuous reasoning, but it always stops short of the conclusion that it itself may be the cause of its fears. It does go so far as to recognize that its agitation "confuses the faculties which I need so urgently for the work before me." But it never considers the possibility that the regularity of the "whistling" might be its own breathing; that the enemy it fears might be itself.

There is character in action in this story; there are conflict and suspense, and though the story ends with the narrator's statement, "But all remained unchanged," there have been a resolution and a change. The difference in the creature since the beginning of the story is that though it still does not have the security it has been seeking, it now blames itself for not having been industrious enough in youth to plan and build a better burrow. The irony is that the only part of the creature's life it did *not* waste was its youth, when it did not try to find an impossibility: security against the riskiness of life and the inevitability of death.

Questions

1. "The Burrow" is an allegory, a kind of fiction in which the characters, objects, and events are to be taken not as real but as standing for some set of ideas (see p. 41). Each object in an allegory must be equated with some object in the set of ideas.

   For example, using for the set of ideas the sensitivity and problems of a creative artist like an author, the burrow might be equated with the author's works—each "cell" a story he has written, hoarding in it the experiences he has collected; the Castle Keep, the story the author himself regards as his masterpiece; the creature would be the author, agonizing over his writing, never satisfied with it, fearful always that it will not be successful, fearful that the public (small fry and imagined beast) will deny him recognition, fearful that he will never achieve the perfection he drives himself to achieve. When the author leaves his work long enough to visit the outside world (the forest) he is trying to view objectively what he has written, but he has to return to it, unable, he discovers, to view it with the eyes of the world, so obsessed has he become. The author is so swallowed up by his work that he becomes his work; he ages and weakens as he struggles to improve his writing (digging and rebuilding), and eventually dies, himself and his work entombed. (See Kafka's biographical sketch on p. 457.)

Develop an allegorical interpretation of "The Burrow" based on a point-to-point equation for the objects in the story by applying them to a political set of ideas or a psychological set of ideas or an architectural set of ideas. In so doing, try to find metaphorical equivalents for the creature, the burrow, the labyrinthine tunnels, the "cells," the Castle Keep, the small fry, the enemy, the moss-covered entry, the forest, the stillness, the whistling sound, etc.

2. Did you experience a feeling of tediousness, restlessness, or frustration as you read the story? If so, how is this effect consistent with the content of the story? How does the author employ language to achieve such an effect?

3. Does the creature in the burrow have a sense of guilt? If so, what could his sin be? If there is no sin, then why does he have such a sense of guilt?

4. Macabre though the story is, what element of humor can you detect in it?

5. How can "The Burrow" be interpreted as an affirmation of humanity? as a rejection of humanity?

6. How does the way in which "The Burrow" is written harmonize with the construction of the burrow and its ingenious system of coordinated and intersecting tunnels?

The Guest

Albert Camus

The schoolmaster was watching the two men climb toward him. One was on horseback, the other on foot. They had not yet tackled the abrupt rise leading to the schoolhouse built on the hillside. They were toiling onward, making slow progress in the snow, among the stones, on the vast expanse of the high, deserted plateau. From time to time the horse stumbled. Without hearing anything yet, he could see the breath issuing from the horse's nostrils. One of the men, at least, knew the region. They were following the trail although it had disappeared days ago under a layer of dirty white snow. The schoolmaster calculated that it would take them half an hour to get onto the hill. It was cold; he went back into the school to get a sweater.

He crossed the empty, frigid classroom. On the blackboard the four rivers of France, drawn with four different colored chalks, had been flowing toward their estuaries for the past three days. Snow had suddenly fallen in mid-October after eight months of drought without the transition of rain, and the twenty pupils, more or less, who lived in the villages scattered over the plateau had stopped coming. With fair weather they would return. Daru now heated only the single room that was his lodging, adjoining the classroom and giving also onto the plateau to the east. Like the class windows, his window looked to the south too. On that side the school was a few kilometers from the point where the plateau began to slope toward the south. In clear weather could be seen the purple mass of the mountain range where the gap opened onto the desert.

Somewhat warmed, Daru returned to the window from which he had first seen the two men. They were no longer visible. Hence they must have tackled the rise. The sky was not so dark, for the snow had stopped falling during the night. The morning had opened with a dirty light which had scarcely become brighter as the ceiling of clouds lifted. At two in the afternoon it seemed as if the day were merely beginning. But still this was better than those three days when the thick snow was falling amidst unbroken darkness with little gusts of wind that rattled the double door of the classroom. Then Daru had spent long hours in his room, leaving it only to go to the shed and feed the chickens or get some coal. Fortunately the delivery truck from Tadjid, the nearest village to the north, had brought his supplies two days before the blizzard. It would return in forty-eight hours.

Besides, he had enough to resist a siege, for the little room was cluttered with bags of wheat that the administration left as a stock to distribute to those of his pupils whose families had suffered from the drought. Actually they had all been victims because they were all poor. Every day Daru would distribute a ration to the children. They had missed it, he knew, during these bad days. Possibly one of the fathers or big brothers would come this afternoon and he could supply them with grain. It was just a matter of carrying them over to the next harvest. Now shiploads of wheat were arriving from France and the worst was over. But it would be hard to forget that poverty, that army of ragged ghosts wandering in the sunlight, the plateaus burned to a cinder month after month, the earth shriveled up little by little, literally scorched, every stone bursting into dust under one's foot. The sheep had died then by thousands and even a few men, here and there, sometimes without anyone's knowing.

In contrast with such poverty, he who lived almost like a monk in his remote schoolhouse, nonetheless satisfied with the little he had and with the rough life, had felt like a lord with his whitewashed walls, his narrow couch, his unpainted shelves, his well, and his weekly provision of water and food. And suddenly this snow, without warning, without the foretaste of rain. This is the way the region was, cruel to live in, even without men—who didn't help matters either. But Daru had been born here. Everywhere else, he felt exiled.

He stepped out onto the terrace in front of the schoolhouse. The two men were now halfway up the slope. He recognized the horseman as Balducci, the old gendarme he had known for a long time. Balducci was holding on the end of a rope an Arab who was walking behind him with hands bound and head lowered. The gendarme waved a greeting to which Daru did not reply, lost as he was in contemplation of the Arab dressed in a faded blue jellaba, his feet in sandals but covered with socks of heavy raw wool, his head surmounted by a narrow, short chèche. They were approaching. Balducci was holding back his horse in order not to hurt the Arab, and the group was advancing slowly.

Within earshot, Balducci shouted: "One hour to do the three kilo-

meters from El Ameur!" Daru did not answer. Short and square in
his thick sweater, he watched them climb. Not once had the Arab
raised his head. "Hello," said Daru when they got up onto the terrace.
"Come in and warm up." Balducci painfully got down from his horse
without letting go the rope. From under his bristling mustache he
smiled at the schoolmaster. His little dark eyes, deep-set under a
tanned forehead, and his mouth surrounded with wrinkles made him
look attentive and studious. Daru took the bridle, led the horse to the
shed, and came back to the two men, who were now waiting for him in
the school. He led them into his room. "I am going to heat up the
classroom," he said. "We'll be more comfortable there." When he entered the room again, Balducci was on the couch. He had undone the
rope tying him to the Arab, who had squatted near the stove. His
hands still bound, the *chèche* pushed back on his head, he was looking
toward the window. At first Daru noticed only his huge lips, fat,
smooth, almost Negroid; yet his nose was straight, his eyes were dark
and full of fever. The *chèche* revealed an obstinate forehead and, under the weathered skin now rather discolored by the cold, the whole
face had a restless and rebellious look that struck Daru when the Arab,
turning his face toward him, looked him straight in the eyes. "Go into
the other room," said the schoolmaster, "and I'll make you some mint
tea." "Thanks," Balducci said. "What a chore! How I long for re-
tirement." And addressing his prisoner in Arabic: "Come on, you."
The Arab got up and, slowly, holding his bound wrists in front of him,
went into the classroom.

With the tea, Daru brought a chair. But Balducci was already en-
throned on the nearest pupil's desk and the Arab had squatted against
the teacher's platform facing the stove, which stood between the desk
and the window. When he held out the glass of tea to the prisoner,
Daru hesitated at the sight of his bound hands. "He might perhaps be
untied." "Sure," said Balducci. "That was for the trip." He started to
get to his feet. But Daru, setting the glass on the floor, had knelt beside the Arab. Without saying anything, the Arab watched him with
his feverish eyes. Once his hands were free, he rubbed his swollen
wrists against each other, took the glass of tea, and sucked up the burning liquid in swift little sips.

"Good," said Daru. "And where are you headed?"

Balducci withdrew his mustache from the tea. "Here, son."

"Odd pupils! And you're spending the night?"

"No. I'm going back to El Ameur. And you will deliver this fellow
to Tinguit. He is expected at police headquarters."

Balducci was looking at Daru with a friendly little smile.

"What's this story?" asked the schoolmaster. "Are you pulling my leg?"

"No, son. Those are the orders."

"The orders? I'm not . . ." Daru hesitated, not wanting to hurt the old Corsican. "I mean, that's not my job."

"What! What's the meaning of that? In wartime people do all kinds of jobs."

"Then I'll wait for the declaration of war!"

Balducci nodded.

"O.K. But the orders exist and they concern you too. Things are brewing, it appears. There is talk of a forthcoming revolt. We are mobilized, in a way."

Daru still had his obstinate look.

"Listen, son," Balducci said. "I like you and you must understand. There's only a dozen of us at El Ameur to patrol throughout the whole territory of a small department and I must get back in a hurry. I was told to hand this guy over to you and return without delay. He couldn't be kept there. His village was beginning to stir; they wanted to take him back. You must take him to Tinguit tomorrow before the day is over. Twenty kilometers shouldn't faze a husky fellow like you. After that, all will be over. You'll come back to your pupils and your comfortable life."

Behind the wall the horse could be heard snorting and pawing the earth. Daru was looking out the window. Decidedly, the weather was clearing and the light was increasing over the snowy plateau. When all the snow was melted, the sun would take over again and once more would burn the fields of stone. For days, still, the unchanging sky would shed its dry light on the solitary expanse where nothing had any connection with man.

"After all," he said, turning around toward Balducci, "what did he do?" And, before the gendarme had opened his mouth, he asked: "Does he speak French?"

"No, not a word. We had been looking for him for a month, but they were hiding him. He killed his cousin."

"Is he against us?"

"I don't think so. But you can never be sure."

"Why did he kill?"

"A family squabble, I think. One owed the other grain, it seems. It's not at all clear. In short, he killed his cousin with a billhook. You know, like a sheep, *kreezk!*"

Balducci made the gesture of drawing a blade across his throat and the Arab, his attention attracted, watched him with a sort of anxiety. Daru felt a sudden wrath against the man, against all men with their rotten spite, their tireless hates, their blood lust.

But the kettle was singing on the stove. He served Balducci more tea, hesitated, then served the Arab again, who, a second time, drank avidly. His raised arms made the jellaba fall open and the schoolmaster saw his thin, muscular chest.

"Thanks, kid," Balducci said. "And now, I'm off."

He got up and went toward the Arab, taking a small rope from his pocket.

"What are you doing?" Daru asked dryly.

Balducci, disconcerted, showed him the rope.

"Don't bother."

The old gendarme hesitated. "It's up to you. Of course, you are armed?"

"I have my shotgun."

"Where?"

"In the trunk."

"You ought to have it near your bed."

"Why? I have nothing to fear."

"You're crazy, son. If there's an uprising, no one is safe, we're all in the same boat."

"I'll defend myself. I'll have time to see them coming."

Balducci began to laugh, then suddenly the mustache covered the white teeth.

"You'll have time? O.K. That's just what I was saying. You have always been a little cracked. That's why I like you, my son was like that."

At the same time he took out his revolver and put it on the desk.

"Keep it; I don't need two weapons from here to El Ameur."

The revolver shone against the black paint of the table. When the gendarme turned toward him, the schoolmaster caught the smell of leather and horseflesh.

"Listen, Balducci," Daru said suddenly, "every bit of this disgusts me, and first of all your fellow here. But I won't hand him over. Fight, yes, if I have to. But not that."

The old gendarme stood in front of him and looked at him severely.

"You're being a fool," he said slowly. "I don't like it either. You don't get used to putting a rope on a man even after years of it, and you're even ashamed—yes, ashamed. But you can't let them have their way."

"I won't hand him over," Daru said again.

"It's an order, son, and I repeat it."

"That's right. Repeat to them what I've said to you: I won't hand him over."

Balducci made a visible effort to reflect. He looked at the Arab and at Daru. At last he decided.

"No, I won't tell them anything. If you want to drop us, go ahead; I'll not denounce you. I have an order to deliver the prisoner and I'm doing so. And now you'll just sign this paper for me."

"There's no need. I'll not deny that you left him with me."

"Don't be mean with me. I know you'll tell the truth. You're from hereabouts and you are a man. But you must sign, that's the rule."

Daru opened his drawer, took out a little square bottle of purple ink, the red wooden penholder with the "sergeant-major" pen he used for making models of penmanship, and signed. The gendarme carefully folded the paper and put it into his wallet. Then he moved toward the door.

"I'll see you off," Daru said.

"No," said Balducci. "There's no use being polite. You insulted me."

He looked at the Arab, motionless in the same spot, sniffed peevishly, and turned away toward the door. "Good-by, son," he said. The door shut behind him. Balducci appeared suddenly outside the window and then disappeared. His footsteps were muffled by the snow. The horse stirred on the other side of the wall and several chickens fluttered in fright. A moment later Balducci reappeared outside the window leading the horse by the bridle. He walked toward the little rise without turning around and disappeared from sight with the horse following him. A big stone could be heard bouncing down. Daru walked back toward the prisoner, who, without stirring, never took his eyes off him. "Wait," the schoolmaster said in Arabic and went toward the bedroom. As he was going through the door, he had a second thought, went to the desk, took the revolver, and stuck it in his pocket. Then, without looking back, he went into his room.

For some time he lay on his couch watching the sky gradually close over, listening to the silence. It was this silence that had seemed painful to him during the first days here, after the war. He had requested a post in the little town at the base of the foothills separating the upper plateaus from the desert. There, rocky walls, green and black to the north, pink and lavender to the south, marked the frontier of eternal summer. He had been named to a post farther north, on the plateau itself. In the beginning, the solitude and the silence had been hard for him on these wastelands peopled only by stones. Occasionally, furrows suggested cultivation, but they had been dug to uncover a certain kind of stone good for building. The only plowing here was to harvest rocks. Elsewhere a thin layer of soil accumulated in the hollows would be scraped out to enrich paltry village gardens. This is the way it was: bare rock covered three quarters of the region. Towns sprang up, flourished, then disappeared; men came by, loved one another or fought bitterly, then died. No one in this desert, neither he nor his guest, mattered. And yet, outside this desert neither of them, Daru knew, could have really lived.

When he got up, no noise came from the classroom. He was amazed at the unmixed joy he derived from the mere thought that the Arab might have fled and that he would be alone with no decision to make. But the prisoner was there. He had merely stretched out between the stove and the desk. With eyes open, he was staring at the ceiling. In that position, his thick lips were particularly noticeable, giving him a pouting look. "Come," said Daru. The Arab got up and followed him. In the bedroom, the schoolmaster pointed to a chair near the table under the window. The Arab sat down without taking his eyes off Daru.

"Are you hungry?"

"Yes," the prisoner said.

Daru set the table for two. He took flour and oil, shaped a cake in a frying-pan, and lighted the little stove that functioned on bottled gas. While the cake was cooking, he went out to the shed to get cheese, eggs, dates, and condensed milk. When the cake was done he set it on the window sill to cool, heated some condensed milk diluted with water, and beat up the eggs into an omelette. In one of his motions he knocked against the revolver stuck in his right pocket. He set the bowl down, went into the classroom, and put the revolver in his desk drawer. When he came back to the room, night was falling. He put on the light and served the Arab. "Eat," he said. The Arab took a piece of the cake, lifted it eagerly to his mouth, and stopped short.

"And you?" he asked.

"After you. I'll eat too."

The thick lips opened slightly. The Arab hesitated, then bit into the cake determinedly.

The meal over, the Arab looked at the schoolmaster. "Are you the judge?"

"No, I'm simply keeping you until tomorrow."

"Why do you eat with me?"

"I'm hungry."

The Arab fell silent. Daru got up and went out. He brought back a folding bed from the shed, set it up between the table and the stove, perpendicular to his own bed. From a large suitcase which, upright in a corner, served as a shelf for papers, he took two blankets and arranged them on the camp bed. Then he stopped, felt useless, and sat down on his bed. There was nothing more to do or to get ready. He had to look at this man. He looked at him, therefore, trying to imagine his face bursting with rage. He couldn't do so. He could see nothing but the dark yet shining eyes and the animal mouth.

"Why did you kill him?" he asked in a voice whose hostile tone surprised him.

The Arab looked away.

"He ran away. I ran after him."

He raised his eyes to Daru again and they were full of a sort of woeful interrogation. "Now what will they do to me?"

"Are you afraid?"

He stiffened, turning his eyes away.

"Are you sorry?"

The Arab stared at him openmouthed. Obviously he did not understand. Daru's annoyance was growing. At the same time he felt awkward and self-conscious with his big body wedged between the two beds.

"Lie down there," he said impatiently. "That's your bed."

The Arab didn't move. He called to Daru:

"Tell me!"

The schoolmaster looked at him.

"Is the gendarme coming back tomorrow?"

"I don't know."

"Are you coming with us?"

"I don't know. Why?"

The prisoner got up and stretched out on top of the blankets, his feet toward the window. The light from the electric bulb shone straight into his eyes and he closed them at once.

"Why?" Daru repeated, standing beside the bed.

The Arab opened his eyes under the blinding light and looked at him, trying not to blink.

"Come with us," he said.

In the middle of the night, Daru was still not asleep. He had gone to bed after undressing completely; he generally slept naked. But when he suddenly realized that he had nothing on, he hesitated. He felt vulnerable and the temptation came to him to put his clothes back on. Then he shrugged his shoulders; after all, he wasn't a child and, if need be, he could break his adversary in two. From his bed he could observe him, lying on his back, still motionless with his eyes closed under the harsh light. When Daru turned out the light, the darkness seemed to coagulate all of a sudden. Little by little, the night came back to life in the window where the starless sky was stirring gently. The schoolmaster soon made out the body lying at his feet. The Arab still did not move, but his eyes seemed open. A faint wind was prowling around the schoolhouse. Perhaps it would drive away the clouds and the sun would reappear.

During the night the wind increased. The hens fluttered a little and then were silent. The Arab turned over on his side with his back to Daru, who thought he heard him moan. Then he listened for his guest's breathing, become heavier and more regular. He listened to that breath so close to him and mused without being able to go to sleep. In this room where he had been sleeping alone for a year, this presence bothered him. But it bothered him also by imposing on him a sort of brotherhood he knew well but refused to accept in the present circumstances. Men who share the same rooms, soldiers or prisoners, develop a strange alliance as if, having cast off their armor with their clothing, they fraternized every evening, over and above their differences, in the ancient community of dream and fatigue. But Daru shook himself; he didn't like such musings, and it was essential to sleep.

A little later, however, when the Arab stirred slightly, the schoolmaster was still not asleep. When the prisoner made a second move, he stiffened, on the alert. The Arab was lifting himself slowly on his arms with almost the motion of a sleepwalker. Seated upright in bed, he waited motionless without turning his head toward Daru, as if he were listening attentively. Daru did not stir; it had just occurred to him that the revolver was still in the drawer of his desk. It was better to act at once. Yet he continued to observe the prisoner, who, with the same slithery motion, put his feet on the ground, waited again, then began to stand up slowly. Daru was about to call out to him when the Arab began to walk, in a quite natural but extraordinarily silent way. He was heading toward the door at the end of the room that opened into the shed. He lifted the latch with precaution and went out, pushing the door behind him but without shutting it. Daru had not stirred. "He is running away," he merely thought. "Good riddance!" Yet he listened attentively. The hens were not fluttering; the guest must be on the plateau. A faint sound of water reached him, and he didn't know what it was until the Arab again stood framed in the doorway, closed the door carefully, and came back to bed without a sound. Then Daru turned his back on him and fell asleep. Still later he seemed, from the depths of his sleep, to hear furtive steps around the schoolhouse. "I'm dreaming! I'm dreaming!" he repeated to himself. And he went on sleeping.

When he awoke, the sky was clear; the loose window let in a cold, pure air. The Arab was asleep, hunched up under the blankets now, his mouth open, utterly relaxed. But when Daru shook him, he started dreadfully, staring at Daru with wild eyes as if he had never seen him and such a frightened expression that the schoolmaster stepped back. "Don't be afraid. It's me. You must eat." The Arab nodded his head and said yes. Calm had returned to his face, but his expression was vacant and listless.

The coffee was ready. They drank it seated together on the folding bed as they munched their pieces of the cake. Then Daru led the Arab under the shed and showed him the faucet where he washed. He went back into the room, folded the blankets and the bed, made his own bed and put the room in order. Then he went through the classroom and out onto the terrace. The sun was already rising in the blue sky; a soft, bright light was bathing the deserted plateau. On the ridge the snow was melting in spots. The stones were about to reappear. Crouched on the edge of the plateau, the schoolmaster looked at the deserted expanse. He thought of Balducci. He had hurt him, for he had sent him off in a way as if he didn't want to be associated with him. He could still hear the gendarme's farewell and, without knowing why, he felt strangely empty and vulnerable. At that moment, from the other side of the schoolhouse, the prisoner coughed. Daru listened to him almost despite himself and then, furious, threw a pebble that whistled through the air before sinking into the snow. That man's stupid crime revolted him, but to hand him over was contrary to honor. Merely thinking of it made him smart with humiliation. And he cursed at one and the same time his own people who had sent him this Arab and the Arab too who had dared to kill and not managed to get away. Daru got up, walked in a circle on the terrace, waited motionless, and then went back into the schoolhouse.

The Arab, leaning over the cement floor of the shed, was washing his

teeth with two fingers. Daru looked at him and said: "Come." He
went back into the room ahead of the prisoner. He slipped a hunting-
jacket on over his sweater and put on walking-shoes. Standing, he
waited until the Arab had put on his *chèche* and sandals. They went
into the classroom and the schoolmaster pointed to the exit saying:
"Go ahead." The fellow didn't budge. "I'm coming," said Daru.
The Arab went out. Daru went back into the room and made a package of pieces of rusk, dates, and sugar. In the classroom, before going
out, he hesitated a second in front of his desk, then crossed the threshold and locked the door. "That's the way," he said. He started toward the east, followed by the prisoner. But, a short distance from the
schoolhouse, he thought he heard a slight sound behind them. He retraced his steps and examined the surroundings of the house; there was
no one there. The Arab watched him without seeming to understand.
"Come on," said Daru.

They walked for an hour and rested beside a sharp peak of lime-
stone. The snow was melting faster and faster and the sun was drinking up the puddles at once, rapidly cleaning the plateau, which gradually dried and vibrated like the air itself. When they resumed walking,
the ground rang under their feet. From time to time a bird rent the
space in front of them with a joyful cry. Daru breathed in deeply the
fresh morning light. He felt a sort of rapture before the vast familiar
expanse, now almost entirely yellow under its dome of blue sky. They
walked an hour more, descending toward the south. They reached a
level height made up of crumbly rocks. From there on, the plateau
sloped down, eastward, toward a low plain where there were a few
spindly trees and, to the south, toward outcroppings of rock that gave
the landscape a chaotic look.

Daru surveyed the two directions. There was nothing but the sky on
the horizon. Not a man could be seen. He turned toward the Arab,
who was looking at him blankly. Daru held out the package to him.
"Take it," he said. "There are dates, bread, and sugar. You can hold
out for two days. Here are a thousand francs too." The Arab took the
package and the money but kept his full hands at chest level as if he
didn't know what to do with what was being given him. "Now look,"
the schoolmaster said as he pointed in the direction of the east, "there's
the way to Tinguit. You have a two-hour walk. At Tinguit you'll find
the administration and the police. They are expecting you." The
Arab looked toward the east, still holding the package and the money
against his chest. Daru took his elbow and turned him rather roughly
toward the south. At the foot of the height on which they stood could

be seen a faint path. "That's the trail across the plateau. In a day's walk from here you'll find pasturelands and the first nomads. They'll take you in and shelter you according to their law." The Arab had now turned toward Daru and a sort of panic was visible in his expression. "Listen," he said. Daru shook his head: "No, be quiet. Now I'm leaving you." He turned his back on him, took two long steps in the direction of the school, looked hesitantly at the motionless Arab, and started off again. For a few minutes he heard nothing but his own step resounding on the cold ground and did not turn his head. A moment later, however, he turned around. The Arab was still there on the edge of the hill, his arms hanging now, and he was looking at the schoolmaster. Daru felt something rise in his throat. But he swore with impatience, waved vaguely, and started off again. He had already gone some distance when he again stopped and looked. There was no longer anyone on the hill.

Daru hesitated. The sun was now rather high in the sky and was beginning to beat down on his head. The schoolmaster retraced his steps, at first somewhat uncertainly, then with decision. When he reached the little hill, he was bathed in sweat. He climbed it as fast as he could and stopped, out of breath, at the top. The rock-fields to the south stood out sharply against the blue sky, but on the plain to the east a steamy heat was already rising. And in that slight haze, Daru, with heavy heart, made out the Arab walking slowly on the road to prison.

A little later, standing before the window of the classroom, the schoolmaster was watching the clear light bathing the whole surface of the plateau, but he hardly saw it. Behind him on the blackboard, among the winding French rivers, sprawled the clumsily chalked-up words he had just read: "You handed over our brother. You will pay for this." Daru looked at the sky, the plateau, and, beyond, the invisible lands stretching all the way to the sea. In this vast landscape he had loved so much, he was alone.

Notes

This story is one of six in the author's collection *The Exile and the Kingdom.* In all the stories, set in Algeria, the author deals with the human problems of solitude and exile. In "The Guest," two kinds of solitude are illuminated. One is the loneliness of an individual when he cannot comprehend why the offer of brotherhood to another turns against him. The other is the loneliness of the same individual when he is aware of what he has done and realizes that it was neces-

sary for him to do what he did regardless of the consequences. Born
in the Algerian plateau, Daru felt exiled everywhere else, but he is
exiled here, too. The unexplained handwriting on the blackboard
suggests that Daru has exposed himself to reprisals. He has offended
his old friend, the gendarme Balducci, and the prisoner has chosen
punishment rather than freedom. All three characters are isolated
from each other, each in his own social or asocial realm; consequently,
each suffers exile from the "kingdom" where he could find unstinted
love and understanding.

Questions

1. Analyze, interpret, and evaluate "The Guest" by answering the questions that appear on page 43-44 of the chapter "The Art of Short Fiction."

2. In the light of your analysis and interpretation, and keeping in mind that this story is not an allegory (see p. 42), try to explain "the clumsily chalked-up words" scrawled on the blackboard: "You handed over our brother. You will pay for this."

So Much Unfairness
of Things

C. D. B. Bryan

The Virginia Preparatory School lies just off the Shirley Highway between Washington, D.C., and Richmond. It is a small Southern school with dull red brick dormitories and classroom buildings, quiet old school buildings with quiet old Southern names—Page House, Stuart Hall, Randolph Hall, Breckinridge, Pinckney, and Coulter. The high brick wall that surrounds the school is known as the Breastworks, and the shallow pond behind the football field is the Crater. V.P.S. is an old school, with an old school's traditions. A Virginia Department of Conservation sign commemorates the use of the school by Union troops as a military hospital in 1861, and every October the school celebrates "Liberation Day," in honor of the day in 1866 when the school reopened.

Graduates of the Virginia Preparatory School who have not returned for some years are shocked by the glass-and-steel apartment houses and cinder-block ramblers that have sprung up around the school grounds, but once they have driven along the Breastworks and passed through the ornate wrought-iron East Gate, they see, with satisfaction, that the school has not changed. Neither have its customs. For example, new boys, or "toads," still must obey the Toad Code. They must be courteous to old boys and faculty. They must know the school song and cheers by the end of the second week. They must know the names of all members of the faculty and the varsity football team. They must hold doors open for old boys and see that old boys are served first in the dining room. And they must "run relay"—meaning that they have to wake up the old boys in the morning when they wish to be wakened and see that they are not disturbed when they wish to sleep.

Philip Sadler Wilkinson was fourteen; he was an old boy. The new boy shook him lightly. "Mr. Wilkinson? Mr. Wilkinson? It's five-thirty, sir. You asked me to wake you up."

Next year the new boy would be permitted to call Philip Sadler Wilkinson "P.S.," like the others. He watched P.S. stretch, turn over, and go back to sleep. "Sir? Hey! Wake up!"

P.S. rolled out of his metal cot, rubbed his eyes, felt around the top of his desk for his glasses, put them on, and looked at the new boy.

"Toad?"

"Yes, sir?"

"What is the date?"

"Thursday, the seventh of June."

"How much longer do we have until the end of the school year?"

"Seven days, twenty-three hours, and"—the new boy looked at his wristwatch—"and thirteen minutes, sir."

P.S. smiled. "Are you sure?"

"No, sir."

"Ah-hah! Ah-HAH! Toad, assume the position!"

The new boy locked his knees and bent over and grabbed his ankles.

"What is a 'toad,' toad?" P.S. asked.

"Sir, a toad is a loathsome warty creature who eats insects and worms, sir. A toad is the lowest form of amphibian. A toad is despicable."

"Well, well, now, straighten those knees, toad." P.S. looked at the new boy and saw that his face was turning red with strain. "Toad, are you in pain?"

"No, sir," the new boy lied.

"Then you may straighten up."

The new boy massaged his calves. "Honest to God, P.S., you're a sadist."

"No, no, wait till next year. You'll be pulling the same thing on some toad yourself. I had it done to me, you had it done to you. And did I detect you calling me by my rightful name?"

The new boy smiled.

"Ah, God, you toads will never learn. Assume the position."

The new boy started to bend over again.

"Oh, hell, go away," P.S. said. The new boy started out of the door and P.S. called him back. "Hey, toad? You gonna kill the Latin exam?"

"I hope so."

"How do you conjugate the verb 'to spit'?"

"*Exspuo, exspuere, exspui—*"

"Good God, no!" P.S. laughed. "It's *spitto, spittere, ach tui, splattus!*"
The new boy groaned and left the room.

P.S. looked at his watch. It was twenty minutes to six. He could
hear the new boy waking up the boy in the next room. P.S. picked up
his water glass and toothbrush and tiptoed down the corridor. He
stopped at Charlie Merritt's room and knocked softly.

"Who is it?"

"It's me, Charlie."

"Oh, hey, P.S. Come on in."

P.S. pushed aside the curtain of the cubicle. Charlie was sitting at
his desk, studying.

"Morning," P.S. whispered.

"Morning."

"Studying the Latin?"

"Yep."

"You know how to conjugate the verb 'to spit'?"

"Yep," Charlie said. "*Spitto, spittere, ach—*"

"O.K., O.K.!" P.S. laughed. "You gonna kill the exam?"

"I hope so. You think you'll pass it?"

"Doubt it. I haven't passed one yet." P.S. looked over at Charlie's
bureau. "Say, Charlie? Can I borrow your toothpaste? I'm out."

"Sure, but roll it from the bottom of the tube, will you?"

P.S. picked up the toothpaste and went down the hall to the bathroom. Mabrey, the head monitor, was shaving. P.S. watched him in
the mirror.

"You must have had a porcupine for a father," P.S. said. "You've got
the heaviest beard in school."

Mabrey began to shave the length of his neck.

"How come you got such a heavy beard?" P.S. asked. "We all know
you like little boys."

"Wilkinson, you're about as funny as a rubber crutch."

"Cut your throat! Cut your throat!" P.S. began to dance around behind Mabrey, sprinkling voodoo potions on the top of the older student's head. "Monkey dust! Monkey dust! Oh, black Pizzoola! Great
Kubla of the Ancient Curse! Make this bad man cut his throat!"

Mabrey cursed and a small red stain began to seep through the lather
on his throat. "P.S., will you *get out of here!*"

P.S. stared, eyes wide open, at the broadening stain. "My God! My
God! It worked!"

Mabrey undid the towel from around his waist and snapped P.S.'s
skinny behind. P.S. yelped and jumped away. "Hey, Mr. Mabrey, sir?

Hey, Mabrey? I'm sorry, I really am. I didn't know it would work."

"What would work?"

"My voodoo curse. I didn't know it would make you cut yourself."

"For God's sake, P.S., what're you talking about? I cut a pimple. Will you leave me alone before I throw you out of a closed window?"

P.S. was quiet for a moment. Then he moved over to the washbasin next to Mabrey and looked at himself in the mirror. He ran his fingers through his light-brown hair and pushed his glasses higher on his nose. "Hey, Mabrey? Do you think I'm fresh? I mean, I have great respect for you—you being the head monitor and all. I mean it. Sometimes I worry. I mean, do you think I'm too fresh?"

Mabrey finished rinsing his face. "P.S., kid," he said as he dried himself, "you're all right. You're a nice guy. And I'm willing to bet that if you could only learn to throw a baseball from center field to second base overhand, you might turn out to be a pretty fair little baseball player."

"*Overhand!* Whaddya mean 'overhand'? They call me 'Deadeye Wilkinson.'" P.S. wound up with an imaginary baseball and threw it as hard as he could. Then he pantomimed being the second baseman. He crouched and caught the incoming ball at his knees and thrust his hand down to tag out the runner. "*Safe!*" he shouted. "I mean, out! Out! Out!"

"Too late," Mabrey said, and laughed. "An umpire never changes his decision."

"I meant *out,*" P.S. said.

Mabrey disappeared down the hall.

P.S. brushed his teeth, being careful to squeeze the toothpaste from the bottom of the tube. He looked at himself in the mirror and chanted, "*Fuero, fueris, fuerit, fuerimus, fueritis, fuerint!*" He examined his upper lip and was disappointed. He wished that he didn't have such a young face. He wished he had a heavy beard, like Mabrey. He washed his face, wet his hair down, and walked back into Charlie's room. Charlie was P.S.'s best friend. He was very short. The other boys kidded him about being an engineer for Lionel trains. P.S. was very tall and thin, and he had not yet grown into his height. At fourteen he was already six feet tall, and he had a tendency to stoop to compensate. He and Charlie were known as Mutt and Jeff. When P.S. entered the room, Charlie was curled up on his bed studying his Latin notes. He didn't look up until P.S. dropped the toothpaste tube on his pillow.

"Rolled from the bottom," P.S. said.

"Hey, how do you expect to pass your Latin exam if you don't study? I heard you and Mabrey clowning around in the can."

"If I don't study!" P.S. said. "Do you know how long I've studied for this exam? Two years! If I flunk it again this year, I get to keep the trophy."

"What trophy?"

"For God's sake, I don't know what trophy. But I'll get something, for sure. I've spent the last two weeks practically doing nothing but studying Latin. I recopied all my notes. I underlined practically the whole book. And I memorized all the irregular verbs. Come on, come on, ask me anything. God, if I don't pass it this year, I've had it. Come on, ask me anything."

"O.K., what's the word for 'ridge'?"

"The word for 'ridge'?" P.S. stalled.

"Yep."

P.S. thought for a moment. "Look, I don't know. Make it two out of three."

"The word for 'ridge' is *'iugum.'* " Charlie looked at his notes. "O.K., two out of three. What's the word for 'crowd'? And 'troop,' as in 'a troop of cavalry'?"

"The word for 'crowd' is *'turba, turbae.'* . . . What was the other one?"

" 'Troop of cavalry.' "

" 'Cavalry' is *'equitatus.'* . . . I don't know. What is 'troop'?"

" 'Troop' is *'turma.'* " Charlie laughed. "Well, you got one out of three."

"Did I get partial credit for the 'cavalry'?"

"Nope."

"Jesus, I hope Dr. Fairfax is more lenient than you are."

"He won't be," Charlie said.

"If I flunk the Latin exam again this year . . ."

"How come you flunked it last year?"

"How come anybody flunks an exam? I didn't know the answers. Boy, Charlie, I don't know what I'm going to do with you. If you weren't such a nice guy and lend me your toothpaste and things like that all the time, I'd probably feed you to the—to the what's-their-name fish. Those fish who eat people in South America all the time."

"Well, since you don't know what to do with me, as a start why don't you let me study?"

"Sure. Sure, O.K. . . . O.K., be a grind. See if I care."

P.S. walked back to his cubicle and pulled his Ullman and Henry

"Latin II" from his unpainted bookcase. First he studied the irregular verbs in the back of the book. Then he went over his vocabulary list. He concentrated for as long as he could; then he leaned out of his window to look at the shadows of the trees directly below, dropped a penny out of the window to see if a squirrel would pick it up, checked his window sill to see if the cookie crumbs he had left for the mocking-bird were still there. He turned back to his Latin book and leafed through the Forestier illustrations of Roman soldiers. He picked up the picture his father had given him last Christmas. Within the frame were four small round photographs of Wilkinsons in uniform. There was his father as an infantry major during the Second World War, his grandfather as a captain in the field artillery during the First World War, his great-great-grandfather as a corporal in a soft gray Confederate uniform, and a great-great-great-great something or other in a dark uniform with a lot of bright buttons. P.S. didn't know who the last picture was of. He imagined it to be somebody from the Revolutionary War. P.S. had seen the oil portrait the photograph had been taken from hanging in the hallway of his grandfather's house. P.S. had the long, thin nose of the other Wilkinsons in the pictures, but he still had the round cheeks of youth and the perfect eyebrows. He was the fifteenth of his family to attend the Virginia Preparatory School. Among the buildings at V.P.S. there was a Wilkinson Memorial Library and a Sadler Gymnasium. When P.S. was packing to begin his first year at the school, his father had said, "Son, when your great-grand-father went off to V.P.S., his father gave him a dozen silk handker-chiefs and a pair of warm gloves. When your grandfather went off to V.P.S., his father gave him a dozen silk handkerchiefs and a pair of warm gloves. When I went off to V.P.S., your grandfather gave me a dozen silk handkerchiefs and a pair of warm gloves. And now here are a dozen silk handkerchiefs and a pair of warm gloves for you."

P.S. looked at the brightly patterned Liberty-silk handkerchiefs and the fuzzy red mittens. No thirteen-year-old ever wore red mittens, except girls, and particularly not fuzzy red mittens. And P.S. knew he would never dare to wear the silk handkerchiefs.

"Well, thank you very much, Dad," he had said.

"That's all right, son."

P.S. left the red mittens behind when he went away to V.P.S. He used two of the silk handkerchiefs to cover the top of his bureau and bookcase, gave one other away to a girl, and hid the rest beneath his underwear on the second shelf of his bureau. His father had done very well at the school; he had been a senior monitor, editor-in-chief of the

yearbook, and a distance runner in winter and spring track. P.S. hoped
he would do as well, but he knew he had disappointed his father so far.
When he flunked the Latin examination last year and tried to explain
to his father that he just could not do Latin, he could see the disbelief
in his father's eyes. "My God, son, you just didn't study. 'Can't do
Latin,' what nonsense!" But P.S. knew that studying had nothing to
do with it. His father said that no Wilkinson had ever flunked at
V.P.S.; P.S. was the first. His father was not the kind to lose his temper. P.S. wished he were. When P.S. had done something wrong, his
father would just look at him and smile sadly and shake his head. The
boy had never felt particularly close to his father. He had never been
able to talk to or with his father. He had found the best means of getting along with his father was to keep out of his way. He had given up
their ever sharing anything. He had no illusions about leading a cal-
endar-picture life with his father—canoeing or hunting together. He
could remember trying to get his father to play catch with him and
how his father would always say, "Not now, son, not now." But there
were certain occasions that his father felt should be shared with P.S.
These were the proper father-son occasions that made P.S. feel like
some sort of ornament. There would be Father's Day, or the big football game of the season. P.S. would be told to order two tickets, and
the afternoon of the game he and his father would watch the first half
together. His father remembered all of the cheers and was shocked
when P.S. didn't remember some of the words to the school song. At the
half, his father would disappear to talk to his friends and P.S. would be
left alone to watch the overcoats or umbrellas. After the game, P.S.
would wander back to the field house, where the alumni tables were set
up. He would locate his father and stand next to him until his father
introduced him to the persons he was talking to. Then his father
would say, "Run along, son. I'll meet you back in your room." So, P.S.
would go back to his room and wait for his father to come by. The boy
would straighten up the bed, dust the bureau, and sweep the floor.
And then after a long wait his father would come in and sit down.
"Well, how are you, son?" the conversation would always start. And
P.S. would answer, "Fine, thank you, sir." His father would look
around the room and remark about its not being large enough to swing
a cat in, then there would be two or three anecdotes about the times
when he was a boy at V.P.S., and then he would look at his watch and
say, "Well, I guess I'd better be pushing off." His father would ask
him if there was anything he needed, and P.S. would say that he didn't
think there was anything. His father would give him a five-dollar bill

and drive away. And P.S., with enormous relief, would go look for
Charlie. "Did you and your dad have a good time?" Charlie would
ask. "Sure," P.S. would say. And that would end the conversation.

P.S. knew that his father loved him, but he also knew better than to
expect any sign of affection. Affection always seemed to embarrass his
father. P.S. remembered his first year at school, when his father had
first come up to see him. He had been very happy to see his father, and
when they were saying goodbye P.S. stepped forward as usual to kiss
him and his father drew away. P.S. always made it a point now to
shake hands with his father. And at fourteen respect and obedience
had taken the place of love.

P.S. picked up his Latin notes and went over the translations he had
completed. He wished he knew what questions would be asked. In
last year's exam there were questions from all over the book, and it
made the exam very difficult to study for, if they were going to do that.
He pictured himself handing in the finished examination to Dr. Fairfax
and saying, "Sir? Wilkinsons do not flunk. Please grade my exam accordingly."

P.S. looked at his wristwatch. The dining hall would begin serving
breakfast in fifteen minutes. He made his bed and put on a clean pair
of khakis and a button-down shirt. He slipped into his old white bucks
and broke a lace tying them, and pulled out the shorter piece and
threaded what was left through the next eyelet up, as the older boys
did. He tidied up his room for inspection, picked up his notes, and
went back to Charlie's room. Charlie was sweeping the dust into the
hall. The new boy on duty that day would be responsible for sweeping
the halls and emptying all trash baskets. P.S. entered and sat down on
the bed.

"Jesus Christ, P.S.! I just made the bed!"

"O.K., O.K., I'll straighten it up when I leave." P.S. ran his fingers
across the desk top. "Merritt, two demerits—dust. . . . Hey, you
know what, Charlie?"

Charlie dusted the desk and then said, "What?"

"You're such a grump in the morning. I sure'd hate to be married to
you."

"Well, I wouldn't worry about that. In the first place, my parents
wouldn't approve."

"I'm not so sure that my family would want me to marry a Merritt,
either. I think you'd have to take my family name. I mean you're just
not our class, you know what I mean?"

"P.S., buddy, you're in a class all by yourself."

"Well, anyway, what I mean is that you're such a grump in the morn-ing that I can see someday your wife coming in—if you ever find a girl who's foolish enough to marry you. But I mean, she might come in some morning and give you grapefruit juice instead of orange juice and you'll probably bite her hand off or something."

"Or *something*." Charlie laughed.

P.S. punched Charlie on the arm. "Garbage mind! God all mighty!"

"What do you mean? I didn't say anything. You've got the dirty mind. All I said was 'or something' and you say I've got a garbage mind."

"Well, you know what I meant."

"I don't know anything at all."

P.S. looked at Charlie for a moment, then he laughed. "I'm not going to take advantage of your last remark. I'm much too good a sport to rake you over the coals when you place your ample foot in your ample mouth."

"*Ample foot!*" Charlie held up his foot. "I've got a very small foot. It's a sign of good breeding."

"Only in horses, Twinkletoes, only in horses."

"Horses, *horses!* What do horses have to do with it?"

"Ask me no questions and I'll tell you no lies." P.S. leafed through Charlie's notes. "Hey, the exam's at ten-thirty, isn't it?"

"Yep. If you flunk Latin again, will they make you go to summer school?"

"Probably. I really think it's archaic the way they make you pass Latin to get out of this place."

"Boy, I sure hope I pass it," Charlie said.

"You will. You will. You're the brain in the class."

"Come on, let's go to chow."

"That's what I've been waiting for, my good buddy, my good friend, old pal of mine." P.S. jumped off the bed, scooped up his notebook, and started out of the room.

"Hey!" Charlie said. "What about the bed?"

At eight o'clock chapel, P.S. knelt in the pew and prayed: *"Dear God, I pray that I pass my Latin exam this morning. . . . If I can pass this exam, then I'll do anything you want me to do. . . . God, please. If I don't pass this exam, I've really had it. . . . They must have made these pews for midgets; I never fit in them right. . . . How am I ever going to get out to Colorado this summer unless I pass that exam? . . . Please God, I don't want a high grade, all I want is to pass . . . and you don't have to help me on the others. . . . I don't want to pass this exam for myself only. I mean, it means a lot to my family. My father will be very disappointed if I flunk the exam. . . .* I wonder if Charlie will be able to go out to Colorado with me. . . . *God bless Mom, God bless Dad, God bless Grandpa Sadler and Grandma Sadler, God bless Grandpa Wilkinson and Granny Wilkinson, God bless all my relatives I haven't mentioned. . . . Amen. And . . . and God? Please, please help me to pass this exam."*

At ten-fifteen, P.S. and Charlie fell in step and walked over to Randolph Hall, where the examination was to be held.

"Well, if we don't know it now, we never will," Charlie said.

"Even if I did know it now, I wouldn't know it tomorrow." P.S. reached into his pants pocket and pulled out his lucky exam tie. It was a stained and unravelled blue knit. As they walked up the path, he was careful to tie the tie backward, the wide end next to his shirt, the seam facing out. Then he checked his watch pocket to see that his lucky silver dollar was there.

"What's the Latin for 'then'?" Charlie asked.

"*'Tum,'*" P.S. answered. "Tums for your *tum*my."

"What's the word for 'thence,' or 'from there'?"

"*'Inde.'*" P.S. began to sing: "*Inde* evening *byde* moonlight you could *hearde*—"

"For God's sake, P.S.!" Charlie laughed.

"You don't like my singing?"

"Not much."

"You know? I'm thinking of joining the choir and glee club next year. You know why? They've got a couple of dances next fall. One with St. Catharine's and another with St. Tim's. You wanta try out with me?"

"I don't know. I can't sing."

"Who's gonna sing?" P.S. grabbed Charlie's arm and growled, "Baby, I'm no singer, I'm a lover!"

"Lover? Who says you're a lover?"

"Ask me no questions and I'll tell you no lies."

P.S. and Charlie walked up the worn wooden steps of Randolph Hall to the third-floor study hall, where the Latin examination was to be given. They both were in the upper study hall, since they were underclassmen still. P.S.'s desk was in the back corner of the study hall, against the wall. He sat down and brushed the dust off the top of his desk with his palm. Someone had traced a hand into the wood.

Others had traced and retraced the hand and deepened the grooves. They had added fingernails and rings. P.S. had added a Marlboro tattoo. He lifted the desk top and, searching for his pencil sharpener, saw that he had some more Latin translations in his desk. He read them through quickly and decided it was too late to learn anything from them. He pulled out his pencil sharpener and closed his desk. The study hall was filling with boys, who took their places at their desks and called back and forth to each other in their slow Southern voices. It was a long, thin room with high windows on either side, and the walls were painted a dirty yellow. Between the windows were framed engravings of Roman ruins and Southern generals. The large fluorescent lights above the desks buzzed and blinked into life. A dark, curly-haired boy sat down in the desk next to P.S. and began to empty his pockets of pencils and pens.

"Hey, Jumbo," P.S. said. "You gonna kill the exam?"

"I hope so. If I can get a good grade on it, then I don't have to worry so much about my math exam tomorrow."

"Well, if we don't know it now we never will."

"You're right."

Jumbo had played second-string tackle on the varsity this year. He was expected to be first-string next year, and by his final year, the coaches thought, he might become an All-Virginia High School tackle. Jumbo was a sincere, not very bright student who came from a farm in Virginia and wanted to be a farmer when he finished college. P.S. had sat next to Jumbo all year, but they had never become particularly close friends. Jumbo lived in a different dormitory and had a tendency to stick with the other members of the football team. But P.S. liked him, and Jumbo was really the only member of the football team that he knew at all.

P.S. looked up at the engraving of General Robert E. Lee and his horse, Traveller. He glanced over at Jumbo. Jumbo was cleaning his fingernails with the tip of his automatic pencil.

"Well, good luck," P.S. said.

"Good luck to you."

"I'll need it."

P.S. stood up and looked for Charlie. "Hey! Hey, Charlie?" Charlie turned around. "Yeah?"

"*Piggo, piggere, squeely, gruntum!*"

"For God's sake, P.S.!"

"Hey, P.S.?" someone shouted. "You gonna flunk it again this year?"

"No, no, I don't think so," P.S. answered in mock seriousness. "In point of fact, as the good Dr. Fairfax would say—in point of fact, I might just come out with the highest grade in class.   After all, I'm such a brain."

The noise in the study hall suddenly stopped; Dr. Fairfax had entered.   The Latin instructor walked to the back of the study hall, where P.S. was sitting.

"And what was all that about, Wilkinson?"

"Sir, I was telling the others how I'm the brain in your class."

"Indeed?" Dr. Fairfax asked.

"Yes, sir.   But I was only kidding."

"Indeed," the Latin instructor said, and the other students laughed.

Dr. Fairfax was large man with a lean, aesthetic face, which he tried to hide with a military mustache.   He had taught at the Virginia Preparatory School since 1919.   P.S.'s father had had Dr. Fairfax for a Latin instructor.   When P.S. read "Goodbye, Mr. Chips," he had kept thinking of Dr. Fairfax.   The Latin instructor wore the same suit and vest all winter.   They were always immaculate.   The first day of spring was marked by Dr. Fairfax's appearance in a white linen suit, which he always wore with a small blue bachelor's-button.   Before a study hall last spring, someone had placed an alarm clock set to go off during the middle of study hall in one of the tall wastepaper baskets at the rear of the room.   The student had then emptied all of the pencil sharpeners and several ink bottles into the basket and covered all this with crumpled-up pad paper.   When the alarm clock went off, Dr. Fairfax strode down the aisle and reached into the wastepaper basket for the clock.   When he lifted it out, the sleeve of his white linen jacket was covered with ink and pencil shavings.   There was a stunned silence in the study hall as Dr. Fairfax looked at his sleeve.   And then Dr. Fairfax began to laugh.   The old man sat down on one of the desk tops and laughed and laughed, until finally the students had enough nerve to join him.   The next day, he appeared in the same linen suit, but it was absolutely clean.   Nobody was given demerits or punished in any manner.   Dr. Fairfax was P.S.'s favorite instructor.   P.S. watched him separate the examination papers and blue books into neat piles at the proctor's desk.   Dr. Fairfax looked up at the electric clock over the study-hall door and then at his thin gold pocket watch.   He cleared his throat.   "Good morning, gentlemen."

"GOOD MORNING, SIR!" the students shouted.

"Gentlemen, there will be no talking during the examination.   In the two hours given you, you will have ample time to complete all of the necessary work.   When the bell sounds signifying the end of examination, you will cease work immediately. In point of fact, anyone found working after the bell will be looked upon most unfavorably. When you receive your examinations, make certain that the print is legible. Make sure that you place your names on each of your blue books. If you have any difficulty reading the examination, hold your hand above your head and you will be given a fresh copy. The tops of your desks should be cleared of all notes, papers, and books. Are there any questions? . . . If not, will Baylor and you, Grandy, and . . . and Merritt . . . will the three of you please pass out the examinations."

P.S. watched Charlie get up and walk over to the desk.

Dr. Fairfax reached into his breast pocket and pulled out a pair of steel-rimmed spectacles. He looked out across the room. "We are nearing the end of the school year," he said. "Examinations always seem to cause students an undue amount of concern. I assure you, I can well remember when I was a student at V.P.S. In point of fact, I was not so very different from some of you—"

The instructor was interrupted by a rasping Bronx cheer. He looked quickly over in the direction of the sound. "Travers, was that you?"

"No, sir."

"Brandon, was that you?"

The student hesitated, then answered, "Yes, sir."

"Brandon, I consider that marked disrespect, and it will cost you ten demerits."

"Aww, sir—"

"Fifteen." Dr. Fairfax cleared his throat again. "Now, if I may continue? . . . Good. There are a few important things to remember when taking an examination. First, do not get upset when you cannot at once answer all of the questions. The examination is designed—"

P.S. stopped listening. Charlie was walking down the aisle toward him.

"Hey, Charlie," he whispered, "give me an easy one."

"There will be no favoritism on my part."

"How does it look?"

"Tough."

"Oh, God!"

"Merritt and Wilkinson?" Dr. Fairfax said. "That last little bit of conversation will cost you each five demerits."

The Latin instructor looked up at the electric clock again. "When you receive your examinations, you may begin. Are there any questions? . . . If not, gentlemen, it might be well for us to remember this ancient Latin proverb: 'Abusus non tollit usum.'" Dr. Fairfax waited

for the laugh. There was none. He cleared his throat again. "Perhaps
. . . perhaps we had better ask the class brain what the proverb means.
Wilkinson?"

P.S. stood up. "'*Abusus non tollit usum,*' sir?"

"That's right."

"Something like 'Abuse does not tolerate the use,' sir?"

"What does the verb '*tollo, tollere, sustuli, sublatus*' mean?"

"To take away, sir."

"That's right. The proverb, then, is 'Abuse does not take away the
use,' or, in the context I was referring to, just because you gentlemen
cannot do Latin properly does not mean that it should not be done at
all."

"Yes, sir," P.S. said, and he sat down.

Dr. Fairfax unfolded his newspaper, and P.S. began to read the examination. He picked up his pencil and printed in large letters on the
cover of his blue book:

> PHILIP SADLER WILKINSON
>
> LATIN EXAMINATION
>
> LATIN II—DR. FAIRFAX
>
> VIRGINIA PREPARATORY SCHOOL
>
> 7 JUNE 1962—BOOK ONE (1)

Then he put down his pencil, stretched, and began to work.

P.S. read the examination carefully. He saw that he would be able
to do very little of it from memory, and felt the first surge of panic
moisten his palms. He tried to translate the first Latin-to-English
passage. He remembered that it fell on the right-hand side of the page
in his Ullman and Henry, opposite the picture of the Roman galley.
The picture was a still taken from the silent-movie version of "Ben-
Hur." He recognized some of the verbs, more of the nouns, and finally
he began to be able to translate. It was about the Veneti ships, which
were more efficient than the Roman galleys because they had high
prows and flat keels. He translated the entire passage, put down his
pencil, and stretched again.

An hour later, P.S. knew he was in trouble. The first translation and
the vocabulary section were the only parts of the exam he had been
able to do without too much difficulty. He was able to give the rule
and examples for the datives of agent and possession. The English-to-
Latin sentences were the most difficult. He had been able to do only
one of those. For the question "How do you determine the tense of the

infinitive in indirect statement?" he wrote, "You can determine the tense by the construction of the sentence and by the word endings," and hoped he might get some credit. The two Latin-to-English passages counted twenty points apiece. If he could only do that second translation, he stood a chance of passing the examination. He recognized the adverb *"inde,"* but saw that it didn't help him very much. The examination was halfway over. He tried to count how many points he had made so far on the examination. He thought he might have somewhere between fifty and fifty-five. Passing was seventy. If he could just translate that second passage, he would have the points he needed to pass. Dr. Fairfax never scaled the grades. P.S. had heard that one year the Latin instructor flunked everybody but two.

He glanced over at Jumbo. Then he looked back down at his own examination and swore under his breath. Jumbo looked over at him and smiled. P.S. pantomimed that he could not answer the questions, and Jumbo smiled again. P.S. slid his glasses off and rubbed his eyes. He fought down the panic, wiped his hands on his pants legs, and looked at the passage again. He couldn't make any sense out of the blur of the words. He squinted, looked at them, put on his glasses again, and knew that he was in trouble.

He leaned over his desk and closed his eyes. *Dear God, please help me on this examination . . . please, God, please . . . I must pass this examination. . . .* He opened his eyes and looked carefully around to see if anyone had seen him praying. The others were all working hard on the examination. P.S. looked up again at the engraving on the wall above his desk. Beneath the portrait was the caption "Soon after the close of the War Between the States, General Robert E. Lee became the head of a school for young men. General Lee made this statement when he met with his students for the first time: 'We have but one rule in this school, and that is that every student must be a gentleman.'" They left out that other rule, P.S. thought. They left out the one that says you have to have Latin to graduate! Or is that part of being a gentleman, too?

He read the Latin-to-English passage through twice, then he read it through backward. He knew he had seen the passage before. He even remembered seeing it recently. But where? He knew that the passage dealt with the difficulties the Romans were having in fortifying their positions, but there were so many technical words in it that he could not get more than five of the twenty points from the translation, and he needed at least fifteen to pass. . . . He was going to flunk. *But I can't flunk! I can't flunk! I've got to pass!*

308   SO MUCH UNFAIRNESS OF THINGS

P.S. knew if he flunked he wouldn't be able to face his father. No matter what excuse P.S. gave, his father would not believe he hadn't loafed all term.

He looked at the passage and tried to remember where he had seen it. And then his mouth went dry. He felt the flush burn into the back of his neck and spread to his cheeks. He swallowed hard. *The translation's in my desk! . . . It's in my desk! . . . Jesus . . . oh, Jesus! . . . It's the translation on the top of the stack in my desk . . . in my desk!*

All he would have to do would be to slip the translation out of his desk, copy it, put it away, and he would pass the examination. All of his worries would be over. His father would be happy that he passed the examination. He wouldn't have to go to summer school. He and Charlie could go out to Colorado together to work on that dude ranch. He would be through with Latin forever. His Latin grade would never pull his average down again. Everything would be all right. Everything would be fine. All he would have to do would be to copy that one paragraph. Everyone cheated. Maybe not at V.P.S. But in other schools they bragged about it. . . . Everyone cheated in one way or another. Why should that one passage ruin everything? Who cared what problems the Romans had!

P.S. glanced over at Jumbo. Jumbo was chewing on his pencil eraser as he worked on the examination. Dr. Fairfax was still reading his newspaper. P.S. felt his heart beat faster. It began beating so hard that he was certain Jumbo could hear it. P.S. gently raised his desk top and pretended to feel around for a pencil. He let his blue book slide halfway off his desk so it leaned in his lap. Then he slid the translation under his blue book and slid the blue book and notes back onto his desk. He was certain that everyone had seen him—that everyone knew he was about to cheat. He slowly raised his eyes to look at Dr. Fairfax, who went on reading. P.S. covered part of the notes with his examination and began to copy the rest into his blue book. He could feel the heat in his cheeks, the dryness in his mouth. *Dear God . . . God, please don't let them catch me! . . . Please!*

He changed the smooth translation into a rough one as he copied, so that it would match his other translation.

From these things the army was taught the nature of the place and how the slope of the hill and the necessity of the time demanded more than one plan and order for the art of war. Different legions, some in one part, others in another, fought the enemy. And the view was obstructed by very thick hedges. Sure support could not be placed, nor could it be seen what work would be necessary in which part, nor could all the commands be administered by one man. Therefore, against so much unfairness of things, various consequences ensued.

He put down his pencil and looked around the study hall. No one was watching. P.S. carefully slid the translation back into his desk. He looked to see if the translation gave him any words that might help him on the rest of the examination. His heart was still beating wildly in his chest, and his hands shook. He licked his lips and concentrated on behaving normally. *It's over. . . . It's over. . . . I've cheated, but it's all over and no one said anything!*

He began to relax.

Fifteen minutes later, Dr. Fairfax stood up at his desk, looked at the electric clock, then down at his pocket watch. He cleared his throat and said, "Stop!"

Several students groaned. The rest gathered up their pencils and pens.

"Make certain you have written out the pledge in full and signed it," Dr. Fairfax said.

P.S. felt the physical pain of fear again. He opened his blue book and wrote, "I pledge on my honor as a gentleman that I have neither given nor received unauthorized assistance on this examination." He hesitated; then he signed his name.

"Place your examination inside your blue book," Dr. Fairfax continued. "Make certain that you put your name on your blue book. . . . Baylor? If you and, uh, Ferguson and Showalter will be good enough to pick up the examinations, the rest of you may go. And, um, gentlemen, your grades will be posted on the front door of my office no sooner than forty-eight hours from now. In point of fact, any attempt to solicit your grade any sooner than that will result in bad temper on my part and greater severity in the marking of papers. Are there any questions? . . . If not, gentlemen, dismissed."

The students stood up and stretched. An immediate, excited hum of voices filled the study hall. P.S. looked down at his exam paper. He slid it into his blue book and left it on his desk.

Charlie was waiting at the door of the study hall. "Well, P.S., how'd the brain do?"

"You know it's bad luck to talk about an exam before the grades are posted."

"I know. I'm just asking how you think you did."

"I don't know," P.S. said.

"Well, well, I mean, do you think you passed?"

"*I don't know!*"

"Whooey!" Charlie whistled. "And you called *me* a grump!"

They walked down the stairs together. At the bottom, Charlie asked P.S. if he was going to go to lunch.

"No, I don't think so," P.S. said. "I'm not feeling so well. I think I'll lie down for a while. I'll see ya."

"Sure," Charlie said. "See ya."

In his cubicle in Memorial Hall, P.S. took off his lucky exam tie. He put his silver dollar back onto his bookcase. He reached inside the hollow copy of "Gulliver's Travels" for the pack of cigarettes he kept there. Then he walked down the corridor to the bathroom, stepped into one of the stalls, and locked the door. He lit the cigarette and leaned his forehead against the cool green marble divider. He was sick with fear and dread. *It's over! It's all over!* he said, trying to calm himself. He did not like the new knowledge he had of himself. He was a cheater. He rolled his forehead back and forth against the stone, pressing his forehead into it, hurting himself. P.S. had broken the Honor Code of the school, and he was scared.

I shouldn't have cheated! What if someone had seen me! I shouldn't have cheated! . . . Maybe somebody did see me. . . . Maybe Dr. Fairfax will know I cheated when he sees my exam. . . . Maybe somebody will check my desk after the exam and find the copy of the translation. . . . I cheated. Jesus, I cheated! . . . Stupid, God-damned fool. . . . What if somebody finds out! . . . Maybe I should turn myself in. . . . I wonder if they'd kick me out if I turned myself in. . . . It would prove that I really am honest, I just made a mistake, that's all. . . . I'll tell them I couldn't help it. . . . Maybe they'll just give me a reprimand.

But P.S. knew that if he turned himself in, they would still tell his parents he had cheated, so what good would that do? His father would be just as angry. Even more so, since Wilkinsons don't cheat, either. P.S. knew how ashamed his father would make him feel. His father would have to tell others that P.S. had cheated. It was a part of the Southern tradition. "My son has disgraced me. It is better that you hear it from me than somebody else." His father would do something like that. And having other people know he had cheated would be too much shame to bear. And even if he did turn himself in, the school

would make him take another exam. . . . And he'd flunk that one, too.
. . . He knew it. . . . *Oh, God, what am I going to do?*

If he didn't turn himself in and no one had seen him, then who would
know? He would never cheat again. If he could just get away with it
this one time. Then everything would be O.K. Nobody need ever
know—except himself. And P.S. knew he would never be able to forget
that he had cheated. Maybe if he turned himself in, it would be better
in the long run. *What long run? What the hell kind of long run will I
have if I turn myself in? Everybody in the school will know I cheated,
no matter whether I turn myself in or not. . . . They won't remember
me for turning myself in. . . . They'll remember that I cheated in the
first place. . . .*

P.S. wanted to cry, but he couldn't. He dropped the cigarette into
the toilet and flushed it down. Then he went over to the sink and
rinsed his mouth out. He had some chewing gum in his room; that
would cover the smell of his smoking. He looked at himself in the
mirror. He couldn't see any change since this morning, and yet he felt
so different. He looked at his eyes to see if there were lines under
them now. *What shall I do?* he asked his reflection. *What the hell
shall I do?* He turned on the cold water and rinsed his face. He dried
himself on a towel someone had left behind, and walked back down the
corridor to his room. He brushed aside the curtain, entered the
cubicle, and stopped, frozen with fear. Mabrey, the head monitor, was
sitting on P.S.'s bed.

"Wilkinson," Mabrey said, "would you mind coming with me?"

He called me "Wilkinson," not P.S. . . . not P.S.! "Where do you
want to go?"

"Just outside for a few minutes."

"What about?"

Mabrey got up from the bed. "Come on, P.S."

"What . . . what do you want me for?"

"We want to talk to you."

We! WE! P.S. picked up his jacket and started to put it on.

"You won't need your jacket," Mabrey said.

"It doesn't matter, I'll wear it anyway."

P.S. followed Mabrey out of the dormitory. *I didn't have a chance
to turn myself in,* he thought. *I didn't have a chance to choose. . . .
Oh, God damn it! . . . God damn it!*

"You think you'll make the varsity baseball team next year?"
Mabrey asked.

"I don't know," P.S. said. *What is he talking about baseball for?*

The new boy who had wakened P.S. passed them on the walk. He said hello to both Mabrey and P.S. He received no answer, and shrugged.

Mabrey and P.S. took the path to the headmaster's office. P.S. could feel the enormous weight of the fear building up inside him again. Mabrey opened the door for P.S. and ushered him into the headmaster's waiting room. Nelson, a pale, fat-faced senior, was sitting there alone. He was the secretary of the Honor Committee. P.S. had always hated him. The other members of the Honor Committee were Mabrey, the vice-president; Linus Hendricks, the president; Mr. Seaton, the headmaster; and Dr. Fairfax, who served as faculty adviser. Mabrey motioned that P.S. was to sit down in the chair facing the others—the only straight-backed wooden chair in the room. Every now and then, Nelson would look up at P.S. and shake his head. The door to the headmaster's office opened and Mr. Seaton came out, followed by Linus Hendricks, Dr. Fairfax, and—*My God, what is Jumbo doing here! Don't tell me he cheated, too! He was sitting right next to me!* Jumbo walked out of the room without looking at P.S.

Linus Hendricks waited for the others to seat themselves, then he sat down himself and faced P.S. "Well, P.S., I imagine you know why you're here."

P.S. looked at Hendricks. Hendricks was the captain of the football team. He and Mabrey were the two most important undergraduates in the school.

"Well, P.S.?" Hendricks repeated.

"Yes, sir," P.S. said.

He could feel them all staring at him. He looked down at his hands folded in his lap. He could see clearly every line in his thumb knuckle. He could see the dirt caught under the corner of his fingernail, and the small blue vein running across the knuckle.

He looked up at Dr. Fairfax. He wanted to tell him not to worry. He wanted to tell him that he was sorry, so very sorry.

The headmaster, Mr. Seaton, was a young man. He had just become the headmaster of V.P.S. this year. He liked the students, and the students liked him. He was prematurely bald, and smiled a lot. He had a very young and pretty wife, and some of the students were in love with her and fought to sit at her table in the dining room. Mr. Seaton liked to play tennis. He would play the students and bet his dessert that he would win. And most of the time he would lose, and the students were enormously pleased to see the headmaster of the school have to get up from the table and pay his bets. Mr. Seaton would walk very quickly across the dining hall, his bald head bent to hide his smile. He would swoop up to a table, drop the dessert, and depart, like a bombing airplane. P.S. could tell that the headmaster was distressed he had cheated.

Linus Hendricks crossed his legs and sank back into the deep leather armchair. Mabrey and Nelson leaned forward as though they were going to charge P.S.

"P.S.," Hendricks said. "You're here this afternoon because the Honor Committee has reason to suspect that you may have cheated on the Latin exam this morning. We must ask you whether or not this is true."

P.S. raised his head and looked at Hendricks. Hendricks was wearing a bright striped tie. P.S. concentrated on the stripes. Thick black, thin white, medium green, thin white, and thick black.

"P.S., did you, or did you not, cheat on the Latin examination?"

P.S. nodded.

"Yes or no, P.S.?" Hendricks asked.

P.S. no longer felt anything. He was numb with misery. "Yes," he said, in a small, tired voice. "Yes, I cheated on the examination. But I was going to turn myself in. I was going to turn myself in, I swear I was."

"If you were going to turn yourself in, why didn't you?" Nelson asked.

"I couldn't. . . . I couldn't yet. . . ." P.S. looked at Dr. Fairfax. "I'm sorry, sir. I'm terribly sorry. . . ." P.S. began to cry. "I'm so ashamed. . . . Oh, God. . . ." P.S. tried to stop crying. He couldn't. The tears stung his eyes. One tear slipped into the inside of his glasses and puddled across the bottom of the lens. He reached into his back pocket for a handkerchief, but he had forgotten to bring one. He started to pull out his shirttail, and decided he'd better not. He wiped his face with the side of his hand.

Mr. Seaton walked over to P.S. and gave him his handkerchief. The headmaster rested his hand on P.S.'s shoulder. "Why P.S.? Why did you cheat?"

P.S. couldn't answer.

"P.S., you were the last boy I expected this of. Why did you feel you had to cheat on this exam?"

"I don't know, sir."

"But P.S., you must have had some reason."

Nelson said, "Answer the headmaster when he's asking you a question, Wilkinson."

P.S. looked up at him with such loathing that Nelson looked away.

Mr. Seaton crouched down next to P.S. "You must have been aware of the penalty for cheating."

P.S. nodded.

"Then why, in God's name, did you risk expulsion just to pass the examination?"

"Sir—sir, I flunked Latin last year, sir. I knew I'd flunk it this year, too. I—I knew I couldn't pass a Latin exam ever."

"But why did you *cheat?*"

"Because . . . because, sir, I had to pass the exam."

The headmaster ran his hand across his forehead. "P.S., I'm not trying to trick you, I'm only trying to understand why you did this thing. Why did you bring the notes into the exam with you?"

"Sir, Mr. Seaton, I didn't bring the notes in, they were in my desk. If they hadn't been, I wouldn't be here. I didn't want to cheat. I didn't *mean* to cheat. I—It was just the only way I could pass the exam."

Nelson rested his pudgy arms on the sides of his leather armchair and looked at the headmaster and then back to P.S. Then he said, "Wilkinson, you have been in V.P.S. for two years. You must be familiar, I imagine, with the Honor Code. In fact, in your study hall there is a small wooden plaque above the proctor's desk. On it is carved the four points of the Honor Code: 'I will not lie. I will not steal. I will not cheat. I will report anyone I see doing so.' You are familiar with them, aren't you?"

"Of course I'm familiar with them," P.S. said impatiently.

"Why did you think you were so much better than everyone else that you could ignore it?"

"I don't think I'm better than everyone else, Nelson," P.S. said.

"Well, you sure aren't! The others don't cheat." Nelson sat back again, very satisfied with himself.

Dr. Fairfax came from behind the chairs and stood next to P.S. "Unless you hold your tongue, Nelson—unless you hold your tongue, I shall personally escort you out of here."

"But, sir," Nelson whined. "I'm only trying to—"

"SHUT UP!" Dr. Fairfax roared. He returned to the back of the room.

Mr. Seaton spoke again. "P.S., if you had flunked this exam, you would have been able to take another. Perhaps you would have passed the reëxamination. Most boys do."

"I wouldn't have, sir," P.S. said. "I just cannot do Latin. You

could have given me fifty examinations, sir. And I don't mean any disrespect, but I would have flunked all fifty of them."

Mabrey asked the headmaster if he could speak. Then he turned
to P.S. "P.S., we—all of us have been tempted at some time or another
to cheat. All of us have either resisted that temptation or, perhaps, we
were lucky enough to get away with it. I think that what we want to
know is what *made* you cheat. Just having to pass the exam isn't enough.
I know you, P.S. I may know you better than anyone else in the room,
because I've shared the same floor in the dorm with you for this year.
And we were on the same floor when you were a toad. You're not the
kind who cheats unless he has a damn good—" Mabrey glanced over at
the headmaster. "Excuse me, sir. I didn't mean to swear."

The headmaster nodded and indicated that Mabrey was to continue.

"What I mean is this, P.S. I know you don't care how high your
grade is, just so long as you keep out of trouble. . . . You're one of
the most popular boys in your class. Everybody likes you. Why
would you throw all of this over, just to pass a Latin exam?"

"I don't know. I don't know. . . . I had to pass the exam. If I
flunked it again, my father would kill me."

"What do you mean he would 'kill' you?" Mr. Seaton asked.

"Oh, nothing, sir. I mean—I don't mean he would hurt me. He
would just—Oh, God, sir, I don't know how to explain it to you. If I
flunked the exam again, he'd just make me feel so, I don't know . . .
ashamed . . . so terrible. I just couldn't take it again."

There was a moment of silence in the room. P.S. began to cry again.
He could tell the headmaster still didn't understand why he had
cheated. He looked down at his hands again. With his index finger
he traced the veins that crossed the back of his hand. He looked over
at the wooden arm of his straight-backed chair. He could see the little
drops of moisture where his hand had squeezed the arm of the chair.
He could make out every grain of wood, every worn spot. He took off
his glasses and rubbed his eyes. He tried taking deep breaths, but each
time his breath would be choked off.

Hendricks cleared his throat and recrossed his legs. "P.S.," he said,
"we have your examination here. You signed your name to the pledge
at the end of the exam. You swore on your honor that you had not
cheated." Hendricks paused. P.S. knew what he was driving at.

"If I hadn't signed my name to the pledge, you would have known I
had cheated right away," P.S. explained. "I didn't want to break my
honor again. I was going to turn myself in, honest I was."

"You didn't, though," Nelson said.

"I would have!" P.S. said. But he still wasn't sure whether he would have or not. He knew he never would be certain.

"So, we've got you on lying and cheating," Nelson said. "How do we know you haven't stolen, too?"

Dr. Fairfax grabbed the lapels of Nelson's jacket, pulled him out of the chair, and pushed him out of the room. The old man closed the door and leaned against it. He wiped his brow and said, "Mr. Seaton, sir, I trust you won't find fault with my actions. That young Nelson has a tendency to bother me. In point of fact, he irritates me intensely."

P.S. looked gratefully at Dr. Fairfax. The old man smiled sadly. Mabrey was talking quietly to Hendricks. Mr. Seaton sat down in Nelson's chair and turned to P.S. "I know this is a difficult question. Would you—would you have turned Jumbo in had you seen him cheating?"

P.S. felt the blood drain from his face. *So Jumbo turned me in! . . . Jumbo saw me! . . . Sitting next to me all year! . . . Jumbo turned me in! Why, in God's name?*

He looked up at the others. They were all waiting for his answer. He had the most curious feeling of aloofness, of coldness. If he said yes, that he would have turned Jumbo in, it would be a lie, and he knew it. If he answered yes, it would please the headmaster, though. Because it would mean that P.S. still had faith in the school system. If he said no, he wouldn't have turned Jumbo in, it would be as good as admitting that he would not obey the fourth part of the Honor Code— "I will report anyone I see doing so." He waited a moment and then answered, "I don't know. I don't know whether I would have turned Jumbo in or not."

"Thank you very much, P.S.," the headmaster said.

P.S. could tell that Mr. Seaton was disappointed in his answer.

"Gentlemen, do you have any further questions you would like to ask Wilkinson?"

"Nothing, sir," Hendricks answered.

The headmaster looked over at Dr. Fairfax, who shook his head. "Well, then, P.S., if you don't mind, we'd like you to sit in my office until we call for you."

P.S. got up and started for the door.

"Have you had any lunch?" Dr. Fairfax asked.

"No, sir. But I'm not very hungry."

"I'll have Mrs. Burdick bring in some milk and cookies."

"Thank you, sir."

The door opened and P.S. stood up as Mr. Seaton walked over to his desk and eased himself into the swivel chair. P.S. had been sitting alone in the headmaster's office for several hours.

"Sit down, please," the headmaster said. He picked up a wooden pencil and began to roll it back and forth between his palms. P.S. could hear the click of the pencil as it rolled across the headmaster's ring. Mr. Seaton laid the pencil aside and rubbed his cheek. His hand moved up the side of his face and began to massage his temple. Then he looked up at P.S. and said, "The Honor Committee has decided that you must leave the school. The penalty for cheating at V.P.S. is immediate expulsion. There cannot be any exceptions."

P.S. took a deep breath and pushed himself back into the soft leather seat. Then he dropped his hands into his lap and slumped. He was beyond crying; there was nothing left to cry about.

"Your father is waiting for you in the other room," Mr. Seaton said. "I've asked him to wait outside for a few minutes, because I want to speak to you alone. I want you to understand why the school had to make the decision to expel you. The school—this school—is only as good as its honor system. And the honor system is only as good as the students who live by it."

P.S. cleared his throat and looked down at his fingernails. He wished the headmaster wouldn't talk about it. He knew why the school had to expel him. It was done. It was over with. What good would it do to talk about it?

"The honor system, since it is based on mutual trust and confidence, no doubt makes it easier for some students to cheat," the headmaster said. "I am not so naïve as to believe that there aren't any boys who cheat here. Unfortunately, our honor system makes it easy for them to do so. These boys have not been caught. Perhaps they will never be caught. But I feel that it was far better for you to have been caught right away, P.S., because you are not a cheater. Notice that I said you *are* not a cheater instead of you *were* not a cheater. . . . Yes, you cheated this one time. I do not need to ask whether you cheated before. I know you haven't. I know also that you will not cheat again. I was frankly stunned when I heard that you had cheated on Dr. Fairfax's examination. You were the last boy I would have expected to cheat. I am still not entirely satisfied by the reasons you gave for cheating. I suppose a person never is. Maybe it is impossible to give reasons for such an act." Mr. Seaton began massaging his temple again. "P.S., the most difficult thing that you must try to understand is that Jumbo did the right thing. Jumbo was correct in turning you in."

P.S. stiffened in the chair. "Yes, sir," he said.

"If no one reported infractions, we would have no Honor Code. The Code would be obeyed only when it was convenient to obey it. It would be given lip service. The whole system would break down. The school would become just another private school, instead of the respected and loved institution it now is. Put yourself in Jumbo's shoes for a moment. You and Jumbo are friends—*believe me*, you are friends. If you had heard what Jumbo said about you in here, and how it hurt him to turn you in, you would know what a good friend Jumbo is. You have been expelled for cheating. You will not be here next fall. But Jumbo will be. Jumbo will stay on at V.P.S., and the other students will know that he was the one who turned you in. When I asked you whether you would have turned Jumbo in, you said that you didn't know. You and I both know from your answer that you wouldn't have turned Jumbo in. Perhaps the schoolboy code is still stronger in you than the Honor Code. Many students feel stronger about the schoolboy code than the Honor Code. No one likes to turn in a friend. A lot of boys who don't know any better, a lot of your friends, will never forgive Jumbo. It will be plenty tough for him. Just as it is tough on anybody who does his duty. I think—I honestly think that Jumbo has done you a favor. I'm not going to suggest that you be grateful to him. Not yet. That would be as ridiculous as my saying something as trite as 'Someday you will be able to look back on this and laugh.' . . . P.S., you will *never* be able to look back on this and laugh. But you may be able to understand." The headmaster looked at his wristwatch and then said, "I'm going to leave you alone with your father for a few minutes; then I suggest you go back to your room and pack. The other students won't be back in the dormitories yet, so you can be alone." He got up from behind the desk. P.S. rose also. He looked down at the milk and cookies Mrs. Burdick had left him. There was half a glass of milk and three cookies left.

The headmaster looked at P.S. for a moment and then he said, "I'm sorry you have been expelled, P.S. You were a good student here. One of the most popular boys in your class. You will leave behind a great many good friends."

"Thank you, sir," P.S. said.

"I'll see you before you and your father leave."

"Yes, sir."

The headmaster walked into the waiting room. P.S. could hear Dr. Fairfax talking, and then his father. The door closed, and P.S. sat down to wait for his father. He could feel the fear building up inside of him again. He did not know what to say to his father. What could he say? He sipped the last of the milk as the door opened. P.S. put down the glass and stood up.

Stewart Wilkinson closed the door behind him and looked at his son. He wanted to hold the boy and comfort him, but Phil looked so solid, so strong, standing there. Why isn't he crying, he wondered, and then he told himself that he wouldn't have cried, either; that the boy had had plenty of time to cry; that he would never cry in front of his father again. He tried to think of something to say. He knew that he often was clumsy in his relations with Phil, and said the wrong thing, and he wondered whether he had been that sensitive at his son's age. He looked down at the plate of cookies and the empty milk glass.

"Where did you get the milk and cookies, son?"

"Mrs. Burdick brought them to me, sir."

He never calls me "Dad" now, Stewart Wilkinson said to himself. Always "sir." . . . My own son calls me "sir." . . .

"Did you thank her?"

"Yes, sir."

Stewart Wilkinson walked over to the couch next to his son and sat down. The boy remained standing.

"Phil, son, sit down, please."

"Yes, sir."

Looking at his son, Stewart Wilkinson could not understand why they had grown apart during the last few years. He had always remained close to his father. Why wasn't it the same between him and the boy who sat so stiff beside him, so still in spite of the horror he must have gone through during the past few hours?

"I'm sorry, sir."

"Yes . . . yes, son, I know you are. . . . I'm terribly sorry myself. Sorry for you. . . . Mr. Seaton told me another boy turned you in, is that right?"

P.S. nodded.

"He also told me that he believes you would have turned yourself in had you been given enough time."

"I don't know whether I would have or not. I never had a chance to find out."

"I think you would have. I think you would have."

He waited for his son to say something; then, realizing there was nothing the boy could say, he spoke again. "I was talking to Dr. Fair-fax outside—you knew he was my Latin teacher, too?"

"Yes, sir."

"We always used to be able to tell when the first day of spring came, because Dr. Fairfax put on his white linen suit."

"Yes, sir."

"At any rate, that man thinks very highly of you, Phil. He is very upset that you had to be expelled. I hope you will speak to him before we go. He's a good man to have on your side."

"I want to speak to him."

"Phil . . . Phil . . ." Stewart Wilkinson thought for a minute. He wanted so desperately what he said to be the right thing to say. "Phil, I know that I am partly responsible for what has happened. I must have in some way pressured you into it. I wanted your marks to be high. I wanted you to get the best education that you could. V.P.S. isn't the best school in the country, but it's a damn fine one. It's a school that has meant a lot to our family. But that doesn't matter so much. I mean, that part of it is all over with. I'm sorry that you cheated, because I know you're not the cheating kind. I'm also sorry because you are going to have to face the family and get it over with. This is going to be tough. But they'll all understand. I doubt that there is any of us who have never cheated in one way or another. But it will make them very proud of you if you can go see them and look them in the eye."

He picked up one of the cookies and began to bite little pieces out of the edge. Then he shook his head sadly, in the gesture P.S. knew so well. "Ah, God, son, it's so terrible that you have to learn these lessons when you are young. I know that you don't want me to feel sorry for you, but I can't help it. I'm not angry with you. I'm a little disappointed, perhaps, but I can understand it, I think. I suppose I must appear as an ogre to you at times. But Phil, I—If I'm tough with you, it's just because I'm trying to help you. Maybe I'm too tough." Stewart Wilkinson looked over at his son. He saw that the boy was watching him. He felt a little embarrassed to have revealed so much of himself before his son. But he knew they were alike. He knew that Phil was really his son. They already spoke alike, already laughed at the same sort of things, appreciated the same things. Their tastes were pretty much the same. He knew that, if anything, he was too much like the boy to be able to help him. And also that the problem was the boy's own, and that he would resent his father's interfering.

"Phil, I'll go speak with Mr. Seaton for a little while, and then I'll come on over and help you pack. If you'd like, I'll pack for you and you can sit in the car."

"No, that's all right, sir, I'll pack. I mean, most of the stuff is packed up already. I'll meet you over there."

Stewart Wilkinson rose with his son. Again he wanted to hold the boy, to show him how much he loved him.

"I'll be through packing in a few minutes. I'll meet you in my room," P.S. said.

"Fine, son."

Together they carried the footlocker down the staircase of Memorial Hall. P.S. stopped at the door, balanced the footlocker with one hand, then pulled the heavy door open. The door swung back before they could get through. Stewart Wilkinson stumbled and P.S. said, "I'm sorry."

They carried the footlocker across the small patch of lawn between the front of Memorial Hall and the main drive and slid the footlocker into the back of the station wagon.

"How much more is there, son?"

"A couple of small boxes, some books, and a couple of pictures."

Stewart Wilkinson pulled a silk handkerchief out of his back pocket and wiped his brow. "You think we can get all of them in one more trip?"

"I think so, sir. At least, we can try."

They turned back toward the dormitory. Stewart Wilkinson rested his hand on his son's shoulder as they walked back across the lawn. "Phil, Mr. Seaton told me that he thinks he might be able to get you into Hotchkiss. How does that sound to you?"

"It's a funny name for a school."

"Hotchkiss, funny? Why?"

"I don't know, it just sounds funny."

"Well, do you think you'd like to go there?"

"Sure. I mean I don't know. I haven't given it much thought."

Stewart Wilkinson laughed. "I guess you haven't."

The boy looked worriedly at his father for a moment. He wondered whether his father was making fun of him. And then he saw the humor in his remark and laughed, too.

They brought the last of the boxes down from the room and slid them into the car and closed the tailgate.

"Did you get a chance to talk to Dr. Fairfax?"

"Yes, sir. He came by the room while I was packing."

"What did he say?"

"I don't know. I mean he was sorry I was going and all that, but he said I'd get along fine anywhere and that it wasn't the end of the world."

"Did he say 'in point of fact'?"

"Yeah." P.S. laughed. "He said, 'Well, boy, you'll do all right. In point of fact, you have nothing to worry about.' I really like old Doc Fairfax."

They went around the side of the car and climbed in.

"Anything you've forgotten? Books out of the library, equipment in the gym? Anybody special you want to see before we go home?"

"No, Dad, thanks, that's all—Hey, wait a minute, could you, Dad?" P.S. got out of the car. "It's Charlie—Charlie Merritt. I'd like to say goodbye to him."

"Sure, son, take your time."

The two boys spoke together for a moment, standing in the road; then they shook hands. Stewart Wilkinson turned off the engine and watched as the boys walked back up the road toward him. As they drew near, he got out of the station wagon.

"Dad, this is Charlie Merritt. . . . Charlie, you remember my father."

"Yes, sir. How are you, sir?"

"Fine, thank you, Charlie."

"Sir, Mr. Wilkinson, I'm sorry about P.S. getting kicked out and all." Stewart Wilkinson nodded.

"He's just sorry because I won't be around to borrow his toothpaste any more. He likes to lend it to me because I always roll it from the top and lose the cap."

P.S. and Charlie laughed.

"Hey, P.S.?" Charlie said. "Does this mean you're not going to have to work off the five demerits Doc Fairfax gave us this morning?"

"What did you two get five demerits for?" Stewart Wilkinson asked.

"We were talking before the exam," P.S. said.

Father and son looked at each other, and then P.S. turned away. It was clear that he was thinking about the exam and his cheating again. And then the boy took a deep breath and smiled. "You know? It's funny," he said. "I mean, it seems that that exam took place so long ago. . . . Well, Charlie." P.S. stuck out his hand and Charlie took it. "Well, I guess we'd better get going. I'll see you around, O.K.?"

"Sure, P.S.," Charlie said.

The two boys shook hands again solemnly. Then Charlie shook hands with P.S.'s father. P.S. and Stewart Wilkinson got back into the station wagon.

Charlie walked around to P.S.'s window. "Hey, P.S.? Make sure you let me hear from you this summer, O.K.?"

"Sure, Charlie. Take care of yourself."

They drove around the school drive, by the Wilkinson Memorial Library and the Sadler Gymnasium, and then they turned down the slight hill toward the Breastworks, and as they passed through the ornate, wrought-iron gate P.S. began to cry.

Questions

1. How is the aura of tradition of the prep school emphasized in the opening paragraph, which describes the setting of the story? Why should this tradition receive so conspicuous a position as the opening scene?
2. How does the author's choice of the name and nickname of the central character give us clues to the kind of boy he is? What other details of information give us a picture of his personality? How else is the characterization developed?
3. What effect does tradition have on P.S.?
4. Why does he want to pass the Latin exam so badly? Is it because he wants to go to Colorado or because of his father's probable disappointment? These are the reasons P.S. states in his prayer. Is there another more important reason?
5. What details of modernity contrast with the recurrent images of tradition? For example, note this juxtaposition of images: "Between the windows were framed engravings of Roman ruins and Southern generals. The large fluorescent lights above the desks buzzed and blinked with life."
6. Why did the author choose to make the exam a *Latin* exam? What is the effect of the repetition of Latin words?
7. Consider P.S.'s effort to study for the exam and the process he goes through while taking the exam up to the point at which for the second time he "knew he was in trouble." What really *is* his trouble?
8. Are you shocked when P.S. actually cheats? Do you feel sympathy for him?
9. What is the source of the title? Why does the wording sound so odd? Why are the title and the way it is worded appropriate to the entire story?

10. How does the narrator lead the reader right into the consciousness and conscience of P.S.?

11. Compare and contrast the Honor Code and the Toad Code. Compare and contrast the Honor Code and the "schoolboy code."

12. What kind of person is Dr. Fairfax? Why does he become so angry at Nelson in the headmaster's office? Does he not agree that P.S.'s punishment is just?

13. Why did Jumbo "turn P.S. in"? Why would P.S. not have done the same to Jumbo? For whom will "things be tougher"—Jumbo, who broke the "schoolboy code," or P.S., who broke the Honor Code?

14. Discuss the irony of P.S.'s attitude toward his father before and after P.S.'s cheating, and the irony of the father's attitude before he sent P.S. to military school and after P.S. was expelled.

15. Why or why not is the "point" of the story that "honesty is the best policy"?

16. What does P.S.'s father have in common with the father in Björnstjerne Björnson's short-short story "The Father"?

17. What does P.S. call his father toward the end of the story? How does this term of address contribute to the resolution of one of the conflicts in the internal action? (See p. 28.)

Man Alone: General Questions

1. Simple irony is the presentation of an appearance that is the opposite of reality (see p. 42). However, sometimes irony is so complex that it becomes paradoxical or ambiguous: what seems to be ironical at first glance is not ironical upon further examination—when two apparent opposites turn out to be not mutually exclusive at all. In "Bartleby the Scrivener," it is ironic that by shunning society in order to assert his individuality, Bartleby loses both his social identification and his individuality, for he dies. His employer, however, submerges his individuality by being socially responsible (for Bartleby) and asserts his individuality by not conforming to the rest of the society's rejection of Bartleby. In reconciling his two apparently conflicting desires (to be an individual and to be a socially responsible person), Bartleby's employer affirms the ambiguity of his humanity.

   Explain the simple and complex ironies of "So Much Unfairness of Things" and "The Burrow."

2. What are the causes of the loneliness of man as illustrated by each of the four stories in this section?

3. In each case, how could the loneliness be overcome? How dependent on someone else would each of the lonely characters have to be in order to overcome his loneliness?

4. To what degree are the characters who sacrifice individual conviction for the sake of social conformity admirable or not admirable? To what degree are the characters who shun society for the sake of individual conviction admirable or not? How can a man compromise conviction in order to save himself from loneliness? How can a man prefer to die rather than compromise his personal convictions?

5. Define *loneliness* by finding descriptions and images in the four stories about how characters appear, act, and feel when they are isolated from human society whether or not by their own choice.

MORE STORIES ABOUT MAN ALONE

"Alibi Ike" by Ring Lardner
"Molly Morgan" by John Steinbeck
"Of This Time, of That Place" by Lionel Trilling
"Old Mortality" by Katherine Anne Porter
"The Duchess and the Smugs" by Pamela Frankau
"The Quiet Man" by Maurice Walsh
"The Second Tree from the Corner" by E. B. White
"The Undefeated" by Ernest Hemingway
"The Yellow Wallpaper" by Charlotte Perkins Gilman
"Young Goodman Brown" by Nathaniel Hawthorne

Mortality and Imagination

Introduction

As mentioned in the chapter "The Art of Short Fiction," one of many aesthetic theories regards man's mortality as the fundamental impulse from which his creativity as an artist springs. If man did not know that he must die and therefore is limited by time, he would lack the motivation to create art. He would not feel the need to leave something enduring behind when he dies.

The unknown beyond death is probably the most urgent subject of man's questionings. His imagination seeks to supply the answers to the mystery of life and death, answers which his conscious experiences cannot fully provide with certainty. His remarkable mind goes as far as it can, through science, to analyze nature, guided by hypotheses that his curiosity and imagination help him to establish on the basis of his observations. Often he finds objective answers to and proof of his hypotheses. But even when he does not, the artistic impulse, inspired by his curiosity and inspiring of his imagination, keeps him exploring.

Man's imagination helps him find some answers to questions about the unknowable. To be sure, they are not answers that he can prove scientifically, but they are answers based on his hope and his faith and are answers that he can believe. These answers constitute various convictions that man has about himself, his fellow man, and God. Religious beliefs have inspired many great works of art which in turn have helped people to come to better terms with their mortality. "The Sisters" is a work of art in short fiction that deals with questions of religious belief as well as of faith and lack of faith in man. "Benediction" also reveals how man's imagination has devised rituals which inspire and reinforce his religious faith. "The Man of Adamant" is concerned with the relationship between man's religious and social beliefs and also illustrates Hawthorne's moral attitude toward mortality as well as his imaginative talent for writing fantasy.

An author's imagination can help him express through fantasy his feelings about mortality. Edgar Allan Poe wrote detective stories, horror stories, and fantasies. One of his most fantastic is "Metzengerstein," in which his imagination so transcends reality that readers are hard pressed to find even the truth of fiction in it. Nobel prize winner John Steinbeck in "The Affair at 7, Rue de M——" has used his imagination to write a fantasy that is a parody of an Edgar Allan Poe fantasy.

Through his imagination, man can express his ideas of timelessness, which in reality he cannot experience. Man, through his art, however, can manipulate time. An author can make time move backwards and forwards in the world of a story, as Hawthorne does in "The Man of Adamant" and as Joyce does in "The Sisters." By pointing out the meaning of life and giving a story universality, an author, who is limited by time in his own individual life, can achieve and convey a sense of timelessness. By directing his thoughts to man's place in the whole of mankind, he can touch eternity. The reader, identifying with the universality of the characters and action of a story, derives, in turn, a sense of timelessness from what the author has conveyed. By applying imagination to the fact of his mortality in artistic expression, man can believe in the immortality of mankind.

The Man of Adamant

AN APOLOGUE

Nathaniel Hawthorne

In the old times of religious gloom and intolerance lived Richard Digby, the gloomiest and most intolerant of a stern brotherhood. His plan of salvation was so narrow, that, like a plank in a tempestuous sea, it could avail no sinner but himself, who bestrode it triumphantly, and hurled anathemas against the wretches whom he saw struggling with the billows of eternal death. In his view of the matter, it was a most abominable crime—as, indeed, it is a great folly—for men to trust to their own strength, or even to grapple to any other fragment of the wreck, save this narrow plank, which, moreover, he took special care to keep out of their reach. In other words, as his creed was like no man's else, and being well pleased that Providence had intrusted him alone, of mortals, with the treasure of a true faith, Richard Digby determined to seclude himself to the sole and constant enjoyment of his happy fortune.

"And verily," thought he, "I deem it a chief condition of Heaven's mercy to myself, that I hold no communion with those abominable myriads which it hath cast off to perish. Peradventure, were I to tarry longer in the tents of Kedar, the gracious boon would be revoked, and I also be swallowed up in the deluge of wrath, or consumed in the storm of fire and brimstone, or involved in whatever new kind of ruin is ordained for the horrible perversity of this generation."

So Richard Digby took an axe, to hew space enough for a tabernacle in the wilderness, and some few other necessaries, especially a sword and gun, to smite and slay any intruder upon his hallowed seclusion, and plunged into the dreariest depths of the forest. On its verge, however, he paused a moment, to shake off the dust of his feet against the village where he had dwelt, and to invoke a curse on the meeting-house, which he regarded as a temple of heathen idolatry. He felt a curiosity, also, to see whether the fire and brimstone would not rush down from heaven at once, now that the one righteous man had provided for his own safety. But, as the sunshine continued to fall peacefully on the cottages and fields, and the husbandmen labored and children played, and as there were many tokens of present happiness, and nothing ominous of a speedy judgment, he turned away, somewhat disappointed. The farther he went, however, and the lonelier he felt himself, and the thicker the trees stood along his path, and the darker the shadow overhead, so much the more did Richard Digby exult. He talked to himself as he strode onward; he read his Bible to himself as he sat beneath the trees; and, as the gloom of the forest hid the blessed sky, I had almost added, that, at morning, noon, and eventide, he prayed to himself. So congenial was this mode of life to his disposition, that he often laughed to himself, but was displeased when an echo tossed him back the long loud roar.

In this manner he journeyed onward three days and two nights, and came, on the third evening, to the mouth of a cave, which, at first sight, reminded him of Elijah's cave at Horeb, though perhaps it more resembled Abraham's sepulchral cave at Machpelah. It entered into the heart of a rocky hill. There was so dense a veil of tangled foliage about it, that none but a sworn lover of gloomy recesses would have discovered the low arch of its entrance, or have dared to step within its vaulted chamber, where the burning eyes of a panther might encounter him. If Nature meant this remote and dismal cavern for the use of man, it could only be to bury in its gloom the victims of a pestilence, and then to block up its mouth with stones, and avoid the spot forever after. There was nothing bright nor cheerful near it, except a bubbling fountain, some twenty paces off, at which Richard Digby hardly threw away a glance. But he thrust his head into the cave, shivered, and congratulated himself.

"The finger of Providence hath pointed my way!" cried he, aloud, while the tomb-like den returned a strange echo, as if some one within were mocking him. "Here my soul will be at peace; for the wicked will not find me. Here I can read the Scriptures, and be no more provoked with lying interpretations. Here I can offer up acceptable prayers, because my voice will not be mingled with the sinful supplications of the multitude. Of a truth, the only way to heaven leadeth through the narrow entrance of this cave,—and I alone have found it!"

In regard to this cave it was observable that the roof, so far as the imperfect light permitted it to be seen, was hung with substances resembling opaque icicles; for the damps of unknown centuries, dripping down continually, had become as hard as adamant; and wherever that moisture fell, it seemed to possess the power of converting what it bathed to stone. The fallen leaves and sprigs of foliage, which the wind had swept into the cave, and the little feathery shrubs, rooted near the threshold, were not wet with a natural dew, but had been embalmed by this wondrous process. And here I am put in mind that Richard Digby, before he withdrew himself from the world, was supposed by skilful physicians to have contracted a disease for which no remedy was written in their medical books. It was a deposition of calculous particles within his heart, caused by an obstructed circulation of the blood; and, unless a miracle should be wrought for him, there was danger that the malady might act on the entire substance of the organ, and change his fleshy heart to stone. Many, indeed, affirmed that the process was already near its consummation. Richard Digby, however, could never be convinced that any such direful work was going on within him; nor when he saw the sprigs of marble foliage, did his heart even throb the quicker, at the similitude suggested by these once tender herbs. It may be that this same insensibility was a symptom of the disease.

Be that as it might, Richard Digby was well contented with his sepulchral cave. So dearly did he love this congenial spot, that, instead of going a few paces to the bubbling spring for water, he allayed his thirst with now and then a drop of moisture from the roof, which, had it fallen anywhere but on his tongue, would have been congealed into a pebble. For a man predisposed to stoniness of the heart, this surely was unwholesome liquor. But there he dwelt for three days more, eating herbs and roots, drinking his own destruction, sleeping, as it were, in a tomb, and awaking to the solitude of death, yet esteeming this horrible mode of life as hardly inferior to celestial bliss. Perhaps superior; for above the sky, there would be angels to disturb him. At the close of the third day, he sat in the portal of his mansion, reading the Bible aloud, because no other ear could profit by it, and reading it amiss, because the rays of the setting sun did not penetrate the dismal depth of shadow round about him, nor fall upon the sacred page. Suddenly, however, a faint gleam of light was thrown over the volume, and raising his eyes, Richard Digby saw that a young woman stood before the mouth of the cave, and that the sunbeams bathed her white garment, which thus seemed to possess a radiance of its own.

"Good evening, Richard," said the girl; "I have come from afar to find thee."

The slender grace and gentle loveliness of this young woman were at once recognized by Richard Digby. Her name was Mary Goffe. She

had been a convert to his preaching of the word in England, before he
yielded himself to that exclusive bigotry which now enfolded him with
such an iron grasp that no other sentiment could reach his bosom.
When he came a pilgrim to America, she had remained in her father's
hall; but now, as it appeared, had crossed the ocean after him, impelled
by the same faith that led other exiles hither, and perhaps by love almost as holy. What else but faith and love united could have sustained
so delicate a creature, wandering thus far into the forest, with her
golden hair dishevelled by the boughs, and her feet wounded by the
thorns? Yet, weary and faint though she must have been, and af-
frighted at the dreariness of the cave, she looked on the lonely man
with a mild and pitying expression, such as might beam from an angel's
eyes, towards an afflicted mortal. But the recluse, frowning sternly
upon her, and keeping his finger between the leaves of his half-closed
Bible, motioned her away with his hand.

"Off!" cried he. "I am sanctified, and thou art sinful. Away!"

"O Richard," said she, earnestly, "I have come this weary way because I heard that a grievous distemper had seized upon thy heart; and
a great Physician hath given me the skill to cure it. There is no other
remedy than this which I have brought thee. Turn me not away,
therefore, nor refuse my medicine; for then must this dismal cave be
thy sepulchre."

"Away!" replied Richard Digby, still with a dark frown. "My heart
is in better condition than thine own. Leave me, earthly one; for the
sun is almost set; and when no light reaches the door of the cave, then
is my prayer-time."

Now, great as was her need, Mary Goffe did not plead with this
stony-hearted man for shelter and protection, nor ask anything whatever for her own sake. All her zeal was for his welfare.

"Come back with me!" she exclaimed, clasping her hands,—"come
back to thy fellow-men; for they need thee, Richard, and thou hast ten-
fold need of them. Stay not in this evil den; for the air is chill, and the
damps are fatal; nor will any that perish within it ever find the path to
heaven. Hasten hence, I entreat thee, for thine own soul's sake; for
either the roof will fall upon thy head, or some other speedy destruction is at hand."

"Perverse woman!" answered Richard Digby, laughing aloud,—for he
was moved to bitter mirth by her foolish vehemence,—"I tell thee that
the path to heaven leadeth straight through this narrow portal where I
sit. And, moreover, the destruction thou speakest of is ordained, not
for this blessed cave, but for all other habitations of mankind, through-

out the earth. Get thee hence speedily, that thou mayst have thy share!"

So saying, he opened his Bible again, and fixed his eyes intently on the page, being resolved to withdraw his thoughts from this child of sin and wrath, and to waste no more of his holy breath upon her. The shadow had now grown so deep, where he was sitting, that he made continual mistakes in what he read, converting all that was gracious and merciful to denunciations of vengeance and unutterable woe on every created being but himself. Mary Goffe, meanwhile, was leaning against a tree, beside the sepulchral cave, very sad, yet with something heavenly and ethereal in her unselfish sorrow. The light from the setting sun still glorified her form, and was reflected a little way within the darksome den, discovering so terrible a gloom that the maiden shuddered for its self-doomed inhabitant. Espying the bright fountain near at hand, she hastened thither, and scooped up a portion of its water in a cup of birchen bark. A few tears mingled with the draught, and perhaps gave it all its efficacy. She then returned to the mouth of the cave, and knelt down at Richard Digby's feet.

"Richard," she said, with passionate fervor, yet a gentleness in all her passion, "I pray thee, by thy hope of heaven, and as thou wouldst not dwell in this tomb forever, drink of this hallowed water, be it but a single drop! Then, make room for me by thy side, and let us read together one page of that blessed volume; and, lastly, kneel down with me and pray! Do this, and thy stony heart shall become softer than a babe's and all be well."

But Richard Digby, in utter abhorrence of the proposal, cast the Bible at his feet, and eyed her with such a fixed and evil frown, that he looked less like a living man than a marble statue, wrought by some dark-imagined sculptor to express the most repulsive mood that human features could assume. And, as his look grew even devilish, so, with an equal change did Mary Goffe become more sad, more mild, more pitiful, more like a sorrowing angel. But, the more heavenly she was, the more hateful did she seem to Richard Digby, who at length raised his hand, and smote down the cup of hallowed water upon the threshold of the cave, thus rejecting the only medicine that could have cured his stony heart. A sweet perfume lingered in the air for a moment, and then was gone.

"Tempt me no more, accursed woman," exclaimed he, still with his marble frown, "lest I smite thee down also! What hast thou to do with my Bible?—what with my prayers?—what with my heaven?"

No sooner had he spoken these dreadful words, than Richard Digby's heart ceased to beat; while—so the legend says—the form of Mary Goffe melted into the last sunbeams, and returned from the sepulchral cave to heaven. For Mary Goffe had been buried in an English church-yard, months before; and either it was her ghost that haunted the wild forest, or else a dream-like spirit, typifying pure Religion.

Above a century afterwards, when the trackless forest of Richard Digby's day had long been interspersed with settlements, the children of a neighboring farmer were playing at the foot of a hill. The trees, on account of the rude and broken surface of this acclivity, had never been felled, and were crowded so densely together as to hide all but a few rocky prominences, wherever their roots could grapple with the soil. A little boy and girl, to conceal themselves from their playmates, had crept into the deepest shade, where not only the darksome pines, but a thick veil of creeping plants suspended from an overhanging rock, combined to make a twilight at noonday, and almost a midnight at all other seasons. There the children hid themselves, and shouted, repeating the cry at intervals till the whole party of pursuers were drawn thither, and, pulling aside the matted foliage, let in a doubtful glimpse of daylight. But scarcely was this accomplished, when the little group uttered a simultaneous shriek, and tumbled headlong down the hill, making the best of their way homeward, without a second glance into the gloomy recess. Their father, unable to comprehend what had so startled them, took his axe, and, by felling one or two trees, and tearing away the creeping plants, laid the mystery open to the day. He had discovered the entrance of a cave, closely resembling the mouth of a sepulchre, within which sat the figure of a man, whose gesture and attitude warned the father and children to stand back, while his visage wore a most forbidding frown. This repulsive person-age seemed to have been carved in the same gray stone that formed the walls and portal of the cave. On minuter inspection, indeed, such blemishes were observed as made it doubtful whether the figure were really a statue, chiselled by human art, and somewhat worn and de-faced by the lapse of ages, or a freak of Nature, who might have chosen to imitate, in stone, her usual handiwork of flesh. Perhaps it was the least unreasonable idea, suggested by this strange spectacle, that the moisture of the cave possessed a petrifying quality, which had thus awfully embalmed a human corpse.

There was something so frightful in the aspect of this Man of Ada-mant, that the farmer, the moment that he recovered from the fascina-tion of his first gaze, began to heap stones into the mouth of the cavern. His wife, who had followed him to the hill, assisted her husband's efforts. The children, also, approached as near as they durst, with their little hands full of pebbles, and cast them on the pile. Earth was then thrown into the crevices, and the whole fabric overlaid with sods. Thus all traces of the discovery were obliterated, leaving only a marvellous legend, which grew wilder from one generation to another, as the children told it to their grandchildren, and they to their posterity, till few believed that there had ever been a cavern or a statue, where now they saw but a grassy patch on the shadowy hill-side. Yet grown people avoid the spot, nor do children play there. Friendship, and Love, and Piety, all human and celestial sympathies, should keep aloof from that hidden cave; for there still sits, and, unless an earthquake crumble down the roof upon his head, shall sit forever, the shape of Richard Digby, in the attitude of repelling the whole race of mortals,— not from heaven,—but from the horrible loneliness of his dark, cold sepulchre!

Commentary

Man's attitude toward the inevitability of death determines what he does with his life. Knowing that he will die but not knowing what lies beyond death, he has employed his imagination to speculate on his mortality. Many works of fiction have death as their subject. Hawthorne's story is a satirical allegory (see p. 42) on Puritanism, "the old times of religious gloom and intolerance," when the concept of death was that of fire-and-brimstone punishment of man for his original sin of having been alive at all.

The subtitle, "An Apologue" (see p. 17), reveals at once that the story is intended to be an allegory and a parable that will teach a moral lesson. The lesson is explicitly stated throughout the narrative: man's unpardonable sin is an egotistical spiritual pride. The man who holds himself so superior to other mortals that he will not associate with them, that he will not concur with their ideas of God and mercy, that he will misread the Bible, is the worst sinner, for his heart has turned to stone. The man who chooses death in life, isolation from God and man, will turn to stone when he dies instead of finding life in death, union with God and man in heaven.

The title, like the subtitle of "Bartleby," contains an ambiguous word, *adamant*. It is upon this ambiguity that the allegory turns. At the literal level of the story, *adamant* is a noun meaning "a hard stone." At the deeper, metaphorical level of meaning, the word is an adjective meaning "obdurate," "resisting," "hard." Richard Digby, who literally turns to stone, does so because he has treated people in a heartless, stony way.

Unlike "The Burrow," which the reader may interpret in a point-to-point equation according to his own choice of a set of meanings, "The Man of Adamant" is explicit in what each object represents. The dark sepulchral cave is the gloomy view of death. The sunny sky is the hopeful view of heaven. Richard Digby wears the fixed evil frown of the devil. Mary Goffe, radiant in a white gown bathed in sunbeams, is a heavenly angel, pure Religion. The moisture of the cave is an impure embalming substance, bigotry, whereas the bubbling fountain is living water; and human kindness, purified by the sun, is God's mercy. To teach the lesson, not only is there a metaphorical representation for each object in the story, but there is also the alternate order in which the images of light and dark, cave and fountain, sun and shadow are presented to effect contrast.

That Richard Digby's Puritanical view is the one being satirized is made clear not only by the tone of the allegory and the contrast of the images, but also by the final episode. Here, the farmer and children from a later generation with a different attitude toward life and death, literally bury the repulsive statue of Digby, thus symbolically burying the repulsive view of death in life and punishment thereafter. The new view of life in death is a hopeful one from heaven, not one of "repelling the whole race of mortals . . . from the horrible loneliness of his dark, cold sepulchre."

Questions

1. The personification of abstract ideas is frequently emphasized in allegorical literature like Hawthorne's tales and John Bunyan's *Pilgrim's Progress* by capitalization of the words for those ideas. Hence, in "The Man of Adamant," we find the words Nature, Heaven, Religion, Providence, Friendship, and Love and Piety. In terms of the story, however, notice that these are all affirmative abstractions. The negative abstractions present in the story are not capitalized. What are the negative abstractions, and why are they not capitalized?
2. Find passages that illustrate Digby's aloofness from society as well as his vindictive hatred of his fellow men.
3. Why does Digby misread the Bible?
4. What is the significance of the image of echoes that recurs so frequently?
5. Who had Richard Digby and Mary Goffe been before their deaths?

How does their previous significance contribute to the irony of the story?

6. The characters of Digby and Mary Goffe illustrate the theme. How does the action contribute to the development of character and consequent projection of theme? How are conflict and suspense achieved? Would the story be better if Digby were aware of his perversion and spiritual suicide? if there were a dramatic external and internal struggle?

7. Look up the allusions "the tents of Kedar," "Elijah's cave at Horeb," and "Abraham's sepulchral cave at Machpelah." How do these references contribute to the total effect of "The Man of Adamant"?

Metzengerstein

Edgar Allan Poe

Pestis eram vivus—moriens tua mors ero.
                                        Martin Luther.

Horror and fatality have been stalking abroad in all ages. Why then give a date to the story I have to tell? Let it suffice to say, that at the period of which I speak, there existed, in the interior of Hungary, a settled although hidden belief in the doctrines of the Metempsychosis. Of the doctrines themselves—that is, of their falsity, or of their proba-bility—I say nothing. I assert, however, that much of our incredulity (as La Bruyère says of all our unhappiness) *"vient de ne pouvoir être seuls."*[1]

But there were some points in the Hungarian superstition which were fast verging to absurdity. They—the Hungarians—differed very essentially from their Eastern authorities. For example. *"The soul,"* said the former—I give the words of an acute and intelligent Parisian— *"ne demeure qu'une seule fois dans un corps sensible: au reste—un cheval, un chien, un homme même, n'est que la ressemblance peu tan-gible de ces animaux."*

The families of Berlifitzing and Metzengerstein had been at variance for centuries. Never before were two houses so illustrious, mutually embittered by hostility so deadly. The origin of this enmity seems to be found in the words of an ancient prophecy—"A lofty name shall have a fearful fall when, as the rider over his horse, the mortality of Metzen-gerstein shall triumph over the immortality of Berlifitzing."

To be sure the words themselves had little or no meaning. But more trivial causes have given rise—and that no long while ago—to conse-quences equally eventful. Besides, the estates, which were contiguous,

---

[1] Mercier, in *"L'an deux mille quatre cent quarante"* seriously maintains the doc-trines of the Metempsychosis, and I. D'Israeli says that "no system is so simple and so little repugnant to the understanding." Colonel Ethan Allen, the "Green Moun-tain Boy," is also said to have been a serious metempsychosist.

had long exercised a rival influence in the affairs of a busy government. Moreover, near neighbors are seldom friends; and the inhabitants of the Castle Berlifitzing might look, from their lofty buttresses, into the very windows of the Palace Metzengerstein. Least of all had the more than feudal magnificence thus discovered a tendency to allay the irritable feelings of the less ancient and less wealthy Berlifitzings. What wonder, then, that the words, however silly, of that prediction, should have succeeded in setting and keeping at variance two families already predisposed to quarrel by every instigation of hereditary jealousy? The prophecy seemed to imply—if it implied anything—a final triumph on the part of the already more powerful house; and was of course remembered with the more bitter animosity by the weaker and less influential.

Wilhelm, Count Berlifitzing, although loftily descended, was, at the epoch of this narrative, an infirm and doting old man, remarkable for nothing but an inordinate and inveterate personal antipathy to the family of his rival, and so passionate a love of horses, and of hunting, that neither bodily infirmity, great age, nor mental incapacity, prevented his daily participation in the dangers of the chase.

Frederick, Baron Metzengerstein, was, on the other hand, not yet of age. His father, the Minister G——, died young. His mother, the Lady Mary, followed him quickly. Frederick was, at that time, in his eighteenth year. In a city, eighteen years are no long period: but in a wilderness—in so magnificent a wilderness as that old principality, the pendulum vibrates with a deeper meaning.

From some peculiar circumstances attending the administration of his father, the young Baron, at the decease of the former, entered immediately upon his vast possessions. Such estates were seldom held before by a nobleman of Hungary. His castles were without number. The chief in point of splendor and extent was the "Palace Metzengerstein." The boundary line of his dominions was never clearly defined; but his principal park embraced a circuit of fifty miles.

Upon the succession of a proprietor so young, with a character so well known, to a fortune so unparalleled, little speculation was afloat in regard to his probable course of conduct. And, indeed, for the space of three days, the behaviour of the heir out-heroded Herod, and fairly surpassed the expectations of his most enthusiastic admirers. Shameful debaucheries—flagrant treacheries—unheard-of atrocities—gave his trembling vassals quickly to understand that no servile submission on their part—no punctilios of conscience on his own—were thenceforward to prove any security against the remorseless fangs of a petty Caligula. On the night of the fourth day, the stables of the Castle Berlifitzing

were discovered to be on fire; and the unanimous opinion of the neighborhood added the crime of the incendiary to the already hideous list
of the Baron's misdemeanors and enormities.

But during the tumult occasioned by this occurrence, the young
nobleman himself, sat apparently buried in meditation, in a vast and
desolate upper apartment of the family palace of Metzengerstein. The
rich although faded tapestry hangings which swung gloomily upon the
walls, represented the shadowy and majestic forms of a thousand illustrious ancestors. *Here,* rich-ermined priests, and pontifical dignitaries, familiarly seated with the autocrat and the sovereign, put a veto on the
wishes of a temporal king, or restrained with the fiat of papal suprem-
acy the rebellious sceptre of the Arch-enemy. *There,* the dark, tall
statures of the Princes Metzengerstein—their muscular war-coursers
plunging over the carcasses of fallen foes—startled the steadiest nerves
with their vigorous expression: and *here,* again, the voluptuous and
swan-like figures of the dames of days gone by, floated away in the
mazes of an unreal dance to the strains of imaginary melody.

But as the Baron listened, or affected to listen, to the gradually increasing uproar in the stables of Berlifitzing—or perhaps pondered
upon some more novel, some more decided act of audacity—his eyes
were turned unwittingly to the figure of an enormous, and unnaturally
colored horse, represented in the tapestry as belonging to a Saracen
ancestor of the family of his rival. The horse itself, in the fore-ground
of the design, stood motionless and statue-like—while, farther back, its
discomfited rider perished by the dagger of a Metzengerstein.

On Frederick's lip arose a fiendish expression, as he became aware of
the direction which his glance had, without his consciousness, assumed.
Yet he did not remove it. On the contrary, he could by no means account for the overwhelming anxiety which appeared falling like a pall
upon his senses. It was with difficulty that he reconciled his dreamy
and incoherent feelings with the certainty of being awake. The longer
he gazed, the more absorbing became the spell—the more impossible
did it appear that he could ever withdraw his glance from the fascination of that tapestry. But the tumult without becoming suddenly more
violent, with a compulsory exertion he diverted his attention to the
glare of ruddy light thrown full by the flaming stables upon the windows of the apartment.

The action, however, was but momentary; his gaze returned mechanically to the wall. To his extreme horror and astonishment, the head of
the gigantic steed had, in the meantime, altered its position. The neck
of the animal, before arched, as if in compassion, over the prostrate

body of its lord, was now extended, at full length, in the direction of the
Baron. The eyes, before invisible, now wore an energetic and human
expression, while they gleamed with a fiery and unusual red; and the
distended lips of the apparently enraged horse left in full view his
sepulchral and disgusting teeth.

Stupefied with terror, the young nobleman tottered to the door. As
he threw it open, a flash of red light, streaming far into the chamber,
flung his shadow with a clear outline against the quivering tapestry;
and he shuddered to perceive that shadow—as he staggered awhile
upon the threshold—assuming the exact position, and precisely filling up
the contour, of the relentless and triumphant murderer of the Saracen
Berlifitzing.

To lighten the depression of his spirits, the Baron hurried into the
open air.   At the principal gate of the palace he encountered three
equerries. With much difficulty, and at the imminent peril of their lives,
they were restraining the convulsive plunges of a gigantic and fiery-
colored horse.

"Whose horse? Where did you get him?" demanded the youth, in a
querulous and husky tone, as he became instantly aware that the mysterious steed in the tapestried chamber was the very counterpart of the
furious animal before his eyes.

"He is your own property, sire," replied one of the equerries, "at
least he is claimed by no other owner. We caught him flying, all smoking and foaming with rage, from the burning stables of the Castle Berlifitzing. Supposing him to have belonged to the old Count's stud of
foreign horses, we led him back as an estray. But the grooms there dis-
claim any title to the creature; which is strange, since he bears evident
marks of having made a narrow escape from the flames."

"The letters W. V. B. are also branded very distinctly on his forehead," interrupted a second equerry; "I supposed them, of course, to be
the initials of Wilhelm Von Berlifitzing—but all at the castle are positive
in denying any knowledge of the horse."

"Extremely singular!" said the young Baron, with a musing air, and
apparently unconscious of the meaning of his words. "He is, as you
say, a remarkable horse—a prodigious horse! although, as you very
justly observe, of a suspicious and untractable character; let him be
mine, however," he added, after a pause, "perhaps a rider like Frederick
of Metzengerstein, may tame even the devil from the stables of Berlifitzing."

"You are mistaken, my lord; the horse, as I think we mentioned, is *not*
from the stables of the Count. If such had been the case, we know our

duty better than to bring him into the presence of a noble of your family."

"True!" observed the Baron, drily; and at that instant a page of the bed-chamber came from the palace with a heightened color, and a precipitate step. He whispered into his master's ear an account of the sudden disappearance of a small portion of the tapestry, in an apartment which he designated; entering, at the same time, into particulars of a minute and circumstantial character; but from the low tone of voice in which these latter were communicated, nothing escaped to gratify the excited curiosity of the equerries.

The young Frederick, during the conference, seemed agitated by a variety of emotions. He soon, however, recovered his composure, and an expression of determined malignancy settled upon his countenance, as he gave peremptory orders that the apartment in question should be immediately locked up, and the key placed in his own possession.

"Have you heard of the unhappy death of the old hunter Berlifitzing?" said one of his vassals to the Baron, as, after the departure of the page, the huge steed which that nobleman had adopted as his own, plunged and curveted, with redoubled fury, down the long avenue which extended from the palace to the stables of Metzengerstein.

"No!" said the Baron, turning abruptly towards the speaker, "dead! say you?"

"It is indeed true, my lord; and, to the noble of your name, will be, I imagine, no unwelcome intelligence."

A rapid smile shot over the countenance of the listener. "How died he?"

"In his rash exertions to rescue a favorite portion of his hunting stud, he has himself perished miserably in the flames."

"I—n—d—e—e—d—!" ejaculated the Baron, as if slowly and deliberately impressed with the truth of some exciting idea.

"Indeed"; repeated the vassal.

"Shocking!" said the youth, calmly, and turned quietly into the palace.

From this date a marked alteration took place in the outward demeanor of the dissolute young Baron Frederick Von Metzengerstein. Indeed, his behavior disappointed every expectation, and proved little in accordance with the views of many a manœuvring mamma; while his habits and manners, still less than formerly, offered anything congenial with those of the neighboring aristocracy. He was never to be seen beyond the limits of his own domain, and, in this wide and social world, was utterly companionless—unless, indeed, that unnatural, impetuous, and fiery-colored horse, which he henceforward continually bestrode, had any mysterious right to the title of his friend.

Numerous invitations on the part of the neighborhood for a long time, however, periodically came in. "Will the Baron honor our festivals with his presence?" "Will the Baron join us in a hunting of the boar?"—"Metzengerstein does not hunt;" "Metzengerstein will not attend," were the haughty and laconic answers.

These repeated insults were not to be endured by an imperious nobility. Such invitations became less cordial—less frequent—in time they ceased altogether. The widow of the unfortunate Count Berlifitzing was even heard to express a hope "that the Baron might be at home when he did not wish to be at home, since he disdained the company of his equals; and ride when he did not wish to ride, since he preferred the society of a horse." This to be sure was a very silly explosion of hereditary pique; and merely proved how singularly unmeaning our sayings are apt to become, when we desire to be unusually energetic.

The charitable, nevertheless, attributed the alteration in the conduct of the young nobleman to the natural sorrow of a son for the untimely loss of his parents;—forgetting, however, his atrocious and reckless behavior during the short period immediately succeeding that bereavement. Some there were, indeed, who suggested a too haughty idea of self-consequence and dignity. Others again (among whom may be mentioned the family physician) did not hesitate in speaking of morbid melancholy, and hereditary ill-health; while dark hints, of a more equivocal nature, were current among the multitude.

Indeed, the Baron's perverse attachment to his lately-acquired charger —an attachment which seemed to attain new strength from every fresh example of the animal's ferocious and demon-like propensities—at length became, in the eyes of all reasonable men, a hideous and unnatural fervor. In the glare of noon—at the dead hour of night—in sickness or in health—in calm or in tempest—the young Metzengerstein seemed riveted to the saddle of that colossal horse, whose intractable audacities so well accorded with his own spirit.

There were circumstances, moreover, which, coupled with late events, gave an unearthly and portentous character to the mania of the rider, and to the capabilities of the steed. The space passed over in a single leap had been accurately measured, and was found to exceed by an astounding difference, the wildest expectations of the most imaginative. The Baron, besides, had no particular *name* for the animal, although all the rest in his collection were distinguished by characteristic appellations. His stable, too, was appointed at a distance from the rest; and with regard to grooming and other necessary offices, none but the owner in person had ventured to officiate, or even to enter the enclosure of that horse's particular stall. It was also to be observed, that although the three grooms, who had caught the steed as he fled from the conflagration at Berlifitzing, had succeeded in arresting his course, by means of a chain-bridle and noose—yet no one of the three could with any certainty affirm that he had, during that dangerous struggle, or at any period thereafter, actually placed his hand upon the body of the beast. Instances of peculiar intelligence in the demeanor of a noble and high-spirited horse are not to be supposed capable of exciting unreasonable attention, but there were certain circumstances which intruded themselves per force upon the most skeptical and phlegmatic; and it is said there were times when the animal caused the gaping crowd who stood around to recoil in horror from the deep and impressive meaning of his terrible stamp—times when the young Metzengerstein turned pale and shrunk away from the rapid and searching expression of his earnest and human-looking eye.

Among all the retinue of the Baron, however, none were found to doubt the ardor of that extraordinary affection which existed on the part of the young nobleman for the fiery qualities of his horse; at least, none but an insignificant and misshapen little page, whose deformities were in every body's way, and whose opinions were of the least possible importance. He (if his ideas are worth mentioning at all,) had the effrontery to assert that his master never vaulted into the saddle, without an unaccountable and almost imperceptible shudder; and that, upon his return from every long-continued and habitual ride, an expression of triumphant malignity distorted every muscle in his countenance.

One tempestuous night, Metzengerstein, awaking from heavy slumber, descended like a maniac from his chamber, and, mounting in hot haste, bounded away into the mazes of the forest. An occurrence so common attracted no particular attention, but his return was looked for with intense anxiety on the part of his domestics, when, after some hours' absence, the stupendous and magnificent battlements of the Palace Metzengerstein, were discovered crackling and rocking to their very foundation, under the influence of a dense and livid mass of ungovernable fire.

As the flames, when first seen, had already made so terrible a progress that all efforts to save any portion of the building were evidently futile, the astonished neighborhood stood idly around in silent, if not apathetic wonder. But a new and fearful object soon riveted the attention of the multitude, and proved how much more intense is the excitement wrought in the feelings of a crowd by the contemplation of human agony, than that brought about by the most appalling spectacles of inanimate matter.

Up the long avenue of aged oaks which led from the forest to the main entrance of the Palace Metzengerstein, a steed, bearing an un-bonneted and disordered rider, was seen leaping with an impetuosity which outstripped the very Demon of the Tempest.

The career of the horseman was indisputably, on his own part, un-controllable. The agony of his countenance, the convulsive struggle of his frame, gave evidence of superhuman exertion: but no sound, save a solitary shriek, escaped from his lacerated lips, which were bitten through and through in the intensity of terror. One instant, and the clattering of hoofs resounded sharply and shrilly above the roaring of the flames and the shrieking of the winds—another, and, clearing at a single plunge the gate-way and the moat, the steed bounded far up the tottering staircases of the palace, and, with its rider, disappeared amid the whirlwind of chaotic fire.

The fury of the tempest immediately died away, and a dead calm sul-lenly succeeded. A white flame still enveloped the building like a shroud, and, streaming far away into the quiet atmosphere, shot forth a glare of preternatural light; while a cloud of smoke settled heavily over the battlements in the distinct colossal figure of—*a horse*.

Notes

The introduction to "Metzengerstein" includes a number of allusions to and French quotations concerning the doctrine of metempsychosis. This doctrine is the theory—in primitive, several Eastern, and even later Western cultures—that souls transmigrate from one body to another for reincarnation. In Buddhism and Hinduism, the passage of a soul into another form or body in the next life is associated with retribution for the sins and accidents of the soul's former life.

The epigraph by Martin Luther means: "A plague was I in my life-time; in death will I be the cause of your death."

The passage that starts in English and ends in French, "Much of our incredulity . . . *vient de ne pouvoir être seuls*," means: "Much of our incredulity comes from not being able to be individuals."

Jean de La Bruyère was a French writer of the 17th century.

The passage "The soul . . . *ne demeure qu' une seule fois dans un corps sensible: au reste—un cheval, un chein, un homme même, n'est que la ressemblance peu tangible de ces animaux* means: "The soul resides only one time in a sensible body: for the rest—a horse, a dog, even the man, is only the scarcely tangible form of these animals."

Louis Sebastien Mercier was a late 18th-century French dramatist, whose plays emphasize the teaching of humanitarian idealism. His book *L'An 2440* ("*L'an deux mille quatre cents quarante*") means "The Year 2440." It is not a play but an imaginative prophecy.

I. D'Israeli is Isaac, father of Benjamin Disraeli, 19th-century Prime Minister of Great Britain. Isaac D'Israeli showed his interest in metempsychosis in his book *Curiosities of Literature*.

Questions

1. "Metzengerstein" is less the horror or detective story that we expect of Edgar Allan Poe than a highly imaginative fantasy. What do the first two paragraphs and the footnote add to the total effect of the story? Would the tale be artistically improved without this "scholarly" touch? Why?

2. At what point in the story did you become aware that the tale is fiction rather than an historical account? Is it convincing as folklore? Why or why not?

3. How does the stiff, elegant style of the language contribute positively to the form? to the content?

4. In the sentence "The rich although faded tapestry hangings which swung *gloomily* upon the walls, represented the shadowy and majestic forms of a thousand illustrious ancestors," is the word *gloomily* necessary to produce the atmosphere of the upper apartment of the Palace Metzengerstein?

5. How might a modern author convey the impression of a young Baron Metzengerstein that Poe conveys in the following:

> The young Frederick, during the conference [with the page of the bedchamber], seemed agitated by a variety of emotions. He soon, however, recovered his composure, and an expression of determined malignancy settled upon his countenance, as he gave peremptory orders that the apartment in question should be immediately locked up, and the key placed in his own possession.

6. Except for the opening paragraph, the tale is related by a third-person-omniscient narrator. How would the story differ were a different point of view employed?

7. Why does the Baron have a "perverse attachment to his lately-acquired charger"?

8. Why is "the insignificant and misshapen little page, whose deformities were in every body's way, and whose opinions were of

the least possible importance" the only one in the Baron's retinue to doubt the Baron's apparent affection for the demon-horse?

9. To what did the neighbors attribute the antisocial behavior of the young Frederick?

10. Why does the Saracen horse in the tapestry come to life? Does he *actually* come to life?

11. Comment on the image of the horse and rider bounding up the staircase of the burning palace. What is the effect of the cloud in the shape of a horse at the end of the story?

12. What does the Countess Berlifitzing mean when she expresses the hope "that the Baron might be at home when he did not wish to be at home, since he disdained the company of his equals; and ride when he did not wish to ride, since he preferred the society of a horse"? And what does the omniscient narrator mean by his editorial comment, "This to be sure was a very silly explosion of hereditary pique; and merely proved how singularly unmeaning our sayings are apt to become, when we desire to be unusually energetic"?

13. How does the fantastic nature (see p. 17) of this story's action clarify the theme?

The Affair at 7, Rue de M——

John Steinbeck

I had hoped to withhold from public scrutiny those rather curious events which have given me some concern for the past month. I knew of course that there was talk in the neighborhood. I have even heard some of the distortions current in my district, stories, I hasten to add, in which there is no particle of truth. However, my desire for privacy was shattered yesterday by a visit of two members of the fourth estate who assured me that the story, or rather *a* story, had escaped the boundaries of my *arrondissement*.

In the light of impending publicity I think it only fair to issue the true details of those happenings which have come to be known as The Affair at 7, rue de M——, in order that nonsense may not be added to a set of circumstances which are not without their *bizarrerie*. I shall set down the events as they happened without comment, thereby allowing the public to judge of the situation.

At the beginning of the summer I carried my family to Paris and took up residence in a pretty little house at 7, rue de M——, a building which in another period had been the mews of the great house beside it. The whole property is now owned and part of it inhabited by a noble French family of such age and purity that its members still consider the Bourbons unacceptable as claimants to the throne of France.

To this pretty little converted stable with three floors of rooms above a well-paved courtyard, I brought my immediate family, consisting of my wife, my three children, two small boys and a grown daughter, and of course myself. Our domestic arrangement in addition to the concierge who, as you might say, came with the house, consists of a French cook of great ability, a Spanish maid and my own secretary, a girl of Swiss nationality whose high attainments and ambitions are only equaled by her moral altitude. This then was our little family group when the events I am about to chronicle were ushered in.

If one must have an agency in this matter, I can find no alternative to placing not the blame but rather the authorship, albeit innocent, on my younger son John who has only recently attained his eighth year, a lively child of singular beauty and buck teeth.

This young man has, during the last several years in America, become not so much an addict as an aficionado of that curious American practice, the chewing of bubble gum, and one of the pleasanter aspects of the early summer in Paris lay in the fact that the Cadet John had neglected to bring any of the atrocious substance with him from America. The child's speech became clear and unobstructed and the hypnotized look went out of his eyes.

Alas, this delightful situation was not long to continue. An old family friend traveling in Europe brought as a present to the children a more than adequate supply of this beastly gum, thinking to do them a kindness. Thereupon the old familiar situation reasserted itself. Speech fought its damp way past a huge wad of the gum and emerged with the sound of a faulty water trap. The jaws were in constant motion, giving the face at best a look of agony while the eyes took on a glaze like those of a pig with a recently severed jugular. Since I do not believe in inhibiting my children I resigned myself to a summer not quite so pleasant as I had at first hoped.

On occasion I do not follow my ordinary practice of laissez-faire. When I am composing the material for a book or play or essay, in a word, when the utmost of concentration is required, I am prone to establish tyrannical rules for my own comfort and effectiveness. One of these rules is that there shall be neither chewing nor bubbling while I am trying to concentrate. This rule is so thoroughly understood by the Cadet John that he accepts it as one of the laws of nature and does not either complain or attempt to evade the ruling. It is his pleasure and my solace for my son to come sometimes into my workroom, there to sit quietly beside me for a time. He knows he must be silent and when he has remained so for as long a time as his character permits, he goes out quietly, leaving us both enriched by the wordless association.

Two weeks ago in the late afternoon I sat at my desk composing a short essay for *Figaro Littéraire*, an essay which later aroused some controversy when it was printed under the title "Sartre Resartus." I had come to that passage concerning the proper clothing for the soul when to my astonishment and chagrin I heard the unmistakable soft plopping sound of a bursting balloon of bubble gum. I looked sternly at my offspring and saw him chewing away. His cheeks were colored with embarrassment and the muscles of his jaws stood rigidly out.

"You know the rule," I said coldly.

To my amazement tears came into his eyes and while his jaws continued to masticate hugely, his blubbery voice forced its way past the huge lump of bubble gum in his mouth.

"I didn't do it," he cried.

"What do you mean, you didn't do it?" I demanded in a rage. "I distinctly heard and now I distinctly see."

"Oh sir!" he moaned, "I really didn't. I'm not chewing it, sir. It's chewing me."

For a moment I inspected him closely. He is an honest child, only under the greatest pressure of gain permitting himself an untruth. I had the horrible thought that the bubble gum had finally had its way and that my son's reason was tottering. If this were so, it were better to tread softly. Quietly I put out my hand. "Lay it here," I said kindly.

My child manfully tried to disengage the gum from his jaws. "It won't let me go," he sputtered.

"Open up," I said and then inserting my fingers in his mouth I seized hold of the large lump of gum and after a struggle in which my fingers slipped again and again, managed to drag it forth and to deposit the ugly blob on my desk on top of a pile of white manuscript paper.

For a moment it seemed to shudder there on the paper and then with an easy slowness it began to undulate, to swell and recede with the exact motion of being chewed while my son and I regarded it with popping eyes.

For a long time we watched it while I drove through my mind for some kind of explanation. Either I was dreaming or some principle as yet unknown had taken its seat in the pulsing bubble gum on the desk. I am not unintelligent. While I considered the indecent thing, a hundred little thoughts and glimmerings of understanding raced through my brain. At last I asked, "How long has it been chewing you?"

"Since last night," he replied.

"And when did you first notice this, this propensity on its part?"

He spoke with perfect candor. "I will ask you to believe me, sir," he said. "Last night before I went to sleep I put it under my pillow as is my invariable custom. In the night I was awakened to find that it was in my mouth. I again placed it under my pillow and this morning it was again in my mouth, lying very quietly. When, however, I became thoroughly awakened, I was conscious of a slight motion and shortly afterward the situation dawned on me that I was no longer master of the gum. It had taken its head. I tried to remove it, sir, and could not. You yourself with all of your strength have seen how difficult it was to extract. I came to your workroom to await your first disengagement, wishing to acquaint you with my difficulty. Oh, Daddy, what do you think has happened?"

The cancerous thing held my complete attention.

"I must think," I said. "This is something a little out of the ordinary, and I do not believe it should be passed over without some investigation."

As I spoke a change came over the gum. It ceased to chew itself and seemed to rest for a while, and then with a flowing movement like those monocellular animals of the order Paramecium, the gum slid across the desk straight in the direction of my son. For a moment I was stricken with astonishment and for an even longer time I failed to discern its intent. It dropped to his knee, climbed horribly up his shirt front. Only then did I understand. It was trying to get back into his mouth. He looked down on it paralyzed with fright.

"Stop," I cried, for I realized that my third-born was in danger and at such times I am capable of a violence which verges on the murderous. I seized the monster from his chin and striding from my workroom, entered the salon, opened the window and hurled the thing into the busy traffic on the rue de M——.

I believe it is the duty of a parent to ward off those shocks which may cause dreams or trauma whenever possible. I went back to my study to find young John sitting where I had left him. He was staring into space. There was a troubled line between his brows.

"Son," I said, "you and I have seen something which, while we know it to have happened, we might find difficult to describe with any degree of success to others. I ask you to imagine the scene if we should tell this story to the other members of the family. I greatly fear we should be laughed out of the house."

"Yes, sir," he said passively.

"Therefore I am going to propose to you, my son, that we lock the episode deep in our memories and never mention it to a soul as long as we live." I waited for his assent and when it did not come, glanced up at his face to see it a ravaged field of terror. His eyes were starting out of his head. I turned in the direction of his gaze. Under the door there crept a paper-thin sheet which, once it had entered the room, grew to a gray blob and rested on the rug, pulsing and chewing. After a moment it moved again by pseudopodian progression toward my son.

I fought down panic as I rushed at it. I grabbed it up and flung it on my desk, then seizing an African war club from among the trophies on the wall, a dreadful instrument studded with brass, I beat the gum until I was breathless and it a torn piece of plastic fabric. The moment I rested, it drew itself together and for a few moments chewed very rapidly as though it chuckled at my impotence, and then inexorably it moved toward my son, who by this time was crouched in a corner moaning with terror.

Now a coldness came over me. I picked up the filthy thing and wrapped it in my handkerchief, strode out of the house, walked three blocks to the Seine and flung the handkerchief into the slowly moving current.

I spent a good part of the afternoon soothing my son and trying to reassure him that his fears were over. But such was his nervousness that I had to give him half a barbiturate tablet to get him to sleep that night, while my wife insisted that I call a doctor. I did not at that time dare to tell her why I could not obey her wish.

I was awakened, indeed the whole house was awakened, in the night by a terrified muffled scream from the children's room. I took the stairs two at a time and burst in the room, flicking the light switch as I went. John sat up in bed squalling, while with his fingers he dug at his half-open mouth, a mouth which horrifyingly went right on chewing. As I looked a bubble emerged between his fingers and burst with a wet plopping sound.

What chance of keeping our secret now! All had to be explained, but with the plopping gum pinned to a breadboard with an ice pick the explanation was easier than it might have been. And I am proud of the help and comfort given me. There is no strength like that of the family. Our French cook solved the problem by refusing to believe it even when she saw it. It was not reasonable, she explained, and she was a reasonable member of a reasonable people. The Spanish maid ordered and paid for an exorcism by the parish priest who, poor man, after two hours of strenuous effort went away muttering that this was more a matter of the stomach than the soul.

For two weeks we were besieged by the monster. We burned it in the fireplace, causing it to splutter in blue flames and melt in a nasty mess among the ashes. Before morning it had crawled through the keyhole of the children's room, leaving a trail of wood ash on the door, and again we were awakened by screams from the Cadet.

In despair I drove far into the country and threw it from my automobile. It was back before morning. Apparently it had crept to the highway and placed itself in the Paris traffic until picked up by a truck tire. When we tore it from John's mouth it had still the nonskid marks of Michelin imprinted in its side.

Fatigue and frustration will take their toll. In exhaustion, with my will to fight back sapped, and after we had tried every possible method to lose or destroy the bubble gum, I placed it at last under a bell jar which I ordinarily use to cover my microscope. I collapsed in a chair to gaze at it with weary defeated eyes. John slept in his little bed under the influence of sedatives backed by my assurance that I would not let the Thing out of my sight.

I lighted a pipe and settled back to watch it. Inside the bell jar the gray tumorous lump moved restlessly about searching for some means of exit from its prison. Now and then it paused as though in thought and emitted a bubble in my direction. I could feel the hatred it had for me. In my weariness I found my mind slipping into an analysis which had so far escaped me.

The background I had been over hurriedly. It must be that from constant association with the lambent life which is my son, the magic of life had been created in the bubble gum. And with life had come intelligence, not the manly open intelligence of the boy, but an evil calculating wiliness.

How could it be otherwise? Intelligence without the soul to balance it must of necessity be evil. The gum had not absorbed any part of John's soul.

Very well, said my mind, now we have a hypothesis of its origin, let us consider its nature. What does it think? What does it want? What does it need? My mind leaped like a terrier. It needs and wants to get back to its host, my son. It wants to be chewed. It must be chewed to survive.

Inside the bell jar the gum inserted a thin wedge of itself under the heavy glass foot and constricted so that the whole jar lifted a fraction of an inch. I laughed as I drove it back. I laughed with almost insane triumph. I had the answer.

In the dining room I procured a clear plastic plate, one of a dozen my wife had bought for picnics in the country. Then turning the bell jar over and securing the monster in its bottom, I smeared the mouth of it with a heavy plastic cement guaranteed to be water-, alcohol- and acidproof. I forced the plate over the opening and pressed it down until the glue took hold and bound the plate to the glass, making an airtight container. And last I turned the jar upright again and adjusted the reading light so that I could observe every movement of my prisoner.

Again it searched the circle for escape. Then it faced me and emitted a great number of bubbles very rapidly. I could hear the little bursting plops through the glass.

"I have you, my beauty," I cried. "I have you at last."

That was a week ago. I have not left the side of the bell jar since, and have only turned my head to accept a cup of coffee. When I go to the bathroom, my wife takes my place. I can now report the following hopeful news.

During the first day and night, the bubble gum tried every means to escape. Then for a day and a night it seemed to be agitated and nervous as though it had for the first time realized its predicament. The third day it went to work with its chewing motion, only the action was speeded up greatly, like the chewing of a baseball fan. On the fourth day it began to weaken and I observed with joy a kind of dryness on its once slick and shiny exterior.

I am now in the seventh day and I believe it is almost over. The gum is lying in the center of the plate. At intervals it heaves and subsides. Its color has turned to a nasty yellow. Once today when my son entered the room, it leaped up excitedly, then seemed to realize its hopelessness and collapsed on the plate. It will die tonight I think and only then will I dig a deep hole in the garden, and I will deposit the sealed bell jar and cover it up and plant geraniums over it.

It is my hope that this account will set straight some of the silly tales that are being hawked in the neighborhood.

Guest Commentary by a Teacher

In "The Affair at 7, Rue de M——," the reader discovers a different author from the one who wrote "Flight" and "The Chrysanthemums," well-known Steinbeck short stories. Here is a writer, tongue-in-cheek, having fun with his subject and, in turn, with his reader. Here is a ridiculous idea taking on significance as a skillful literary technician succeeds with his exaggeration of the short-story pattern of that master fantasy writer, Edgar Allan Poe.

The language, style, and structure of "The Affair at 7, Rue de M——" are all reminiscent of Poe, and the story is no accidental imitation but a carefully delineated parody. The story is full of Poe's customary display of English vocabulary and foreign phrases; it employs the high level of language typical of Poe; and it contains the many details which Poe regarded as necessary to create an impression of truth. The structure particularly resembles Poe's classic "The Facts in the Case of M. Valdemar," with both tales possessing that "singleness of effect" Poe so strongly advocated. It is really only in the unity of time that Steinbeck's story differs technically from Poe's, and that difference is slight.

As in Poe's stories, few characters in this Steinbeck tale are of major importance. There are only the father-narrator, his young son John, and the bubble gum. Other characterizations, however, though brief, are vividly presented so that the reader feels he knows enough about everyone involved.

The tone (see p. 43), maintained consistently, is delightfully pseudoserious. The reader moves quickly into the life of an American family living in Paris, where the father is a writer. It is an upper-class, sophisticated, normal household consisting of a father, mother, three children, and four servants; but it is one day transformed into something frightful and supernatural when a visitor from America brings bubble gum to the children. A wild chain of events is started as John, aged eight, becomes the victim of an evil-ridden piece of gum that refuses to release him from chewing it! No matter what measures are taken—and there are drastic ones—the father is unable to rid John of the gum, which seemingly possesses "life," "intelligence," "and an evil calculating wiliness." It is not until the end of the story, when the gum is weakening under a tightly fastened bell jar, unable to return to John, its "host," for sustenance, that the reader feels that perhaps John is to be saved. And at the same time, the reader realizes how thoroughly he has been spoofed.

Because of the first person point of view (see p. 31) employed by Steinbeck, the tale seems realistic and, thus, believable. The narrator begins almost apologetically and quite deceptively to explain the "rather curious events" which had occurred and which he feels need clarification. The reader is carried along unsuspectingly through five paragraphs of mounting suspense until the introduction of the bubble gum in paragraph 6. Even then, however, the susceptible reader is not quite certain whether the story will develop into a real mystery or a hoax, and that mystification persists until John's horrified admission to his father: "I'm not chewing it, sir. It's chewing me."

From John's muffled confession until the end of the story, each incident is more incredible (see *fantasy,* p. 17) than the one before, and each more fascinating. And the pace is maintained so steadily and successfully that the reader finds no time to question the veracity. The bubble gum is tossed into the Paris traffic and into the Seine River; it is discarded far out in the country; it is burned in the fireplace. Each time, however, the gum returns to plague John. Only after careful, scientific reasoning does the father devise a clever plan to defeat the "monster," and the tragicomic ending evokes a chuckle along with a sigh of relief that at last the nightmarish struggle is ended. This is, indeed, a *different* Steinbeck.

Notes

arrondissement: a municipal subdivision of Paris.
bizarrerie: something fantastic or odd.
Bourbon: French royal family which founded dynasties in France, Italy, and Spain.
concierge: house porter; doorkeeper.
Figaro Littéraire: The *Literary Figaro,* a magazine.
fourth estate: the newspaper business.
mews: a range of stables with coach houses around an open area.
Michelin: a French tire company.
"Sartre Resartus": a reference to Thomas Carlyle's *Sartor Resartus,* which means "the tailor retailored." Steinbeck is punning by using the name of the modern French existentialist philosopher and writer Jean-Paul Sartre.

Questions

1. Give examples of Steinbeck's "use of details to create an impression of truth." In what way does the story differ slightly from the "unity of time" advocated by Poe?
2. How does the author achieve both humorous and melodramatic effects?
3. Is the setting especially significant? Explain.
4. Discuss the author's handling of point of view (see p. 31).
5. Who or what are the characters? Are they believable? Why or why not? (See p. 23.)
6. Why is it incongruous for John to be the victim?
7. Does the title contribute anything to your understanding of the story? For example, why does the author use "M——" in his title instead of naming the street?
8. What, if any, examples of verbal irony or irony of situation (see p. 42) did you discover in the story? What effect do they create?

9. Discuss this statement made by the father-narrator: "Intelligence without the soul to balance it must of necessity be evil."
10. Find examples of words and phrases "reminiscent of Poe." How do they contribute to the characterization of the father?
11. Do you think Steinbeck intended anything but a humorous parody when he wrote the story? If so, what else did he intend?

Commentary, Notes, and Questions by
Mary Jane Richeimer
Evanston Township High School

The Sisters

James Joyce

There was no hope for him this time: it was the third stroke. Night after night I had passed the house (it was vacation time) and studied the lighted square of window: and night after night I had found it lighted in the same way, faintly and evenly. If he was dead, I thought, I would see the reflection of candles on the darkened blind for I knew that two candles must be set at the head of a corpse. He had often said to me: "I am not long for this world," and I had thought his words idle. Now I knew they were true. Every night as I gazed up at the window I said softly to myself the word *paralysis*. It had always sounded strangely in my ears, like the word *gnomon* in the Euclid and the word *simony* in the Catechism. But now it sounded to me like the name of some maleficent and sinful being. It filled me with fear, and yet I longed to be nearer to it and to look upon its deadly work.

Old Cotter was sitting at the fire, smoking, when I came downstairs to supper. While my aunt was ladling out my stirabout he said, as if returning to some former remark of his:

"No, I wouldn't say he was exactly . . . but there was something queer . . . there was something uncanny about him. I'll tell you my opinion. . . ."

He began to puff at his pipe, no doubt arranging his opinion in his mind. Tiresome old fool! When we knew him first he used to be rather interesting, talking of faints and worms; but I soon grew tired of him and his endless stories about the distillery.

"I have my own theory about it," he said. "I think it was one of those . . . peculiar cases. . . . But it's hard to say. . . ."

He began to puff again at his pipe without giving us his theory. My uncle saw me staring and said to me:

"Well, so your old friend is gone, you'll be sorry to hear."

"Who?" said I.

"Father Flynn."

"Is he dead?"

"Mr. Cotter here has just told us. He was passing by the house."

I knew that I was under observation so I continued eating as if the news had not interested me. My uncle explained to old Cotter.

"The youngster and he were great friends. The old chap taught him a great deal, mind you; and they say he had a great wish for him."

"God have mercy on his soul," said my aunt piously.

Old Cotter looked at me for a while. I felt that his little beady black eyes were examining me but I would not satisfy him by looking up from my plate. He returned to his pipe and finally spat rudely into the grate.

"I wouldn't like children of mine," he said, "to have too much to say to a man like that."

"How do you mean, Mr. Cotter?" asked my aunt.

"What I mean is," said old Cotter, "it's bad for children. My idea is: let a young lad run about and play with young lads of his own age and not be . . . Am I right, Jack?"

"That's my principle, too," said my uncle. "Let him learn to box his corner. That's what I'm always saying to that Rosicrucian there: take exercise. Why, when I was a nipper every morning of my life I had a cold bath, winter and summer. And that's what stands to me now. Education is all very fine and large. . . . Mr. Cotter might take a pick of that leg of mutton," he added to my aunt.

"No, no, not for me," said old Cotter.

My aunt brought the dish from the safe and put it on the table.

"But why do you think it's not good for children, Mr. Cotter?" she asked.

"It's bad for children," said old Cotter, "because their minds are so impressionable. When children see things like that, you know, it has an effect. . . ."

I crammed my mouth with stirabout for fear I might give utterance to my anger. Tiresome old red-nosed imbecile!

It was late when I fell asleep. Though I was angry with old Cotter for alluding to me as a child, I puzzled my head to extract meaning from his unfinished sentences. In the dark of my room I imagined that I saw again the heavy grey face of the paralytic. I drew the blankets over my head and tried to think of Christmas. But the grey face still followed me. It murmured; and I understood that it desired to confess something. I felt my soul receding into some pleasant and vicious region; and there again I found it waiting for me. It began to confess to me in a murmuring voice and I wondered why it smiled continually and why the lips were so moist with spittle. But then I remembered that it had died of paralysis and I felt that I too was smiling feebly as if to absolve the simoniac of his sin.

The next morning after breakfast I went down to look at the little house in Great Britain Street. It was an unassuming shop, registered under the vague name of *Drapery*. The drapery consisted mainly of children's bootees and umbrellas; and on ordinary days a notice used to hang in the window, saying: *Umbrellas Re-covered*. No notice was visible now for the shutters were up. A crape bouquet was tied to the doorknocker with ribbon. Two poor women and a telegram boy were reading the card pinned on the crape. I also approached and read:

July 1st, 1895

The Rev. James Flynn (formerly of S. Catherine's Church,

Meath Street), aged sixty-five years.

R. I. P.

The reading of the card persuaded me that he was dead and I was disturbed to find myself at check. Had he not been dead I would have gone into the little dark room behind the shop to find him sitting in his arm-chair by the fire, nearly smothered in his great-coat. Perhaps my aunt would have given me a packet of High Toast for him and this present would have roused him from his stupefied doze. It was always I who emptied the packet into his black snuff-box for his hands trembled too much to allow him to do this without spilling half the snuff about the floor. Even as he raised his large trembling hand to his nose little clouds of smoke dribbled through his fingers over the front of his coat. It may have been these constant showers of snuff which gave his ancient priestly garments their green faded look for the red handkerchief, blackened, as it always was, with the snuff-stains of a week, with which he tried to brush away the fallen grains, was quite inefficacious.

I wished to go in and look at him but I had not the courage to knock. I walked away slowly along the sunny side of the street, reading all the theatrical advertisements in the shop-windows as I went. I found it strange that neither I nor the day seemed in a mourning mood and I felt even annoyed at discovering in myself a sensation of freedom as if I had been freed from something by his death. I wondered at this for, as my uncle had said the night before, he had taught me a great deal. He had studied in the Irish college in Rome and he had taught me to pronounce Latin properly. He had told me stories about the cata-combs and about Napoleon Bonaparte, and he had explained to me the meaning of the different ceremonies of the Mass and of the different vestments worn by the priest. Sometimes he had amused himself by putting difficult questions to me, asking me what one should do in certain circumstances or whether such and such sins were mortal or venial or only imperfections. His questions showed me how complex and mysterious were certain institutions of the Church which I had always regarded as the simplest acts. The duties of the priest towards the Eucharist and towards the secrecy of the confessional seemed so grave to me that I wondered how anybody had ever found in himself the courage to undertake them; and I was not surprised when he told me that the fathers of the Church had written books as thick as the *Post Office Directory* and as closely printed as the law notices in the newspaper, elucidating all these intricate questions. Often when I thought of this I could make no answer or only a very foolish and halting one upon which he used to smile and nod his head twice or thrice. Sometimes he used to put me through the responses of the Mass which he had made me learn by heart; and, as I pattered, he used to smile pensively and nod his head, now and then pushing huge pinches of snuff up each nostril alternately. When he smiled he used to uncover his big discoloured teeth and let his tongue lie upon his lower lip—a habit which had made me feel uneasy in the beginning of our acquaintance before I knew him well.

As I walked along in the sun I remembered old Cotter's words and tried to remember what had happened afterwards in the dream. I remembered that I had noticed long velvet curtains and a swinging lamp of antique fashion. I felt that I had been very far away, in some land where the customs were strange—in Persia, I thought. . . . But I could not remember the end of the dream.

In the evening my aunt took me with her to visit the house of mourning. It was after sunset; but the window-panes of the houses that looked to the west reflected the tawny gold of a great bank of clouds. Nannie received us in the hall; and, as it would have been unseemly to have shouted at her, my aunt shook hands with her for all. The old woman pointed upwards interrogatively and, on my aunt's nodding, proceeded to toil up the narrow staircase before us, her bowed head being scarcely above the level of the banister-rail. At the first landing she stopped and beckoned us forward encouragingly towards the open door of the dead-room. My aunt went in and the old woman, seeing that I hesitated to enter, began to beckon to me again repeatedly with her hand.

I went in on tiptoe. The room through the lace end of the blind was suffused with dusky golden light amid which the candles looked like pale thin flames. He had been coffined. Nannie gave the lead and we three knelt down at the foot of the bed. I pretended to pray but I could not gather my thoughts because the old woman's mutterings distracted me. I noticed how clumsily her skirt was hooked at the back and how the heels of her cloth boots were trodden down all to one side. The fancy came to me that the old priest was smiling as he lay there in his coffin.

But no. When we rose and went up to the head of the bed I saw that he was not smiling. There he lay, solemn and copious, vested as for the altar, his large hands loosely retaining a chalice. His face was very truculent, grey and massive, with black cavernous nostrils and circled by a scanty white fur. There was a heavy odour in the room—the flowers.

We crossed ourselves and came away. In the little room downstairs we found Eliza seated in his arm-chair in state. I grouped my way towards my usual chair in the corner while Nannie went to the sideboard and brought out a decanter of sherry and some wine-glasses. She set these on the table and invited us to take a little glass of wine. Then, at her sister's bidding, she filled out the sherry into the glasses and passed them to us. She pressed me to take some cream crackers also but I declined because I thought I would make too much noise eating them. She seemed to be somewhat disappointed at my refusal and went over quietly to the sofa where she sat down behind her sister. No one spoke: we all gazed at the empty fireplace.

My aunt waited until Eliza sighed and then said:

"Ah, well, he's gone to a better world."

Eliza sighed again and bowed her head in assent. My aunt fingered the stem of her wine-glass before sipping a little.

"Did he . . . peacefully?" she asked.

"Oh, quite peacefully, ma'am," said Eliza. "You couldn't tell when the breath went out of him. He had a beautiful death, God be praised."

"And everything . . . ?"

"Father O'Rourke was in with him a Tuesday and anointed him and prepared him and all."

"He knew then?"

"He was quite resigned."

"He looks quite resigned," said my aunt.

"That's what the woman we had in to wash him said. She said he just looked as if he was asleep, he looked that peaceful and resigned. No one would think he'd make such a beautiful corpse."

"Yes, indeed," said my aunt.

She sipped a little more from her glass and said:

"Well, Miss Flynn, at any rate it must be a great comfort for you to know that you did all you could for him. You were both very kind to him, I must say."

Eliza smoothed her dress over her knees.

"Ah, poor James!" she said. "God knows we done all we could, as poor as we are—we wouldn't see him want anything while he was in it."

Nannie had leaned her head against the sofa-pillow and seemed about to fall asleep.

"There's poor Nannie," said Eliza, looking at her, "she's wore out. All the work we had, she and me, getting in the woman to wash him and then laying him out and then the coffin and then arranging about the Mass in the chapel. Only for Father O'Rourke I don't know what we'd done at all. It was him brought us all them flowers and them two candlesticks out of the chapel and wrote out the notice for the *Freeman's General* and took charge of all the papers for the cemetery and poor James's insurance."

"Wasn't that good of him?" said my aunt.

Eliza closed her eyes and shook her head slowly.

"Ah, there's no friends like the old friends," she said, "when all is said and done, no friends that a body can trust."

"Indeed, that's true," said my aunt. "And I'm sure now that he's gone to his eternal reward he won't forget you and all your kindness to him."

"Ah, poor James!" said Eliza. "He was no great trouble to us. You wouldn't hear him in the house any more than now. Still, I know he's gone and all to that. . . ."

"It's when it's all over that you'll miss him," said my aunt.

"I know that," said Eliza. "I won't be bringing him in his cup of beef-tea any more, nor you, ma'am, sending him his snuff. Ah, poor James!"

She stopped, as if she were communing with the past and then said shrewdly:

"Mind you, I noticed there was something queer coming over him latterly. Whenever I'd bring in his soup to him there I'd find him with his breviary fallen to the floor, lying back in the chair and his mouth open."

She laid a finger against her nose and frowned: then she continued:

"But still and all he kept on saying that before the summer was over he'd go out for a drive one fine day just to see the old house again where we were all born down in Irishtown and take me and Nannie with him.   If we could only get one of them new-fangled carriages that makes no noise that Father O'Rourke told him about, them with the rheumatic wheels, for the day cheap—he said, at Johnny Rush's over the way there and drive out the three of us together of a Sunday evening.   He had his mind set on that. . . . Poor James!"

"The Lord have mercy on his soul!" said my aunt.

Eliza took out her handkerchief and wiped her eyes with it.   Then she put it back again in her pocket and gazed into the empty grate for some time without speaking.

"He was too scrupulous always," she said.   "The duties of the priesthood was too much for him.   And then his life was, you might say, crossed."

"Yes," said my aunt.   "He was a disappointed man.   You could see that."

A silence took possession of the little room and, under cover of it, I approached the table and tasted my sherry and then returned quietly to my chair in the corner.   Eliza seemed to have fallen into a deep revery.   We waited respectfully for her to break the silence: and after a long pause she said slowly:

"It was that chalice he broke. . . .   That was the beginning of it. Of course, they say it was all right, that it contained nothing, I mean. But still. . . .   They say it was the boy's fault.   But poor James was so nervous, God be merciful to him!"

"And was that it?" said my aunt.   "I heard something. . . ."

Eliza nodded.

"That affected his mind," she said.   "After that he began to mope by himself, talking to no one and wandering about by himself.   So one night he was wanted for to go on a call and they couldn't find him anywhere.   They looked high up and low down; and still they couldn't see a sight of him anywhere.   So then the clerk suggested to try the chapel. So then they got the keys and opened the chapel and the clerk and Father O'Rourke and another priest that was there brought in a light for to look for him. . . .   And what do you think but there he was, sitting up by himself in the dark in his confession-box, wide-awake and laughing-like softly to himself?"

She stopped suddenly as if to listen.   I too listened; but there was no sound in the house: and I knew that the old priest was lying still in his coffin as we had seen him, solemn and truculent in death, an idle chalice on his breast.

Eliza resumed:

"Wide-awake and laughing-like to himself. . . .   So then, of course,

when they saw that, that made them think that there was something
gone wrong with him. . . ."

Guest Commentary by a Critic

One of the most complex and disturbing in the sequence [*Dub-liners*], this story is a riddle. Nothing comes quite clear. The name-less boy who tells the story is "puzzled" by hints and "intricate ques-tions," and so are we. Raising such questions, teasing us with pos-sibilities, the story provides no answers. The key sentence, "There was something gone wrong with him," comes last. We may guess what has gone wrong and with what and with whom but we never know, and that seems the point of the story. Fascinated with the unanswerable question, Joyce put riddles into all his major works, which, to be sure, seem riddles too. Stephen Dedalus and Shem confront them, and Mr. Bloom's day ends with the enigma of M'Intosh. It is proper that Joyce, for whom riddle became obsessive theme, began with a riddle that seems designed in part to establish the idea of riddle.

"The Sisters" opens simply enough with night, paralysis, and death, which, as we have seen, point toward the final story. The word "paralysis" is accompanied by two others, "gnomon" and "simony." These three fascinate the boy, sensitive to words, as we too must be, accosting Joyce. Expert in words, he used them for all they are worth; and we, following at a suitable distance, must use the dictionary, of which his talking boy was also amorous. Gnomon, a figure from geom-etry, carries a suggestion of Euclid, hence of intellect. Simony, an ecclesiastical sin, has moral and religious bearing. A gnomon is an imperfect figure, however, and simony is an imperfection. These words, neighbors of paralysis, are there to define it. The paralysis in question, though literally a physical imperfection, is also intellec-tual, moral, and spiritual. Poor James Flynn is the victim and embodi-ment of this syndrome.

Never there in person, poor Father Flynn is talked about by old Cotter and the sisters and thought about or remembered by the boy. Almost nothing happens. The boy inspects the death notice on the door, and, feeling free at last, crosses to the sunny side of the street; later he visits the corpse with his aunt and, having tasted sherry, re-tires to a chair. All the rest is talk and memory, from which, by a gradual and almost static process of disclosure, we learn that Father Flynn, a kindly man, who taught the boy much about ritual, tradition, and the sacraments, was a queer one, untidy, ambiguously smiling, torpid, and probably perverse, a priest whose duties "was too much for him." Unable to face his inadequacies and imperfections, he went mad, laughing to himself in the dark of his confession box, before yielding to paralysis and death.

Taken literally, this disclosure is case history; taken symbolically, it means or can mean many things, all of them doubtful. Only the latter possibility detains us. Who or what is Father Flynn, literally a parish priest, potentially more? Since a priest is a father, the Rev. James Flynn, ascending from his parish, may be *the* father, a kind of archetype of fatherhood or the father principle. In this capacity, suggesting all that the image affords, he could include the idea of God, of the Pope, of fatherland, or of ecclesiastical tradition, a fatherly hand-me-down. If we may take him so, his incapacity, madness, paralysis, and death leave Great Britain Street and environs without fatherly assurance. The boy and the sisters, equally at a loss, attempt to supply his abandoned functions. A pseudo-priest, the boy hears confession in a dream and, waking, sips wine, declining the congregational biscuit; and the sisters, though plainly incapable of fatherhood, attempt to carry on by offering wine and biscuits, which, by parodying the sacrament, maintain tradition. They are doing their best; but one is deaf and both, though they beckon and invite, are ignorant and senile. Fatherhood, so maintained, is in a bad way here.

Those sisters, who enjoy (without seeming to deserve) the title role, are even more puzzling than their clerical brother. Are their names, Nannie and Eliza, significant? Why are there two of them? I should find it easier if there were only one. A poor old woman (the traditional figure) could serve as an image of Ireland or of Ireland's Church, attempting to preserve a dead tradition; but two seem one too many unless one is Ireland, the other the Church or unless the word sister implies nurse or nun. This is dubious. Whatever the number, these survivors and Father Flynn, far from being allegorical signs with a definite meaning, are unassigned symbols, without certain import. We cannot call them this or that. That they offer feelings and ideas associated with religion and country is all we can prudently guess. The encounter of the boy with the priest and his survivors is that of a boy, at once dutiful and uneasy, with what surrounds him in Ireland.

This "Rosicrucian" boy brings up another problem: who or what is central in the story, the boy, the priest, the sisters, or an idea? Since the boy tells us the story in first person, it is tempting to think him

central and his mind our theater. If so, he is to the priest as Marlow
to Kurtz in Conrad's *Heart of Darkness*. Kurtz or Father Flynn is the
enigmatic ostensible object of an inquirer whose real concern is himself. Like Marlow, the boy is uneasy and no more than partly aware
of the mystery he is approaching. From his account, however, we
learn more than he seems to know. At the end, Marlow is almost fully
aware, but the boy, implying much, displaying little, is content to report. If this is a story of sudden awareness, like many of the others in
the book, the awareness is successfully concealed. Doubt alone is
well established. Our knowledge, such as it is, comes from three conflicts: the first within old Cotter between suspicion and prudence, the
second within the boy between affection and uneasiness, and the third
that of the sisters, at once defensive and anxious. Never was subjective
drama more ambiguous.

The methods by which Joyce establishes this ambiguity are various
and appropriate, ranging in kind from the expressive dots of old
Cotter's monologue ("I puzzled my head to extract meaning from his
unfinished sentences.") to conversation, image, rhythm, and dream.
That none of these devices was present in the first version (published in
the *Irish Homestead* in 1904) proves them deliberate. Two devices
from Joyce's twenty-two epiphanies reappear here: the objectively reported, desolating conversation (Eliza's in this case) and the dream.
The boy's nightmare of Father Flynn's heavy grey face, feebly smiling,
and of his murmured confession is one of the most terrible epiphanies
of the story—equal in horror to the boy's waking memory of Flynn:
"When he smiled he used to uncover his big discoloured teeth and
let his tongue lie upon his lower lip—a habit which . . . made me feel
uneasy." The dream, like all else here, is incomplete: "I could not
remember the end of the dream." There is nothing of "scrupulous
meanness" about the hypnotic rhythm or the diction of this dream.

Two carefully elaborated themes, one of confession, the other of
communion, control the imagery. Confession, which begins with that
dream, ends with the confession box where poor mad Father Flynn sits
laughing to himself. The chalice is the principal image of the more
important of these themes. Father Flynn incompetently drops a
chalice; for he was "crossed." When dead, he "loosely" holds a chalice;
and the glass of wine received by the boy at the table (altar) brings this
sequence to its climax. His communion (and we must take this word
literally as well as ecclesiastically) is reluctant and, since the congrega-
tion takes the biscuit, uncongregational. Are we to take this glass of
wine as a kind of Protestant rebellion, as a priestly gesture, or as

partial rejection of communion with Ireland and its Church? All we can be sure of is that father's gone.

William York Tindall

Guest Commentary by Two Critics

Perhaps the best approach to the symbolic meaning of the stories in *Dubliners* is through scrutiny of the first story, "The Sisters." Fortunately, three versions of the story are available for study. The earliest, Joyce's contribution to George Russell's *Irish Homestead,* runs to about sixteen hundred words (half the size of the final version) and is little more than a record of a rambling conversation or two, with incidental description of several Dublin slum dwellers. It is signed "Stephen Daedalus."

The story tells of a boy, Stephen perhaps, whose elderly friend, the Reverend James Flynn, lies dying. The lad maintains a vigil on the sidewalk below. But death occurs when the child is not present, so he hears of the event from grown-ups at supper. The next morning he visits the priest's house. He thinks of the old man, feeble, waking to talk occasionally to the little boy or to complain of his needs to his two sisters, Nannie and Eliza. On the evening of the same day, the boy comes with his aunt to pay formal respects to the dead man. They kneel with deaf Nannie at the coffin, then make small talk about the priest's life. The sisters speak of his life as "crossed," his attitude "disappointed." They date this attitude to the time he dropped and shattered a chalice. This accident is supposed to have affected his mind so that he would laugh to himself in his dark confessional. This draft of the story shows the young Joyce at his blunt, unsubtle worst. An intermediate version of the story, in the collection of John J. Slocum, apparently represents an attempt by Joyce to revise the *Homestead* story. In it Joyce is at work refining his diction, reworking tenses, economizing on superfluous words, making it a neater piece. What he adds to it to bolster its symbolic content will be dealt with shortly.

The final *Dubliners* version of "The Sisters" is to the *Homestead* draft what *A Portrait* is to *Stephen Hero.* The quantity of information in the latter may be greater, but there is more artistry in the former. We learn in the *Homestead* story that Cotter is "the old distiller" and that he owns "prize setters." In *Dubliners* we must assume his occupation from his "talking of faints and worms." In the former we find that Nannie "is almost stone deaf", we learn of her deafness in the final version when all those who talk to her raise their voices. In the short interval between first and last drafts, Joyce had learned to use the symbolist technique of expression through suggestion rather than through explicit telling. Joyce had lengthened the story to almost twice its original size. He had also shifted the emphasis from the sisters to the boy and his environment.

What, specifically, has been added? Joyce had promised earlier to write of the moral paralysis of his country. In this final version he reveals that the priest's malady is paralysis, a word that "sounded to me like the name of some maleficent and sinful being. . . ." Thus, at the beginning of the narrative, the author associates the priest with paralysis, sickness, and vague evil. The dreams and visions of the symbolists also come into play. After death, the "grey face of the paralytic" appears before him, apparently trying to "confess" a sin.

The problem of the relationship of the boy to the priest becomes complicated in the *Dubliners* version. By trying to confess to the lad, Father Flynn shows that he considers Stephen's role a priestly one. After all, the old man has trained him in Latin, in the catechism, and in performing some of the ceremonies of the priesthood. Yet the boy resists: "The duties of the priest toward the Eucharist and . . . confessional seemed so grave to me that I wondered how anybody had ever found in himself the courage to undertake them." Nor can he perform his functions as a Catholic communicant, much less those of priest-confessor. Kneeling with the rest of the mourners at the bier, he "pretended to pray but . . . could not. . . ." In the same way, Stephen, in *A Portrait,* kneels silently while Uncle Charles prays aloud, for the boy can respect, "though he did not share, his piety." Later, offered wine and crackers by the sisters, he hesitates to take the wine and refuses the crackers. So much space is given to the details of the offer, omitted completely from the *Homestead* version and merely mentioned in a sentence in the intermediate draft, that the question arises of Joyce's intention to express symbolically here the boy's hesitation to accept "Communion." Considered from the point of view of Joyce's biography or Stephen's spiritual history, the episode seems significant.

At the time when Joyce was turning his obvious first version of the story into the very delicately symbolic story that we have today, his mind was full of his involuntary conflict with the national religion. Behind him lay his rejection of the life of a Jesuit; immediately before him were the many vital decisions that had to be made: to leave Ireland, to refuse to conform to religious ritual observances, to enter a frightening profession. That the shock of such a conflict was tremendous is clear from Joyce's inability to forget his period of mental strain and emotional turmoil. A man whose life was the literature he created might well have attempted to project his conflict in his short story.

The Father Flynn whose shadowy essence dominates the revised story appears to be illustrative of the, to Joyce, decaying Irish Catholic God. Being a part of the paralyzed Irish environment, the Deity of the church is also paralyzed. With care, Joyce carries through the analogy, not made in the *Homestead* version, in all details. Paralysis, it will be recalled, reminds him of the word "simony." Not only does the church suffer from physical paralysis, but morally it is sick, if the perversion theme may be transferred—as it must be—from the man to the church. (In the specific context of this story, simony may be involved simply in the superior relationship of Flynn to the boy, since the Catholic church defines simony as any exchange of spiritual for temporal things. It can take the form of having the applicant pay homage, "which consists in subserviency, the rendering of undue services.") And much is made of the advisability of keeping the younger generation, represented by the boy narrator, away from the perverted influence of Irish religion, which has "smiled continually" but has been guilty of awful sins.

True, Father Flynn, a surrogate for the Deity, has made friendly overtures to Stephen, as to Joyce. It was possible to rouse him from his "stupefied doze," says Joyce, in a tone reminiscent of Gautier and the early Eliot, by bringing him a contribution of snuff. But so weak and enervated is the old God that "his hands trembled" and the gifts of snuff sprinkled through his fingers and "gave his ancient priestly garments their green faded look. . . ." Yet the father figure had done something for the boy: ". . . taught me to pronounce Latin properly . . . explained to me the meaning of the different ceremonies of the Mass . . . amused himself by putting difficult questions to me. . . ." The old man had ended by trying to make a priest of him and had succeeded in scaring the boy with the awful solemnity of a priest's functions.

Perhaps his spiritual superior might have convinced the boy if he himself had not been so inept in carrying out his own priestly functions. Had not Father Flynn dropped and broken the chalice? Had he not crushed this symbol of spiritual responsibility? Even in death the coffined priest lies silently, "his large hands *loosely* retaining a chalice [italics mine]." An indication of how important Joyce considered this chalice symbol is its evolution from draft to draft. In the first version, the priest grasps a rosary, in the second a cross; but

Joyce saw in time the artistic rightness of placing in the dead man's hand what, as a living man, he could not hold.

The stage is set now in the story for presentation of the boy's symbolic reluctance to accept the ceremonies of his former faith. He cannot pray; he delays drinking the wine and refuses the wafers offered to him by the sisters. The role of Nannie and Eliza assumes an importance that the merely realistic part they play does not apparently justify. After all, Joyce, who took great pains with his story titles, did call the story "The Sisters." They do not represent nuns. As nurses, who minister to the wants of Father Flynn (the God of the church on earth), they may play the symbolic part of priests. As one of their functions is the bestowing of Communion, Joyce has the two sisters offer "Communion" to the unwilling boy. Significantly, the *Homestead* draft makes no mention of food and drink offered to the guests. In the intermediate version, one line is devoted to the offering: "We, as visitors, were given a glass of sherry each." But not until the final version does Joyce spend half a page describing the details of the proffered "Communion." All along, he seems to be groping toward inclusion of this symbolic situation, without grasping yet its full significance.

Taking the sisters as priestly figures helps to give consistency to the details of the story. Nannie is deaf, as in Joyce's opinion the average priest was deaf to the words and needs of docile parishioners. Nannie leads the prayers at the bier of the dead father. Her voice is audible above the voices of the others. Both sisters apparently offer "Communion." Both point out rather weakly the virtues of the impotent, feeble Father Flynn. Throughout the story, too, there is an air of disappointed expectancy as the living await a sign, a voice, a sound from the dead figure of the Catholic faith. As must happen, however, "there was no sound in the house: and I knew that the old priest was lying still in his coffin. . . ."

Critics have almost universally dismissed all the stories in *Dubliners* except "The Dead" as trivial sketches—and let it go at that. Too few have seen the trouble that Joyce took to give more than a surface meaning to his seemingly transparent, harmless stories. Yet even in the fragile narrative of "An Encounter," a richness of symbolic content is evident.

The main outlines of the story are simple and ordinary. Three boys, weary of the unromantic life of schoolboys, decide to play truant for one day and to make an excursion to the old Pigeonhouse Fort. One loses his courage and backs out, leaving the narrator and Mahony to go together. The former, his mind full of "penny dreadful" notions of what adventure and adventurers should be, watches wide-eyed on the docks to catch a glimpse of foreign sailors, whose eyes, he has been led to believe, will be green. He is disappointed. But later in the afternoon, the two boys fall in with an elderly pervert, whose strange conversation they do not quite understand although it makes them uneasy. The narrator suddenly discovers with a shock that the rheumy eyes of their unwholesome acquaintance are "bottle-green." "I turned my eyes away." The boys, worried by the tone of his conversation, depart hurriedly.

The dead and inconclusive note on which the story and the quest for adventure end is, of course, deliberate. The attempt of the boy in "The Sisters" to find a spiritual father and a calling had resulted in rejection and almost in revulsion. The expectation of discovering romance and adventure in Dublin must end in more than frustration—in a souring of childhood dreams of glamour and love. This happens also to the adolescent narrator in "Araby," and his youthful exuberance is permanently dampened.

Marvin Magalaner and Richard M. Kain

Questions

1. Who is the central character in this story? Is it the nameless boy who narrates it? the dead priest?
2. Why is "The Sisters" an appropriate title? How important to the character development and action and theme are the characters Nannie and Eliza, the sisters of the title?
3. Consider the action of the story. How do the characters move and speak? What do their movements and dialogue contribute to the characterization and theme?
4. Compare the boy in this story with the boy in "Patricia, Edith and Arnold." Note that in each case the boy is not given a name. Why not? Compare the real and imagined sense impressions of both boys.
5. At what point in "The Sisters" does the change in the action occur? In whom does it occur? (See p. 26.) How does the point of view of the narration communicate the change? (See p. 31.) What hints as to the opposing forces of the conflict have been given before this reversal?
6. The boy describes one of his memories of Father Flynn: "When he smiled he used to uncover his big discoloured teeth and let his

tongue lie upon his lower lip—a habit which had made me feel uneasy in the beginning of our acquaintance before I knew him well." How does this passage relate to the "broken chalice" and the "idle chalice"?

7. Contrast the invulnerability, the malapropisms ("new-fangled carriages with *rheumatic* wheels"), and the acuteness of the sisters with the narrator's troubled memory of his childhood search for a spiritual creed.

8. The first and last sentences of a work of fiction are often key sentences. In what way do the first and last sentences in this story contribute to its ambiguity?

9. Compare the attitude of the older Marlow toward the younger Marlow in Joseph Conrad's "Youth" with the attitude of the narrator of James Joyce's "The Sisters" toward the boy the narrator is remembering himself to have been.

10. What are the essential points of difference and of similarity between the two guest commentaries on "The Sisters"?

Holiday

Katherine Anne Porter

At that time I was too young for some of the troubles I was having, and I had not yet learned what to do with them. It no longer can matter what kind of troubles they were, or what finally became of them. It seemed to me then there was nothing to do but run away from them, though all my tradition, background, and training had taught me unanswerably that no one except a coward ever runs away from anything. What nonsense! They should have taught me the difference between courage and foolhardiness, instead of leaving me to find it out for myself. I learned finally that if I still had the sense I was born with, I would take off like a deer at the first warning of certain dangers. But this story I am about to tell you happened before this great truth impressed itself upon me—that we do not run from the troubles and dangers that are truly ours, and it is better to learn what they are earlier than later. And if we don't run from the others, we are fools.

I confided to my friend Louise, a former schoolmate about my own age, not my troubles but my little problem: I wanted to go somewhere for a spring holiday, by myself, to the country, and it should be very simple and nice and, of course, not expensive, and she was not to tell anyone where I had gone; but if she liked, I would send her word now and then, if anything interesting was happening. She said she loved getting letters but hated answering them; and she knew the very place for me, and she would not tell anybody anything. Louise had then—she has it still—something near to genius for making improbable persons, places, and situations sound attractive. She told amusing stories that did not turn grim on you until a little while later, when by chance you saw and heard for yourself. So with this story. Everything was just as Louise had said, if you like, and everything was, at the same time, quite different.

"I know the very place," said Louise. "A family of real old-fashioned German peasants, in the deep blackland Texas farm country, a house-

hold in real patriarchal style—the kind of thing you'd hate to live with
but is very nice to visit.   Old father, God Almighty himself, with
whiskers and all; old mother, matriarch in men's shoes; endless daughters and sons and sons-in-law, and fat babies falling about the place;
and fat puppies—my favorite was a darling little black thing named
Kuno—cows, calves, and sheep and lambs and goats and turkeys and
guineas roaming up and down the shallow green hills, ducks and geese
on the ponds.   I was there in the summer when the peaches and water-
melons were in—"

"This is the end of March," I said, doubtfully.

"Spring comes early there," said Louise.   "I'll write to the Müllers
about you, you just get ready to go."

"Just where is this paradise?"

"Not far from the Louisiana line," said Louise.   "I'll ask them to give
you my attic—oh, that was a sweet place!   It's a big room, with the roof
sloping to the floor on each side, and the roof leaks a little when it
rains, so the shingles are all stained in beautiful streaks, all black and
gray and mossy green, and in one corner there used to be a stack of
dime novels, The Duchess, Ouida, Mrs. E.D.E.N. Southworth, Ella
Wheeler Wilcox's poems—one summer they had a lady boarder who
was a great reader, and she went off and left her library.   I loved it!
And everybody was so healthy and goodhearted, and the weather was
perfect. . . .   How long do you want to stay?"

I hadn't thought of this, so I said at random, "About a month."

A few days later I found myself tossed off like an express package
from a dirty little crawling train onto the sodden platform of a country
station, where the stationmaster emerged and locked up the waiting
room before the train had got round the bend.   As he clumped by me
he shifted his wad of tobacco to his cheek and asked, "Where you
goin'?"

"To the Müller farm," I said, standing beside my small trunk and
suitcase with the bitter wind cutting my shoulders through my thin
coat.

"Anybody meet you?" he asked, not pausing.

"They *said* so."

"All right," he said, and got into his little ragged buckboard with a
sway-backed horse and drove away.

I turned my trunk on its side and sat on it facing the wind and the
desolate mud-colored shapeless scene and began making up my first
letter to Louise.   First I was going to tell her that unless she meant to

be a novelist, there was no excuse for her having so much imagination. In daily life, I was going to tell her, there are also such useful things as the plain facts that should be stuck to, through thick and thin. Anything else led to confusion like this. I was beginning to enjoy my letter to Louise when a sturdy boy about twelve years old crossed the platform. As he neared me, he took off his rough cap and bunched it in his thick hand, dirt-stained at the knuckles. His round cheeks, his round nose, his round chin were a cool, healthy red. In the globe of his face, as neatly circular as if drawn in bright crayon, his narrow, long, tip-tilted eyes, clear as pale-blue water, seemed out of place, as if two incompatible strains had collided in making him. They were beautiful eyes, and the rest of the face was not to be taken seriously. A blue woolen blouse buttoned up to his chin ended abruptly at his waist as if he would outgrow it in another half hour, and his blue drill breeches flapped about his ankles. His old clodhopper shoes were several sizes too big for him. Altogether, it was plain he was not the first one to wear his clothes. He was a cheerful, detached, self-possessed apparition against the tumbled brown earth and ragged dark sky, and I smiled at him as well as I could with a face that felt like wet clay.

He smiled back slightly without meeting my eye, motioning for me to take up my suitcase. He swung my trunk to his head and tottered across the uneven platform, down the steps slippery with mud, where I expected to see him crushed beneath his burden like an ant under a stone. He heaved the trunk into the back of his wagon with a fine smash, took my suitcase and tossed it after, then climbed up over one front wheel while I scrambled my way up over the other.

The pony, shaggy as a wintering bear, eased himself into a grudging trot, while the boy, bowed over with his cap pulled down over his ears and eyebrows, held the reins slack and fell into a brown study. I examined the harness, a real mystery. It met and clung in all sorts of unexpected places; it parted company in what appeared to be strategic seats of jointure. It was mended sketchily in risky places with bits of hairy rope. Other seemingly unimportant parts were bound together irrevocably with wire. The bridle was too long for the pony's stocky head, so he had shaken the bit out of his mouth at the start, apparently, and went his own way at his own pace.

Our vehicle was an exhausted specimen of something called a spring wagon, who knows why? There were no springs, and the shallow enclosed platform at the back, suitable for carrying various plunder, was worn away until it barely reached midway of the back wheels, one side of it steadily scraping the iron tire. The wheels themselves spun not dully around and around in the way of common wheels, but elliptically being loosened at the hubs, so that we proceeded with a drunken, hilarious swagger, like the rolling motion of a small boat on a choppy sea.

The soaked brown fields fell away on either side of the lane, all rough with winter-worn stubble ready to sink and become earth again. The scanty leafless woods ran along an edge of the field nearby. There was nothing beautiful in those woods now except the promise of spring, for I detested bleakness, but it gave me pleasure to think that beyond this there might be something else beautiful in its own being, a river shaped and contained by its banks, or a field stripped down to its true meaning, plowed and ready for the seed. The road turned abruptly and was almost hidden for a moment, and we were going through the woods. Closer sight of the crooked branches assured me that spring was beginning, if sparely, reluctantly; the leaves were budding in tiny cones of watery green besprinkling all the new shoots; a thin sedate rain began again to fall, not so opaque as a fog, but a mist that merely deepened overhead, and lowered, until the clouds became rain in one swathing, delicate gray.

As we emerged from the woods, the boy roused himself and pointed forward, in silence. We were approaching the farm along the skirts of a fine peach orchard, now faintly colored with young buds, but there was nothing to disguise the gaunt and aching ugliness of the farmhouse itself. In this Texas valley, so gently modulated with small crests and shallows, "rolling country" as the farmers say, the house was set on the peak of the barest rise of ground, as if the most infertile spot had been thriftily chosen for building a shelter. It stood there staring and naked, an intruding stranger, strange even beside the barns ranged generously along the back, low-eaved and weathered to the color of stone.

The narrow windows and the steeply sloping roof oppressed me; I wished to turn away and go back. I had come a long way to be so disappointed, I thought, and yet I must go on, for there could be nothing here for me more painful than what I had left. But as we drew near the house, now hardly visible except for the yellow lamplight in the back, perhaps in the kitchen, my feelings changed again toward warmth and tenderness, or perhaps just an apprehension that I could feel so, maybe, again.

The wagon drew up before the porch, and I started climbing down. No sooner had my foot touched ground than an enormous black dog of the detestable German shepherd breed leaped silently at me, and as silently I covered my face with my arms and leaped back. "Kuno, down!" shouted the boy, lunging at him. The front door flew open and a young girl with yellow hair ran down the steps and seized the ugly beast by the scruff. "He does not mean anything," she said seriously in English. "He is only a dog."

Just Louise's darling little puppy Kuno, I thought, a year or so older. Kuno whined, apologized by bowing and scraping one front paw on the ground, and the girl holding his scruff said, shyly and proudly, "I teach him that. He has always such bad manners, but I teach him!"

I had arrived, it seemed, at the moment when the evening chores were about to begin. The entire Müller household streamed out of the door, each man and woman going about the affairs of the moment. The young girl walked with me up the porch steps and said, "This is my brother Hans," and a young man paused to shake hands and passed by. "This is my brother Fritz," she said, and Fritz took my hand and dropped it as he went. "My sister Annetje," said the young girl, and a quiet young woman with a baby draped loosely like a scarf over her shoulder smiled and held out her hand. Hand after hand went by, their palms variously younger or older, broad or small, male or female, but all thick hard decent peasant hands, warm and strong. And in every face I saw again the pale, tilted eyes, on every head that taffy-colored hair, as though they might all be brothers and sisters, though Annetje's husband and still another daughter's husband had gone by after greeting me. In the wide hall with a door at front and back, full of cloudy light and the smell of soap, the old mother, also on her way out, stopped to offer her hand. She was a tall strong-looking woman wearing a three-cornered black wool shawl on her head, her skirts looped up over a brown flannel petticoat. Not from her did the young ones get those water-clear eyes. Hers were black and shrewd and searching, a band of hair showed black streaked with gray, her seamed dry face was brown as seasoned bark, and she walked in her rubber boots with the stride of a man. She shook my hand briefly and said in German English that I was welcome, smiling and showing her black-ened teeth.

"This is my girl Hatsy," she told me, "and she will show you to your room." Hatsy took my hand as if I were a child needing a guide. I followed her up a flight of steps steep as a ladder, and there we were, in Louise's attic room, with the sloping roof. Yes, the shingles were stained all the colors she had said. There were the dime novels heaped in the corner. For once, Louise had got it straight, and it was homely and familiar, as if I had seen it before. "My mother says we could give you a better place on the downstairs," said Hatsy, in her soft blurred

English, "but *she* said in her letter you would like it so." I told her indeed I did like it so. She went down the steep stairs then, and her
brother came up as if he were climbing a tree, with the trunk on his
head and the suitcase in his right hand, and I could not see what kept
the trunk from crashing back to the bottom, as he used the left hand to
climb with. He put his burden down and straightened up, wriggling his
shoulders and panting only a little. I thanked him and he pushed his
cap back and pulled it forward again, which I took for some sort of
polite response, and clattered out hugely. Looking out of my window
a few minutes later, I saw him setting off across the fields carrying a
lighted lantern and a large steel trap.

I began changing my first letter to Louise. "I'm going to like it
here. I don't quite know why, but it's going to be all right. Maybe I
can tell you later—"

The sound of the German speech in the household below was part of
the pleasantness, for they were not talking to me and did not expect me
to answer. All the German I understood then was contained in five
small deadly sentimental songs of Heine's, learned by heart; and this
was a very different tongue, Low German corrupted by three generations in a foreign country. A dozen miles away, where Texas and Louisiana melted together in a rotting swamp whose sluggish undertow of
decay nourished the roots of pine and cedar, a colony of French immi-
grants had lived out two hundred years of exile, not wholly incorrup-
tible, but mystically faithful to the marrow of their bones, obstinately
speaking their old French, by then as strange to the French as it was to
the English. I had known many of these families during a certain long
summer happily remembered, and here, listening to another language
nobody could understand except those of this small farming community, I knew that I was again in a house of perpetual exile. These were
solid, practical, hard-bitten, landholding German peasants who stuck
their mattocks into the earth deep and held fast wherever they were,
because to them life and the land were one indivisible thing; but never
in any wise did they confuse nationality with habitation.

I liked the thick warm voices, and it was good not to have to understand what they were saying. I loved that silence which means freedom from the constant pressure of other minds and other opinions and
other feelings, that freedom to fold up in quiet and go back to my own
center, to find out again, for it is always a rediscovery, what kind of
creature it is that rules me finally, makes all the decisions no matter who
thinks they make them, even I; who little by little takes everything away

except the one thing I cannot live without, and who will one day say, "Now I am all you have left—take me." I paused there a good while listening to this muted unknown language which was silence with music in it; I could be moved and touched but not troubled by it, as by the crying of frogs or the wind in the trees.

The catalpa tree at my window would, I noticed, when it came into leaf, shut off my view of the barns and the fields beyond. When in bloom the branches would almost reach through the window. But now they were a thin screen through which the calves, splotchy red and white, moved prettily against the weathered darkness of the sheds. The brown fields would soon be green again; the sheep would not look then as they did now, merely lumps of moving earth, but would be washed by the rains and become clean gray. All the beauty of the landscape now was in the harmony of the valley rolling fluently away to the wood's edge. It was an inland country, with the forlorn look of all unloved things; winter in this part of the South is a moribund coma, not the Northern death sleep with the sure promise of resurrection. But in my South, my loved and never-forgotten country, after her long sickness, with only a slight stirring, an opening of the eyes between one breath and the next, between night and day, the earth revives and bursts into the plenty of spring with fruit and flowers together, spring and summer at once under the hot shimmering blue sky.

The freshening wind promised another light sedate rain to come at evening. The voices below-stairs dispersed, rose again, separately calling from the yards and barns. The old woman strode down the path toward the cow sheds, Hatsy runing behind her. The woman wore her wooden yoke, with the milking pails covered and closed with iron hasps, slung easily across her shoulders, but her daughter carried two tin milking pails on her arm. When they pushed back the bars of cedar which opened onto the fields, the cows came through lowing and crowding, and the calves scampered each to his own dam with reaching, opened mouths. Then there was the battle of separating the hungry children from their mothers when they had taken their scanty share. The old woman slapped their little haunches with her open palm, Hatsy dragged at their halters, her feet slipping wide in the mud, the cows bellowed and brandished their horns, the calves bawled like rebellious babies. Hatsy's long yellow braids whisked round her shoulders, her laughter was a shrill streak of gaiety above the angry cow voices and the raucous shouting of the old woman.

From the kitchen porch below came the sound of splashing water, the creaking of the pump handle, and the stamping boots of men. I sat in the window watching the darkness come on slowly. All the sounds of the place gathered under the roof while the lamps were being lighted. My own small lamp had a handle on the oil bowl, like a cup's. There was also a lantern with a frosted chimney hanging by a nail on the wall. A voice called to me from the foot of my stairs and I looked down into the face of a dark-skinned, flaxen-haired young woman, far advanced in pregnancy, and carrying a prosperous year-old boy on her hip, one arm clutching him to her, the other raised above her head so that her lantern shone upon their heads. "The supper is now ready," she said, and waited for me to come down before turning away.

In the large square room the whole family was gathering at a long table covered with a red checkered cotton cloth, heaped-up platters of steaming food at either end. A crippled and badly deformed servant girl was setting down pitchers of milk. Her head was so bowed over, her face was almost hidden, and her whole body was maimed in some painful, mysterious way, probably congenital, I supposed, though she seemed wiry and tough. Her knotted hands shook continually, her wagging head kept pace with her restless elbows. She ran unsteadily around the table scattering plates, dodging whoever stood in her way; no one moved aside for her, or spoke to her, or even glanced after her when she vanished into the kitchen.

The men moved forward to their chairs. Father Müller took his patriarch's place at the head of the table, Mother Müller looming behind him like a dark boulder. The young men ranged themselves about one side, the married ones with their wives standing back of their chairs to serve them, for three generations in this country had not made them self-conscious or disturbed their ancient customs. The two sons-in-law and three sons rolled down their shirt sleeves before beginning to eat. Their faces were polished with recent scrubbing and their open collars were damp.

Mother Müller pointed to me, then waved her hand at her household, telling off their names rapidly once more. I was a stranger and a guest, so was seated on the men's side of the table, and Hatsy, whose real name turned out to be Huldah, the maiden of the family, was seated on the children's side of the board, attending to them and keeping them in order. These infants ranged from two years to ten, five in number—not counting the one still straddling his mother's hip behind his father's chair—divided between the two married daughters. The children ravened and gorged and reached their hands into the sugar bowl to sprinkle sugar on everything they ate, solemnly elated over their food and paying no attention to Hatsy, who struggled with them only a little less energetically than she did with the calves, and ate almost nothing. She was about seventeen years old, pale-lipped and too thin, and her sleek fine butter-yellow hair, streaked light and dark, real German peasant hair, gave her an air of fragility. But she shared the big-boned structure, the enormous energy and animal force that was like a bodily presence itself in the room; and seeing Father Müller's pale-gray deep-set choleric eyes and high cheekbones, it was easy to trace the family resemblance around the table: it was plain that poor Mother Müller had never had a child of her own—black-eyed, black-haired South Germany people. True, she had borne them, but that was all; they belonged to their father. Even the tawny Gretchen, expecting an-other baby, obviously the pet of the family, with the sly smiling manner of a spoiled child, who wore the contented air of a lazy, healthy young animal, seeming always about to yawn, had hair like pulled taffy and those slanted clear eyes. She stood now easing the weight of her little boy on her husband's chair back, reaching with her left arm over his shoulder to refill his plate from time to time.

Annetje's baby drooled comfortably down her back, while she spooned things from platters and bowls for her husband. Whenever their eyes met, they smiled with a gentle, reserved warmth in their eyes, the smile of long and sure friendship.

Father Müller did not in the least believe in his children's marrying and leaving home. Marry, yes, of course; but must that take a son or daughter from him? He always could provide work and a place in the household for his daughters' husbands, and in time he would do the same for his sons' wives. A new room had lately been built on, to the northeast, Annetje explained to me, leaning above her husband's head and talking across the table, for Hatsy to live in when she should be married. Hatsy turned very beautifully pink and ducked her head almost into her plate, then looked up boldly and said, "*Jah, jah,* I am marrit now soon!" Everybody laughed except Mother Müller, who said in German that girls at home never knew when they were well off —no, they must go bringing in husbands. This remark did not seem to hurt anybody's feelings, and Gretchen said it was nice that I was going to be here for the wedding. This reminded Annetje of something, and she spoke in English to the table at large, saying that the Lutheran pastor had advised her to attend church oftener and put her young ones in Sunday School, so that God would give her a blessing with her next child. I counted around again, and sure enough, with Gretchen's un-born, there were eight children at that table under the age of ten; some-body was going to need a blessing in all that crowd, no doubt. Father

Müller delivered a short speech to his daughter in German, then
turned to me and said, "What I say iss, it iss all craziness to go to
church and pay a preacher goot money to talk his nonsense. Say
rather that he pay me to come and lissen, then I vill go!" His eyes
glared with sudden fierceness above his square speckled gray and yellow beard that sprouted directly out from the high cheekbones. "He
thinks, so, that my time maybe costs nothing? That iss goot! Let him
pay me!"

Mother Müller snorted and shuffled her feet. "Ach, you talk, you
talk! Now you vill make the pastor goot and mad if he hears. Vot ve
do, if he vill not chrissen the babies?"

"You give him goot money, he vill chrissen," shouted Father Müller.
"You vait und see!"

"Ah sure, dot iss so," agreed Mother Müller. "Only do not let him
hear!"

There was a gust of excited talk in German, with much rapping of
knife handles on the table. I gave up trying to understand, but
watched their faces. It sounded like a pitched battle, but they were
agreeing about something. They were united in their tribal skepti-
cisms, as in everything else. I got a powerful impression that they
were all, even the sons-in-law, one human being divided into several
separate appearances. The crippled servant girl brought in more food
and gathered up plates and went away in her limping run, and she
seemed to me the only individual in the house. Even I felt divided
into many fragments, having left or lost a part of myself in every place
I had traveled, in every life mine had touched, above all, in every death
of someone near to me that had carried into the grave some part of my
living cells. But the servant, she was whole, and belonged nowhere.

I settled easily enough into the marginal life of the household ways
and habits. Day began early at the Müllers', and we ate breakfast by
yellow lamplight, with the gray damp winds blowing with spring softness through the open windows. The men swallowed their last cups of
steaming coffee standing, with their hats on, and went out to harness
the horses to the plows at sunrise. Annetje, with her fat baby slung
over her shoulder, could sweep a room or make a bed with one hand,
all finished before the day was well begun; and she spent the rest of the
day outdoors, caring for the chickens and the pigs. Now and then she
came in with a shallow box full of newly hatched chickens, abject dabs
of wet fluff, and put them on a table in her bedroom where she might
tend them carefully on their first day. Mother Müller strode about

hugely, giving orders right and left, while Father Müller, smoothing his whiskers and lighting his pipe, drove away to town with Mother Müller calling out after him final directions and instructions about household needs. He never spoke a word to her or looked at her and appeared not to be listening, but he always returned in a few hours with every commission performed exactly. After I had made my own bed and set my attic in order, there was nothing at all for me to do, and I walked out of this enthusiastic bustle into the lane, feeling extremely useless. But the repose, the almost hysterical inertia of their minds in the midst of this muscular life, communicated itself to me little by little, and I absorbed it gratefully in silence and felt all the hidden knotted painful places in my own mind beginning to loosen. It was easier to breathe, and I might weep, if I pleased. In a very few days I no longer felt like weeping.

One morning I saw Hatsy spading up the kitchen garden plot, and my offer to help, to spread the seeds and cover them, was accepted. We worked at this for several hours each morning, until the warmth of the sun and the stooping posture induced in me a comfortable vertigo. I forgot to count the days, they were one like the other except as the colors of the air changed, deepening and warming to keep step with the advancing season, and the earth grew firmer underfoot with the swelling tangle of crowding roots.

The children, so hungry and noisy at the table, were peaceable little folk who played silent engrossed games in the front yard. They were always kneading mud into loaves and pies and carrying their battered dolls and cotton rag animals through the operations of domestic life. They fed them, put them to bed; they got them up and fed them again, set them to their chores making more mud loaves; or they would harness themselves to their carts and gallop away to a great shady chestnut tree on the opposite side of the house. Here the tree became the *Turnverein*, and they themselves were again human beings, solemnly ambling about in a dance and going through the motions of drinking beer. Miraculously changed once more into horses, they harnessed themselves and galloped home. They came at call to be fed and put to sleep with the docility of their own toys or animal playmates. Their mothers handled them with instinctive, constant gentleness; they never seemed to be troubled by them. They were as devoted and care-taking as a cat with her kittens.

Sometimes I took Annetje's next to youngest child, a baby of two years, in her little wagon, and we would go down through the orchard and into the lane for a short distance. I would turn again into a smaller lane, smoother because less traveled, and we would go slowly between the aisles of mulberry trees where the fruit was beginning to hang and curl like green furry worms. The baby would sit in a compact mound of flannel and calico, her pale-blue eyes tilted and shining under her cap, her little lower teeth showing in a rapt smile. Sometimes several of the other children would follow along quietly. When I turned, they all turned without question, and we would proceed back to the house as sedately as we had set out.

The narrow lane, I discovered, led to the river, and it became my favorite walk. Almost every day I went along the edge of the naked wood, passionately occupied with looking for signs of spring. The changes there were so subtle and gradual, I found one day that branches of willows and sprays of blackberry vine alike were covered with fine points of green; the color had changed overnight, or so it seemed, and I knew that tomorrow the whole valley and wood and edge of the river would be quick and feathery with golden green blowing in the winds.

And it was so. On that day I did not leave the river until after dark and came home through the marsh with the owls and nightjars crying over my head, calling in a strange broken chorus in the woods until the farthest answering cry was a ghostly echo. When I went through the orchard the trees were all abloom with fireflies. I stopped and looked at it for a long time, then walked slowly, amazed, for I had never seen anything that was more beautiful to me. The trees were freshly budded out with pale bloom, the branches were immobile in the thin darkness, but the flower clusters shivered in a soundless dance of delicately woven light, whirling as airily as leaves in a breeze, as rhythmically as water in a fountain. Every tree was budded out with this living, pulsing fire as fragile and cool as bubbles. When I opened the gate their light shone on my hands like fox fire. When I looked back, the shimmer of golden light was there, it was no dream.

Hatsy was on her knees in the dining room, washing the floor with heavy dark rags. She always did this work at night, so the men with their heavy boots would not be tracking it up again and it would be immaculate in the morning. She turned her young face to me in a stupor of fatigue. "Ottilie! Ottilie!" she called loudly, and before I could speak, she said, "Ottilie will give you supper. It is waiting, all ready." I tried to tell her that I was not hungry, but she wished to reassure me. "Look, we all must eat. Now, or then, it's no trouble." She sat back on her heels, and raising her head, looked over the window sill at the orchard. She smiled and paused for a moment and said

happily, "Now it is come spring. Every spring we have that." She
bent again over the great pail of water with her mops.

The crippled servant came in, stumbling perilously on the slippery
floor, and set a dish before me, lentils with sausage and red chopped
cabbage. It was hot and savory and I was truly grateful, for I found I
was hungry, after all. I looked at her—so her name was Ottilie?—and
said, "Thank you." "She can't talk," said Hatsy, simply, stating a fact
that need not be emphasized. The blurred, dark face was neither
young nor old, but crumpled into crisscross wrinkles, irrelevant either
to age or suffering; simply wrinkles, patternless blackened seams as if
the perishable flesh had been wrung in a hard cruel fist. Yet in that
mutilated face I saw high cheekbones, slanted water-blue eyes, the pupils very large and strained with the anxiety of one peering into a darkness full of danger. She jarred heavily against the table as she turned,
her bowed back trembling with the perpetual working of her withered
arms, and ran away in aimless, driven haste.

Hatsy sat on her heels again for a moment, tossed her braids back
over her shoulder, and said, "That is Ottilie. She is not sick now. She
is only like that since she was sick when she was baby. But she can
work so well as I can. She cooks. But she cannot talk so you can understand." She went up on her knees, bowed over, and began to scrub
again, with new energy. She was really a network of thin taut liga-
ments and long muscles elastic as woven steel. She would always
work too hard, and be tired all her life, and never know that this was
anything but perfectly natural; everybody worked all the time, because
there was always more work waiting when they had finished what they
were doing then. I ate my supper and took my plate to the kitchen
and set it on the table. Ottilie was sitting in a kitchen chair with her
feet in the open oven, her arms folded, and her head waggling a little.
She did not see or hear me.

At home, Hatsy wore an old brown corduroy dress and galoshes
without stockings. Her skirts were short enough to show her thin legs,
slightly crooked below the knees, as if she had walked too early.
"Hatsy, she's a good, quick girl," said Mother Müller, to whom praising
anybody or anything did not come easily. On Saturdays, Hatsy took a
voluminous bath in a big tub in the closet back of the kitchen, where
also were stored the extra chamber pots, slop jars, and water jugs. She
then unplaited her yellow hair and bound up the crinkled floss with a
wreath of pink cotton rosebuds, put on her pale-blue China silk dress,

and went to the *Turnverein* to dance and drink a seidel of dark-brown beer with her devoted suitor, who resembled her brothers enough to be her brother. On Sundays, the entire family went to the *Turnverein* after copious washings, getting into starched dresses and shirts, and getting the baskets of food stored in the wagons. The servant, Ottilie, would rush out to see them off, standing with both shaking arms folded over her forehead, shading her troubled eyes to watch them to the turn of the lane. Her muteness seemed nearly absolute; she had no coherent language of signs. Yet three times a day she spread that enormous table with solid food, freshly baked bread, huge platters of vegetables, immoderate roasts of meat, extravagant tarts, strudels, pies—enough for twenty people. If neighbors came in for an afternoon on some holiday, Ottilie would stumble into the big north room, the parlor, with its golden-oak melodeon, a harsh-green Brussels carpet, Nottingham lace curtains, crocheted lace antimacassars on the chair backs, to serve them coffee with cream and sugar and thick slices of yellow cake.

Mother Müller sat but seldom in her parlor, and always with an air of formal unease, her knotted big fingers cramped in a cluster. But Father Müller often sat there in the evenings, where no one ventured to follow him unless commanded; he sometimes played chess with his elder son-in-law, who had learned a good while ago that Father Müller was a good player who abhorred an easy victory, and he dared not do less than put up the best fight he was able, but even so, if Father Müller felt himself winning too often, he would roar, "No, you are not trying! You are not doing your best. Now we stop this nonsense!", and the son-in-law would find himself dismissed in temporary disgrace.

Most evenings, however, Father Müller sat by himself and read *Das Kapital*. He would settle deeply into the red plush base rocker and spread the volume upon a low table before him. It was an early edition in blotty black German type, stained and ragged in its leather cover, the pages falling apart, a very bible. He knew whole chapters almost by heart, and added nothing to, took nothing from, the canonical, once-delivered text. I cannot say at that time of my life I had never heard of *Das Kapital*, but I had certainly never known anyone who had read it, though if anyone mentioned it, it was always with profound disapproval. It was not a book one had to read in order to reject it. And here was this respectable old farmer who accepted its dogma as a religion—that is to say, its legendary inapplicable precepts were just, right, proper, one must believe in them, of course; but life, everyday living, was another and unrelated thing. Father Müller was the wealthiest man in his community; almost every neighboring farmer rented land from him, and some of them worked it on the share system. He explained this to me one evening after he had given up trying to teach me chess. He was not surprised that I could not learn, at least not in one lesson, and he was not surprised either that I knew nothing about *Das Kapital*. He explained his own arrangements to me thus: "These men, they cannot buy their land. The land must be bought, for *Kapital* owns it, and *Kapital* will not give back to the worker the land that is his. Well, somehow, I can always buy land. Why? I do not know. I only know that with my first land here I made good crops to buy more land, and so I rent it cheap, more than anybody else I rent it cheap, I lend money so my neighbors do not fall into the hands of the bank, and so I am not *Kapital*. Someday these workers, they can buy land from me, for less than they can get it anywhere else. Well, that is what I can do, that is all." He turned over a page, and his angry gray eyes looked out at me under his shaggy brows. "I buy my land with my hard work, all my life, and I rent it cheap to my neighbors, and then they say they will not elect my son-in-law, my Annetje's husband, to be sheriff because I am atheist. So then I say, all right, but next year you pay more for your land or more shares of your crops. If I am atheist, I will act like one. So, my Annetje's husband is sheriff, that is all."

He had put a stubby forefinger on a line to mark his place, and now he sank himself into his book, and I left quietly without saying good night.

The *Turnverein* was an octagonal pavilion set in a cleared space in a patch of woods belonging to Father Müller. The German colony came here to sit about in the cool shade, while a small brass band played cloppity country dances. The girls danced with energy and direction, their starched petticoats rustling like dry leaves. The boys were more awkward, but willing; they clutched their partners' waists and left crumpled sweaty spots where they clutched. Here Mother Müller took her ease after a hard week. Her gaunt limbs would relax, her knees spread squarely apart, and she would gossip over her beer with the women of her own generation.

On the other side of the pavilion, Father Müller would sit with the sober grandfathers, their long curved pipes wagging on their chests as they discussed local politics with profound gravity, their hard peasant fatalism tempered only a little by a shrewd worldly distrust of all office-holders not personally known to them, all political plans except their own immediate ones. When Father Müller talked, they listened respectfully, with faith in him as a strong man, head of his own house and his community. They nodded slowly whenever he took his pipe from his mouth and gestured, holding it by the bowl as if it were a stone he was getting ready to throw.

On our way back from the *Turnverein* one evening, Mother Müller said to me, "Well, now, by the grace of Gott it is all settled between Hatsy and her man. It is next Sunday by this time they will be marrit."

All the folk who usually went to the *Turnverein* on Sundays came instead to the Müller house for the wedding. They brought useful presents, mostly bed linen, pillow covers, a white counterpane, with a few ornaments for the bridal chamber; and the bridegroom's gift to the bride was a necklace, a double string of red coral twigs. Just before the short ceremony began, he slipped the necklace over her head with trembling hands. She smiled up at him shakily and helped him disentangle her short veil from the coral, then they joined hands and turned their faces to the pastor, not letting go until time for the exchange of rings—the widest, thickest, reddest gold bands to be found, no doubt— and at that moment they both stopped smiling and turned a little pale. The groom recovered first, and bent over—he was considerably taller than she—and kissed her on the forehead. His eyes were a deep blue, and his hair not really Müller taffy color, but a light chestnut; a good-looking, gentle-tempered boy, I decided, and he looked at Hatsy as if he liked what he saw. They knelt and clasped hands again for the final prayer, then stood together and exchanged the bridal kiss, a very chaste reserved one, still not on the lips. Then everybody came to shake hands and the men all kissed the bride and the women all kissed the groom. Some of the women whispered in Hatsy's ear, and all burst out laughing except Hatsy, who turned red from her forehead to her throat. She whispered in turn to her husband, who nodded in agreement. She then tried to slip away quietly, but the watchful young girls were after her, and shortly we saw her running through the blossoming orchard, holding up her white ruffled skirts, with all the girls in pursuit, shrieking and calling like excited hunters, for the first to overtake and touch her would be the next bride. They returned, breathless, dragging the lucky one with them, and held her, against her ecstatic resistance, while all the young boys kissed her.

The guests stayed on for a huge supper, and Ottilie came in, wearing a fresh blue apron, sweat beaded in the wrinkles of her forehead and around her formless mouth, and passed the food around the table. The men ate first, and then Hatsy came in with the women for the first time, still wearing her square little veil of white cotton net bound on her hair with peach blossoms shattered in the bride's race. After supper, one of the girls played waltzes and polkas on the melodeon, and everyone danced. The bridegroom drew gallons of beer from a keg set up in the hall, and at midnight everybody went away, warmly emotional and happy. I went down to the kitchen for a pitcher of hot water. The servant was still setting things to rights, hobbling between table and cupboard. Her face was a brown smudge of anxiety, her eyes were wide and dazed. Her uncertain hands rattled among the pans, but nothing could make her seem real, or in any way connected with the life around her. Yet when I set my pitcher on the stove, she lifted the heavy kettle and poured the scalding water into it without spilling a drop.

The clear honey green of the early morning sky was a mirror of the bright earth. At the edge of the woods there had sprung a reticent blooming of small white and pale-colored flowers. The peach trees were now each a separate nosegay of shell rose and white. I left the house, meaning to take the short path across to the lane of mulberries. The women were deep in the house, the men were away to the fields, the animals were turned into the pastures, and only Ottilie was visible, sitting on the steps of the back porch peeling potatoes. She gazed in my direction with eyes that fell short of me, and seemed to focus on a point midway between us, and gave no sign. Then she dropped her knife and rose, her mouth opened and closed several times, she strained toward me, motioning with her right hand. I went to her, her hands came out and clutched my sleeve, and for a moment I feared to hear her voice. There was no sound from her, but she drew me along after her, full of some mysterious purpose of her own. She opened the door of a dingy, bitter-smelling room, windowless, which opened off the kitchen, beside the closet where Hatsy took her baths. A lumpy narrow cot and a chest of drawers supporting a blistered looking-glass almost filled the space. Ottilie's lips moved, struggling for speech, as she pulled and tumbled over a heap of rubbish in the top drawer. She took out a photograph and put it in my hands. It was in the old style, faded to a dirty yellow, mounted on cardboard elaborately clipped and gilded at the edges.

I saw a girl child about five years old, a pretty smiling German baby, looking curiously like a slightly elder sister of Annetje's two-year-old, wearing a frilled frock and a prodigious curl of blonde hair on the crown of her head. The strong legs, round as sausages, were encased in long white ribbed stockings, and the square firm feet were laced into old-fashioned soft-soled black boots. Ottilie peered over the picture, twisted her neck, and looked up into my face. I saw the slanted water-blue eyes and the high cheekbones of the Müllers again, mutilated, almost destroyed, but unmistakable. This child was what she had been, and she was without doubt the elder sister of Annetje and Gretchen and Hatsy; in urgent pantomime she insisted that this was so—she patted the picture and her own face, and strove terribly to speak. She pointed to the name written carefully on the back, Ottilie, and touched her mouth with her bent knuckles. Her head wagged in her perpetual nod; her shaking hand seemed to flap the photograph at me in a roguish humor. The bit of cardboard connected her at once somehow to the world of human beings I knew; for an instant some filament lighter than cobweb spun itself out between that living center in her and in me, a filament from some center that held us all bound to our inescapable common source, so that her life and mine were kin, even a part of each other, and the painfulness and strangeness of her vanished. She knew well that she had been Ottilie, with those steady legs and watching eyes, and she was Ottilie still within herself. For a moment, being alive, she knew she suffered, for she stood and shook with silent crying, smearing away her tears with the open palm of her hand. Even while her cheeks were wet, her face changed. Her eyes cleared and fixed themselves upon that point in space which seemed for her to contain her unaccountable and terrible troubles. She turned her head as if she had heard a voice and disappeared in her staggering run into the kitchen, leaving the drawer open and the photograph face downward on the chest.

At midday meal she came hurrying and splashing coffee on the white floor, restored to her own secret existence of perpetual amazement, and again I had become a stranger to her like all the rest, but she was no stranger to me, and could not be again.

The youngest brother came in, holding up an opossum he had caught in his trap. He swung the furry body from side to side, his eyes fairly narrowed with pride as he showed us the mangled creature. "No, it is cruel, even for the wild animals," said gentle Annetje to me, "but boys love to kill, they love to hurt things. I am always afraid he will trap poor Kuno." I thought privately that Kuno, a wolfish, ungracious beast, might well prove a match for any trap. Annetje was full of silent, tender solicitudes. The kittens, the puppies, the chicks, the lambs and calves were her special care. She was the only one of the women who caressed the weanling calves when she set the pans of milk before them. Her child seemed as much a part of her as if it were not

yet born. Still, she seemed to have forgotten that Ottilie was her sister.
So had all the others. I remembered how Hatsy had spoken her name
but had not said she was her sister. Their silence about her was, I realized, exactly that—simple forgetfulness. She moved among them as
invisible to their imaginations as a ghost. Ottilie their sister was something painful that had happened long ago and now was past and done
for; they could not live with that memory or its visible reminder—they
forgot her in pure self-defense. But I could not forget her. She drifted
into my mind like a bit of weed carried in a current and caught there,
floating but fixed, refusing to be carried away. I reasoned it out. The
Müllers, what else could they have done with Ottilie? By a physical
accident in her childhood, she had been stripped of everything but her
mere existence. It was not a society or a class that pampered its in-
valids and the unfit. So long as one lived, one did one's share. This
was her place, in this family she had been born and must die; did she
suffer? No one asked, no one looked to see. Suffering went with life,
suffering and labor. While one lived one worked, that was all, and
without complaints, for no one had time to listen, and everybody had
his own troubles. So, what else could they have done with Ottilie? As
for me, I could do nothing but promise myself that I would forget her,
too; and to remember her for the rest of my life.

Sitting at the long table, I would watch Ottilie clattering about in her
tormented haste, bringing in that endless food that represented all her
life's labors. My mind would follow her into the kitchen, where I
could see her peering into the great simmering kettles, the crowded
oven, her ruined hands always lifting and stirring, and paring and
chopping, her whole body a mere machine of torture. Straight up to
the surface of my mind the thought would come urgently, clearly, as if
driving time toward the desired event: Let it be now, let it be *now*. Not
even tomorrow, no, today. Let her sit down quietly in her rickety chair
by the stove and fold those arms, and let us find her there like that,
with her head fallen forward on her knees. I would wait, hoping she
might not come again, ever again, through that door I gazed at with
wincing eyes, as if I might see something unendurable enter. Then she
would come, and it was only Ottilie, after all, in the bosom of her
family, and one of its most useful and competent members; and they
with a deep right instinct had learned to live with her disaster on its
own terms, and hers; they had accepted and then made use of what
was for them only one more painful event in a world full of troubles,
many of them much worse than this. So, a step at a time, I followed
the Müllers as nearly as I could in their acceptance of Ottilie and the

use they made of her life, for in some way that I could not quite explain to myself, I found great virtue and courage in their steadiness and refusal to feel sorry for anybody, least of all for themselves.

Gretchen bore her child, a son, conveniently between the hours of supper and bedtime, one evening of friendly domestic-sounding rain. The next day brought neighboring women from miles around, and the child was bandied about among them as if he were a new kind of medicine ball. Sedate and shy at dances, emotional at weddings, they were ribald and jocose at birth. Over coffee and beer the talk grew broad, the hearty gutturals were swallowed in the belly of laughter; those honest hard-working wives and mothers saw life for a few hours as a hearty low joke, and it did them good. The baby bawled and suckled like a young calf, and the men of the family came in for a look and added their joyful improprieties.

Cloudy weather drove them home earlier than they had meant to go. The whole sky was lined with smoky black and gray vapor hanging in ragged wisps like soot in a chimney. The edges of the woods turned dull purple as the horizon reddened slowly, then faded, and all across the sky ran a deep shuddering mumble of thunder. All the Müllers hurried about getting into rubber boots and oilcloth overalls, shouting to each other, making their plan of action. The youngest boy came over the ridge of the hill with Kuno helping him to drive the sheep into the fold. Kuno was barking, the sheep were baaing and bleating, the horses freed from the plows were excited; they whinnied and trotted at the lengths of their halters, their ears laid back. The cows were bawling in distress and the calves cried back to them. All the men went out among the animals to round them up and quiet them and get them enclosed safely. Even as Mother Müller, her half-dozen petticoats looped about her thighs and tucked into her hip boots, was striding to join them in the barns, the cloud rack was split end to end by a shattering blow of lightning, and the cloudburst struck the house with the impact of a wave against a ship. The wind broke the windowpanes and the floods poured through. The roof beams strained and the walls bent inward, but the house stood to its foundations. The children were huddled into the inner bedroom with Gretchen. "Come and sit on the bed with me now," she told them calmly, "and be still." She sat up with a shawl around her, suckling the baby. Annetje came then and left her baby with Gretchen, too; and standing at the doorstep with one arm caught over the porch rail, reached down into the furious waters which were rising to the very threshold and dragged in a half-drowned lamb. I followed her. We could not make ourselves heard above the cannonade of thunder, but together we carried the creature into the hall under the stairs, where we rubbed the drowned fleece with rags and pressed his stomach to free him from the water and finally got him sitting up with his feet tucked under him. Annetje was merry with triumph and kept saying in delight, "Alive, alive! Look!"

We left him there when we heard the men shouting and beating at the kitchen door and ran to open it for them. They came in, Mother Müller among them, wearing her yoke and milk pails. She stood there with the water pouring from her skirts, the three-cornered piece of black oilcloth on her head dripping, her rubber boots wrinkled down with the weight of her petticoats. She and Father Müller stood near each other, looking like two gnarled lightning-struck old trees, his beard and oilcloth garments streaming, both their faces suddenly dark and old and tired, tired once for all; they would never be rested again in their lives. Father Müller suddenly roared at her, "Go get yourself dry clothes. Do you want to make yourself sick?"

"Ho," she said, taking off her milk yoke and setting the pails on the floor. "Go change yourself. I bring you dry socks." One of the boys told me she had carried a day-old calf on her back up a ladder against the inside wall of the barn and had put it safely in the hayloft behind a barricade of bales. Then she had lined up the cows in the stable, and sitting on her milking stool in the rising water, she had milked them all. She seemed to think nothing of it.

"Hatsy," she called, "come help with this milk!" Little pale Hatsy came flying, barefoot because she had been called in the midst of taking off her wet shoes. Her new husband followed her, rather shy of his mother-in-law.

"Let me," he said, wishing to spare his dear bride such heavy work, and started to lift the great pails. "No!" shouted Mother Müller, so the poor young man nearly jumped out of his shirt. "Not you. The milk is not business for a man." He fell back and stood there with dark rivulets of mud seeping from his boots, watching Hatsy pour the milk into pans. Mother Müller started to follow her husband to attend him, but said at the door, "Where is Ottilie?", and no one knew, no one had seen her. "Find her," said Mother Müller. "Tell her we want supper, now."

Hatsy motioned to her husband, and together they tiptoed to the door of Ottilie's room and opened it silently. The light from the kitchen showed them Ottilie, sitting by herself, folded up on the edge

of the bed. Hatsy threw the door wide open for more light and called
in a high penetrating voice as if to a deaf person or one at a great
distance, "Ottilie! Suppertime. We are hungry!", and the young pair
left the kitchen to look under the stairway to see how Annetje's lamb
was getting on. Then Annetje, Hatsy, and I began sweeping the
dirty water and broken glass from the floors of the hall and dining
room.

The storm lightened gradually, but the flooding rain continued. At
supper there was talk about the loss of animals and their replacement.
All the crops must be replanted, the season's labor was for nothing.
They were all tired and wet, but they ate heartily and calmly, to
strengthen themselves against all the labor of repairing and restoring
which must begin early tomorrow morning.

By morning the drumming on the roof had almost ceased; from my
window I looked upon a sepia-colored plain of water moving slowly
to the valley. The roofs of the barns sagged like the ridgepoles of a
tent, and a number of drowned animals floated or were caught against
the fences. At breakfast, Mother Müller sat groaning over her coffee
cup. "Ach," she said, "what it is to have such a pain in the head. Here
too." She thumped her chest. "All over. Ach, Gott, I'm sick." She
got up sighing hoarsely, her cheeks flushed, calling Hatsy and Annetje
to help her in the barn.

They all came back very soon, their skirts draggled to the knees, and
the two sisters were supporting their mother, who was speechless and
could hardly stand. They put her to bed, where she lay without moving, her face scarlet. Everybody was confused; no one knew what to
do. They tucked the quilts about her, and she threw them off. They
offered her coffee, cold water, beer, but she turned her head away.
The sons came in and stood beside her and joined the cry: "*Mutter-
chen, Mutti, Mutti,* what can we do? Tell us, what do you need?"
But she could not tell them. It was impossible to ride the twelve miles
to town for a doctor; fences and bridges were down, the roads were
washed out. The family crowded into the room, unnerved, in panic,
lost unless the sick woman should come to herself and tell them what to
do for her. Father Müller came in, and kneeling beside her, he took hold
of her hands and spoke to her most lovingly, and when she did not
answer him, he broke out crying openly, in a loud voice, the great tears
rolling, "Ach, Gott, Gott. A hundert tousand tollars in the bank"—he
glared around at his family and spoke broken English to them, as if he
were a stranger to himself and had forgotten his own language—"and
tell me, tell, what goot does it?"

This frightened them, and all at once, together, they screamed and called and implored her in a tumult utterly beyond control. The noise of their grief and terror filled the place. In the midst of this, Mother Müller died.

In the midafternoon the rain passed, and the sun was a disk of brass in a cruelly bright sky. The waters flowed thickly down to the river, leaving the hill bald and brown, with the fences lying in a flattened tangle, the young peach trees stripped of bloom and sagging at the roots. In the woods had occurred a violent eruption of ripe foliage of a jungle thickness, glossy and burning, a massing of hot peacock green with cobalt shadows.

The household was in such silence, I had to listen carefully to know that anyone lived there. Everyone, even the younger children, moved on tiptoe and spoke in whispers. All afternoon the thud of hammers and the whine of a saw went on monotonously in the barn loft. At dark, the men brought in a shiny coffin of new yellow pine with rope handles and set it in the hall. It lay there on the floor for an hour or so, where anyone passing had to step over it. Then Annetje and Hatsy, who had been washing and dressing the body, appeared in the doorway and motioned. "You bring it in now."

Mother Müller lay in state in the parlor throughout the night, in her black silk dress with a scrap of white lace at the collar and a small lace cap on her hair. Her husband sat in the plush chair near her, looking at her face, which was very contemplative, gentle, and remote. He wept at intervals, silently, wiping his face with a big handkerchief. His daughters brought him coffee from time to time. He fell asleep there toward morning.

The light burned in the kitchen nearly all night, too, and the sound of Ottilie's heavy boots thumping about unsteadily was accompanied by the locust whirring of the coffee mill and the smell of baking bread. Hatsy came to my room. "There's coffee and cake," she said, "you'd better have some," and turned away crying, crumbling her slice in her hand. We stood about and ate in silence. Ottilie brought in a fresh pot of coffee, her eyes bleared and fixed, her gait as aimless-looking and hurried as ever, and when she spilled some on her own hand, she did not seem to feel it.

For a day longer they waited; then the youngest boy went to fetch the Lutheran pastor, and a few neighbors came back with them. By noon many more had arrived, spattered with mud, the horses heaving and sweating. At every greeting the family gave way and wept afresh, as naturally and openly as children. Their faces were drenched and soft with their tears; there was a comfortable relaxed look in the muscles of their faces. It was good to let go, to have something to weep for that nobody need excuse or explain. Their tears were at once a luxury and a cure of souls. They wept away the hard core of secret trouble that is in the heart of each separate man, secure in a communal grief; in sharing it, they consoled each other. For a while, they would visit the grave and remember, and then life would arrange itself again in another order, yet it would be the same. Already the thoughts of the living were turning to tomorrow, when they would be at the work of rebuilding and replanting and repairing—even now, today, they would hurry back from the burial to milk the cows and feed the chickens, and they might weep again and again for several days, until their tears should heal them at last.

On that day I realized, for the first time, not death, but the terror of dying. When they took the coffin out to the little country hearse and I saw that the procession was about to form, I went to my room and lay down. Staring at the ceiling, I heard and felt the ominous order and purpose in the movements and sounds below—the creaking harness and hoofbeats and grating wheels, the muted grave voices—and it was as if my blood fainted and receded with fright, while my mind stayed wide-awake to receive the awful impress. Yet when I knew they were leaving the yard, the terror began to leave me. As the sounds receded, I lay there not thinking, not feeling, in a mere drowse of relief and weariness.

Through my half-sleep I heard the howling of a dog. It seemed to be in a dream, and I was troubled to awaken. I dreamed that Kuno was caught in the trap; then I thought he was really caught, it was no dream and I must wake, because there was no one but me to let him out. I came broad awake, the cry rushed upon me like a wind, and it was not the howl of a dog. I ran downstairs and looked into Gretchen's room. She was curled up around her baby, and they were both asleep. I ran to the kitchen.

Ottilie was sitting in her broken chair with her feet in the edge of the open oven, where the heat had died away. Her hands hung at her sides, the fingers crooked into the palm; her head lay back on her shoulders, and she howled with a great wrench of her body, an upward reach of the neck, without tears. At sight of me she got up and came over to me and laid her head on my breast, and her hands dangled forward a moment. Shuddering, she babbled and howled and waved her arms in a frenzy through the open window over the stripped branches of the orchard toward the lane where the procession had straightened out into formal order. I took hold of her arms where the unnaturally corded muscles clenched and strained under her coarse sleeves; I led her out to the steps and left her sitting there, her head wagging.

In the barnyard there remained only the broken-down spring wagon and the shaggy pony that had brought me to the farm on the first day. The harness was still a mystery, but somehow I managed to join pony, harness, and wagon not too insecurely, or so I could only hope; and I pushed and hauled and tugged at Ottilie and lifted her until she was in the seat and I had the reins in hand. We careened down the road at a grudging trot, the pony jolting like a churn, the wheels spinning elliptically in a truly broad comedy swagger. I watched the jovial antics of those wheels with attention, hoping for the best. We slithered into round pits of green mud and jogged perilously into culverts where small bridges had been. Once, in what was left of the main road, I stood up to see if I might overtake the funeral train; yes, there it was, going inchmeal up the road over the little hill, a bumbling train of black beetles crawling helter-skelter over clods.

Ottilie, now silent, was doubled upon herself, slipping loosely on the edge of the seat. I caught hold of her stout belt with my free hand, and my fingers slipped between her clothes and bare flesh, ribbed and gaunt and dry against my knuckles. My sense of her realness, her humanity, this shattered being that was a woman, was so shocking to me that a howl as doglike and despairing as her own rose in me unuttered and died again, to be a perpetual ghost. Ottilie slanted her eyes and peered at me, and I gazed back. The knotted wrinkles of her face were grotesquely changed, she gave a choked little whimper, and suddenly she laughed out, a kind of yelp but unmistakably laughter, and clapped her hands for joy, the grinning mouth and suffering eyes turned to the sky. Her head nodded and wagged with the clownish humor of our trundling lurching progress. The feel of the hot sun on her back, the bright air, the jolly senseless staggering of the wheels, the peacock green of the heavens: something of these had reached her. She was happy and gay, and she gurgled and rocked in her seat, leaning upon me and waving loosely around her as if to show me what wonders she saw.

Drawing the pony to a standstill, I studied her face for a while and pondered my ironical mistake. There was nothing I could do for Ottilie, selfishly as I wished to ease my heart of her; she was beyond my reach as well as any other human reach, and yet, had I not come nearer to her than I had to anyone else in my attempt to deny and bridge the distance between us, or rather, her distance from me? Well, we were both equally the fools of life, equally fellow fugitives from death. We had escaped for one day more at least. We would celebrate our good luck, we would have a little stolen holiday, a breath of spring air and freedom on this lovely, festive afternoon.

Ottilie fidgeted, uneasy at our stopping. I flapped the reins, the pony moved on, we turned across the shallow ditch where the small road divided from the main traveled one. I measured the sun westering gently; there would be time enough to drive to the river down the lane of mulberries and to get back to the house before the mourners returned. There would be plenty of time for Ottilie to have supper ready. They need not even know she had been gone.

Guest Commentary by a Student

Closely connected with man's recognition of himself as a mortal creature is his admission that death is not a sudden event but one preceded by the gradual erosion of life. The suffering that man learns to identify with living is a symptom of this erosion, an aspect of the problem of man's mortality, and like mortality, suffering is a problem for man's imagination.

The problem of the suffering of life and eventually of mortality concerns Katherine Anne Porter in "Holiday." Since any solution of this problem will be a product of the imagination, it is likely that the emphasis in the development of the theme of "Holiday" will be on internal action rather than on external action. (See p. 25.)

Since the development of the theme will take place in the mind of its protagonist, the protagonist will be the character whose perspective on suffering and mortality is evolving in the course of the story in reaction to the views of others. There is only one character that meets this qualification, the anonymous speaker.

We have little specific information on the troubles the speaker is trying futilely to escape on her "spring holiday," but we soon realize that the conditions at the Müllers' farm provide such a challenge to her that such information would be irrelevant. Two perspectives on the problem of suffering are revealed to us through the narration of the speaker.

The first of these is represented by the Müller family unit, Ottilie excepted, who, in their attitudes, seemed "even the sons-in-law, one human being divided into several separate appearances." Their view of Ottilie's deformation is typical of their attitude toward suffering in general: "they had accepted and then made use of what was for them only one more painful event in a world full of troubles. . . ." The other perspective on suffering is revealed more gradually to the speaker; it is Ottilie's. Until the very end of the story, the narrator sees Ottilie's view as an admirable resignation to a half-life apart from the others.

At first, in the course of the story, the protagonist "found great virtue and courage in their [the Müllers'] steadiness and refusal to feel sorry for anybody, least of all for themselves." But later, when the rest of the Müllers trail off in bereavement to Mother Müller's funeral, the narrator discovers that Ottilie is strongest of all in the face of suffering. In her total isolation, Ottilie never feels the temporary sorrow that the other Müllers feel, and the speaker notes that "she was beyond my reach as well as any other human reach. . . ." Finally, the narrator shares Ottilie's perspective of isolation, realizing "we were both equally the fools of life, equally fellow fugitives from death," and the narrator achieves her sought-after "holiday." The important consequences, thematically speaking, of this and all other incidents in "Holiday" rest on their effect on the attitudes of the speaker toward the problem of suffering and death.

The secret of the vitality of the story derives partly from Miss Porter's masterful choice of setting. The story takes place just at the turning of winter to spring, and appropriately it takes place in a land where "winter . . . is a moribund coma, not the Northern death sleep with the sure promise of resurrection." The author makes the event of seasonal transition coincide with the protagonist's mental transition. For instance, when the narrator arrives, she describes the land around her as "the desolate mud-colored shapeless scene." Just as there was nothing hopeful in her mind but the promise of a solution to her problem, when she arrived: "There was nothing beautiful in those woods now except the promise of spring." Later, when the narrator aligns with the rest of the Müllers in their view of suffering, "The clear honey green of the early morning sky was a mirror of the bright earth." Finally, on the afternoon of her climactic discovery of Ottilie's powerful isolation, the narrator notes: "In the woods had occurred a violent eruption of ripe foliage of a jungle thickness, glossy and burning, a massing of hot peacock green with cobalt shadows."

Another device Miss Porter uses to give her story vitality is irony. As revealed in the last scene, the irony derives from Ottilie's emergence as the strongest character in the story, contrary to the narrator's previous view of her as a pitiful outcast. Ottilie's isolation enables her to enjoy the beauty of the day in spite of her mother's death.

The success of "Holiday" in achieving vitality is a result of Miss Porter's using a literary form suitable to and consistent with content. An internally developed theme is externalized and given color, and irony is used to provide suspense.

Questions

1. How does the narrator's relationship with Ottilie after the scene in the cripple's room differ from her relationship with Ottilie at the end of the story? Can you account for this difference in terms of thematic development?

2. Why is the first-person-central point of view, from which "Holiday" is told, vital to the development of the story's theme through imagery and irony?

3. How does the connotation of the word *holiday* change for the narrator in the course of the story? Is this change consistent with the thematic development?

4. Why is it appropriate that the harness on the Müllers' "spring wagon" be a "real mystery" to the narrator?

5. Father Müller is the source of the Müller "water-clear eyes." How does this fact imply Father Müller's function in the family unit? How does the absence of "water-clear eyes" in Mother Müller relate to her function in the family—and to her death?

6. What events tend to universalize the situation at the Müllers' farm?

7. In identifying with Ottilie, what position does the narrator finally assume with respect to the problem of suffering and mortality?

Commentary and Questions by
William B. Rood, Jr.
Evanston Township High School '60
Northwestern University '64

Benediction

Patricia Collinge

Although Mrs. Engel was not a Catholic, she felt that to be in Rome and not see the Pope was to miss something essential. It was like eating an artichoke and ignoring the heart, she thought, but she had no practical idea how to rectify it. She was aware that the Pope gave a daily benediction from his window overlooking St. Peter's Square, but she and her husband had never been there at the right hour, which was approximately noon. The thing to do was to plan for it and go, she knew, but she was shy about suggesting it, for while she was an Episcopalian, Mr. Engel was a Congregationalist, when he remembered it, and she was not sure how he would take to being publicly blessed. She would go alone some morning when he was having his hair cut, or something, she promised herself, and then, one afternoon, she ran into Miss Murphy.

Half an hour later, she burst in on Mr. Engel, who was sitting on his bed with a number of lira notes spread around him. "What do you think?" she demanded, her eyes shining.

"I know one thing I think," Mr. Engel replied. "Something ought to be done about these ten-thousand-lira notes. No one will change them, and I've got to have something to tip with."

"I know, it's a shame, but who do you think I met buying postcards from the porter?" said his wife, in one breath. "Do you remember Miss Murphy?"

"No," said Mr. Engel.

"Yes, you do. She was on the boat with us coming over. She wore that suit with the funny pockets, and she has a sister who's a nun. Don't you remember her? You danced with her once."

"I never danced with a nun," said Mr. Engel definitely.

"I meant with Miss *Murphy*, the time they had that change-partners waltz. *She* remembers it. She spoke of it twice. Well, anyway, that's who she is, and she's staying right here in the hotel—and where do you think she's taking me?"

"I don't know," said Mr. Engel. "Waltzing?"

"*No*," said Mrs. Engel. "I *wish* you wouldn't spoil things."

Mr. Engel relented. "Where, then?" he asked, gathering his money together.

"Well," said Mrs. Engel, "she's taking me to an audience." Mr. Engel looked vague. "The *Pope*. She's taking me to see the Pope."

"Oh," said Mr. Engel.

"I can't *believe* it," his wife went on. "It won't be like seeing him from the Square, the way anyone can. This is *indoors*." She paused. "Not indoors in his apartments. That's only for very small groups. This one is for several groups combined, so it's sort of biggish. It's to be in St. Peter's."

"The church?"

"The Basilica," Mrs. Engel amended.

"That's more than sort of biggish, that's big. How will you be able to see him there?"

Mrs. Engel glowed. "Miss Murphy has tickets for places in a special stand, like a royal box, or something—I suppose because her sister's a nun. The tickets are a special color. Wasn't it wonderful that she had two? She was going to return one when she met *me*."

"When is it to be?"

"Tomorrow, at noon, but we're going to get there at eleven, because they don't reserve the seats in the box, and we want to be right in front." She beamed at Mr. Engel. "Aren't you excited?"

"Excited?"

"Well, *interested*, then."

"I suppose so," said Mr. Engel, putting his money in his wallet.

Mrs. Engel hesitated. "Do you—do you *mind* my going?" she asked tentatively.

"I don't mind," her husband answered. "I just thought you didn't like crowds."

"We have *seats*," Mrs. Engel said. "We even go in by a private entrance. This isn't a *crowd*—this is an *audience*." She let the word linger, and then went to her wardrobe and surveyed her dresses. "*Now* the thing is, what am I going to wear? Of course, *she's* going to wear black with a mantilla, the way they do, but I don't think I should. . . . Anyway, I haven't got a mantilla," she added, a little wistfully.

"I don't see why you have to dress up for it," said Mr. Engel.

Before Mrs. Engel answered this, she somehow managed to give the impression that she had counted up to ten. "It wouldn't be dressing up if I wore a mantilla. It would be manners—like wearing three feathers when you're presented at court. She pushed her dresses along the hanger rail. "My black is too cocktaily. Do you think my navy blue would do, with my black hat, if I took the flowers off?"

Mr. Engel had collected a dacron shirt and a box of soap flakes, which he shook experimentally. "Remind me to get some more of these," he said, and retired to the bathroom.

Mrs. Engel examined her black hat. Without its trimming, it would be no more than a head covering, but, after all, that was the idea, she supposed. She had one brief vision of herself correct and remote in the mystery of drifting black lace, and dismissed it. Mantillas and Mr. Engel would not mix, she decided. But before she reached for her scissors, she telephoned an order to the porter. If a mantilla was beyond her, the hotel car service was not, and the deference of a limousine she could, and would, contribute.

The next morning, at ten-thirty, Mr. Engel helped Miss Murphy into the symbolic limousine and asked his invariable questions of Mrs. Engel. "Have you got everything? Bag, money, glasses?"

Mrs. Engel, whose mouth was oddly dry, nodded.

"Medals," said Miss Murphy. "Have you your medals?"

Mrs. Engel looked bewildered. "Medals?" She thought of Mr. Engel's Purple Heart. I'm afraid not. Not *with* me."

"Ah, that's too bad," said Miss Murphy. "Any religious article you carry or wear will get the blessing." She indicated a small parcel tucked under her arm. "Rosaries and medals to take home."

"Oh," said Mrs. Engel. "You mean *saints!* I have a St. Christopher medal"—Miss Murphy smiled tolerantly—"but it's on the car at home. Oh dear, I would so love to have a *blessed* St. Christopher." She looked wildly down the street toward the shops. "I suppose there isn't time to——"

"There isn't," said Mr. Engel, "and you're blocking the taxis."

Mrs. Engel looked at him imploringly. "If only I had thought of it in time," she said.

"You'll be late," said Mr. Engel. He urged her in, nodded to the chauffeur, and stood, half waving, as the car started away.

"He's a fine-looking man," said Miss Murphy, "and a grand waltzer. He didn't remember me, though: he didn't know me from Adam."

Mrs. Engel wrenched herself from St. Christopher. "It was your mantilla," she invented hastily. "He's more used to you in a hat." She gave a side glance at Miss Murphy. Remembering some of her less fortunate shipboard costumes, Mrs. Engel thought that the Pope's ruling on dress had much to be said for it. It was not only modest, it was helpful. Miss Murphy looked actually distinguished, Mrs. Engel acknowledged—and wished she could think the same of herself. The denuded hat, softened with a veil ripped from another hat, looked better than she had hoped, and her dark dress was simple, but the total effect, she was afraid, was no more than unobtrusive.

"I would have worn a mantilla, too," she told Miss Murphy, "but I wasn't sure that I *should*."

"It isn't obligatory, it isn't obligatory at all," Miss Murphy assured her, just touching her own black lace. "The Holy Father has relaxed the rule considerably. Of course, this is a public audience. A private one would be another matter altogether."

"Have you been to one like that?" asked Mrs. Engel.

"I've not been to one of any kind," said Miss Murphy, "but there's established procedure for all."

"Is it difficult?" asked Mrs. Engel, seeing herself backing out of St. Peter's. "Will I be able to do it properly?"

"You'll not have to do anything," said Miss Murphy. "Just sit in your place and don't stir till we kneel for the blessing."

"But when the Pope—when the Holy *Father*—comes in," said Mrs. Engel, "don't we do anything then?"

"Well, he won't *come* in, he'll be carried in on his chair," Miss Murphy said. "It may be that we'll stand then, but we'll be told about that, I've no doubt. So relax, now, Mrs. Engel. We've no cause to worry ourselves." She laughed, a shade too brightly, and touched a cross at her throat with trembling fingers. "I'll say a prayer to St. Peter; he'll not let us disgrace him."

Maybe she ought to include St. Christopher, Mrs. Engel thought. He got you places safely; maybe he got you through things safely. She didn't know, but she wished again that she had one of his medals. Then she forgot the medal and everything else, for the car was approaching St. Peter's Square, and she saw how it teemed with people. "We'll never get there!" she exclaimed. "There isn't even room to walk!"

But the car ignored the congested Square and swept to a gateway at its left, where Swiss Guards made splotches of red and yellow against gray stone. A note from Mrs. Engel's guidebook leaped to her memory, and she recognized the entrance they were approaching. It's the Arch of the Bells, she thought, and we're going through it to see the Pope. She caught sight of herself in the car mirror, and made a final, token

gesture. Taking her handkerchief, she quickly, almost with one movement, rubbed off her lipstick.

As Miss Murphy presented her special tickets, the guards at the Arch
saluted, and, as the car rolled through it to a courtyard inside, Mrs.
Engel bowed to them in return. It's like royalty, she thought. Now
they drove up to a wide door, where they waited while a car ahead of
them discharged three ladies in long mantillas and a man with a ribbon
around his neck, from which hung a gold cross. Other crosses and
medals were pinned to the breast of his somber suit. A Papal Count,
Mrs. Engel decided, or a Knight of the Realm—no, of Malta, she cor-
rected herself. Well, anyway, he was *someone,* she was sure, and she
wondered if he would be in their stand. His car moved on, and it
was her own and Miss Murphy's turn to alight. A man with gloves and
badge approved their tickets with a low bow, and Mrs. Engel, her
heart thumping perceptibly, followed Miss Murphy up a short flight of
steps toward the unknown.

Almost at once, there were people. Not guards—not chamberlains,
as Mrs. Engel had half expected—but ordinary, everyday people, all in
what was unmistakably a tearing hurry. "Where did *they* come from?"
Miss Murphy asked, as she and Mrs. Engel headed with the rest down
a long stone corridor. Feet sounded behind them, and four nuns with
winged coifs like flying birds passed on the double. Six young men in
bright red cassocks went by like a flash fire. "Seminarians. They're
always rushing," said Miss Murphy. Two Norwegians and an American soldier skirted Mrs. Engel with the effect of being on skis. "I wonder if we're in the right place," said Miss Murphy, and waved her
special tickets for the attention of an official stationed on the way.

"*Si, si,*" he responded. "*Avanti, avanti.*" Mrs. Engel thought he
sounded impatient, but she reminded herself that most Italians did.

"*Avanti!*" cried a man with a sword, and this time there was no
doubt.

Unconsciously, Miss Murphy increased her speed, infecting Mrs.
Engel, and soon they were almost running. Dignity was receding, and
more and more people were overtaking them, all with the look of men
and women who had just been told that the dam had burst. "Where
do they think they're *going?*" asked Miss Murphy, rebounding from the
impact of several small but solid little girls in white First Communion
dresses.

If Mrs. Engel had an answer, it was smothered by an Italian family that converged on her and bore her through an opening into the arms of a man in a cocked hat. "*Avanti!*" he commanded, and Mrs. Engel found that she was out of the corridor and in the immensity of the church.

"We're all right," said Miss Murphy breathlessly. "We've come around a back way. We're in the transept and the stand can't be far off."

Although the crowds kept them moving, Mrs. Engel could recognize, now, where she was. She was near the canopied High Altar, and the dome was just above. She looked up and gasped. From top to bottom, for as far as she could see, the church was hung with blazing red and studded with lighted candelabra, as if scarlet ribbons had been pinned to the arches with diamond brooches, and there, in front of the lamp-lined tomb of St. Peter, she could just see a dais on which stood a tall chair, its pointed back glinting with gold. She stopped dead.

"*Avanti!*" protested a little man, who was behaving as if he were directing a line of fire buckets.

"We go to the *stand*," said Miss Murphy, waving her tickets again.

"*Si, si, va bene,*" said someone soothingly, and Mrs. Engel and Miss Murphy were propelled up a step or two onto a railed platform covered by what seemed to be a low ceiling, and so choked with occupants that Mrs. Engel could only think of what she had heard of the New York subway at the rush hour. But before she could do more than notice that at least the front rows were decorous with long lines of motionless nuns, a hoarse injunction compelled her on. "*Di sopra!*" it said. "*Di sopra.* Up, please, up."

She nudged Miss Murphy, who was standing stock-still. "We have to go up," Mrs. Engel said. Miss Murphy turned, looking as if she were about to cry. "Up," Mrs. Engel repeated. "We go up."

The press of people impelled them to a stairway, narrow and quivering, that ran eerily up behind the platform and led to a tier above it—a balcony, which Mrs. Engel had mistaken for a ceiling. "It's as bad here," said Miss Murphy, like a Celtic Cassandra. "There's no hope for us at all."

Mrs. Engel looked around her. The first rows up here, like those she had noticed below, were neat with the black-and-white of nuns. Over in one corner, the man with all the medals cowered crestfallen, his ladies crushed against him. Anywhere one could sit, people sat, and where they couldn't sit, they stood. "We should have come earlier," said Miss Murphy inadequately.

"*Mi scusi*," said a Roman matron, squeezing herself into a space where none had existed.

"*Prego*," said Mrs. Engel, and wished she hadn't.

"Pardon," said an American voice, and a man with three cameras flattened her as he pushed by.

"We should have come earlier," said Miss Murphy again, standing as stiff and weighted as the statue of St. Andrew against which the stand was erected.

"Look!" said Mrs. Engel.

At the very back, on a line with St. Andrew's knees, she had spotted a bench that offered a suggestion of space. She steered Miss Murphy, who seemed incapable of independent action, toward it. It was mainly in possession of the Italian family that had engulfed Mrs. Engel in the corridor. "No, no!" they cried in concerted defense. "We save!"

Mrs. Engel took courage. "*Non capisco.* No understand," she said, and hoped it was all right to fib in church. "Well," she said, when she had inserted herself and Miss Murphy in the space, "this isn't so bad."

The balcony was crammed, but it sloped steeply, and it was possible to see the dais. "And there's no one behind us, so we can stand up to see better," she said. She thought a moment. "I mean if that would be correct. Will people *do* that?"

Miss Murphy looked at the excited crowd about her. "I don't know *what* they'll do," she said through tight lips. "I'd put nothing past them."

Mrs. Engel attempted comfort. "They'll settle down," she said, raising her voice against the chatter of several languages. "They'll be wonderful. Look at all those nice nuns."

Miss Murphy stared stonily at the veils and coifs that had pre-empted the front rows of seats. "Why wouldn't they be nice?" she said. "All in the best places, like that."

"Maybe they got here *very* early," Mrs. Engel offered placatingly.

"I'd not be surprised if they'd slept here," said Miss Murphy witheringly.

Mrs. Engel gave up. Miss Murphy was disappointed, and so was she, but, after all, it was worse for Miss Murphy, because the Pope was *her* Pope. Surely, when the time came, it would be all right. Finally putting aside her ideas of royal boxes and velvet chairs, Mrs. Engel admitted to herself that at least the position of the stand was enviable. It faced the dais below, and when the Pope was there and everyone was quiet, they would see him well. She craned for confirmation and drew a breath at what she saw. The transept was checkered with groups of nuns, priests, children, and—"laymen" she supposed was the word—in orderly, squared-off sections. But away from these, stretching back beyond her vision, were masses and masses of people, so dwarfed by the vast space and distances that they had only the dark, packed quality of a homogeneous sticky substance. "Caviar," Mrs. Engel said to herself. "The church is full of caviar." Above the crowd's blackness, the basilica soared in the brilliance of its decorations like a flaming, protective bird. Under the dome, the chair dominated, still waiting for the hush she was sure would herald the coming of the Pope. Dotted near it were Swiss Guards, their uniforms—so improbable by daylight—now as right as votive candles.

"Michelangelo knew what he was doing when he designed those uniforms," Mrs. Engel murmured, to distract Miss Murphy, who sniffed.

"I've read that he did it one day when he was annoyed," she said coldly. "And whoever designed this stand must have been in the same state. It's not safe. Listen to that, will you?"

The stairs were creaking under the strain of heavily ascending feet. "Someone ought to stop them," said Mrs. Engel. "It was full long ago."

A young Irish priest standing near heard her and grinned. "In Italy, there's no such word as full," he said.

"If you ask *me*," said Miss Murphy, "the nuns are the worst. There's twice as many now as there were."

The priest chuckled. "They have a system," he said. "They spread themselves out, with their veils and all, and then move close together when other nuns come. They're a caution!"

They talk about them as if they were *people*, Mrs. Engel noted, amazed, but she supposed it was like being in a family. However, she argued to herself, they surely had more right to good places than—well, someone like herself. Or *sight-seers*, she added scathingly as two stolid British tourists, complete with binoculars, increased the standees. If the nuns had their rights, then so had Miss Murphy hers, and she ought to assert them. Mrs. Engel was getting confused, but she was also getting angry. She glared at the binoculars and turned to Miss Murphy, who had subsided into misery.

Mrs. Engel couldn't bear it. "Get down there, Miss Murphy," she ordered peremptorily. "Get right down there in front."

"Me?" said Miss Murphy, startled. "There's no room there."

"*Make* it!" said Mrs. Engel. "Everyone else does, and you have more right. Go *on*. Tell them your sister's a nun." Miss Murphy looked uncertain. "*Per favore, attenzione*," said Mrs. Engel to the air. "*La sorella della signorina*——" She stopped. "I don't know the Italian for 'nun,'" she said, "but you go *on down.*"

Miss Murphy, suddenly spurred, thrust herself forward. Mrs. Engel watched as she edged and pressed and insinuated herself, inch by inch, down through people, between people, until she was miraculously in a corner of the lower tier, by the railing, where at first she clung, and then knelt, to lean over it for an unobstructed view. Mrs. Engel sighed with relief.

"Why don't you have a go at it yourself?" asked the young priest, who had been watching with amusement.

Mrs. Engel shook her head. "I couldn't," she said, and hoped he would understand. "You see, I'm not a Catholic."

The priest smiled. "Better stay where you are now, anyway," he said. "It's almost time Holy Father was here."

Mrs. Engel froze. In her concern for Miss Murphy, she had almost forgotten the Pope, and he was coming. She straightened her hat and tried to wedge herself more firmly onto the bench. Soon everything would be quiet, she knew, and she wouldn't want to move then or disturb anyone.

"*Mama!*" cried the Italian family beside her, and reached ecstatic hands toward a panting old woman, hung with rosaries, who made her way to them. They pulled her down to the bench almost obliterating Mrs. Engel, and burst into the volubility of people reunited after many years. "They'll stop any moment now," Mrs. Engel told herself, as she was pushed to the very end of the bench. She thought of the hush, and the Pope borne high to the dais, and she gripped her hands together to stop them from shaking. Then, all at once, as if some wordless signal had been given, the shuffling and the chatter were arrested, and a strange intensity took their place, as if something unseen were gathering itself in. From far back in the church came a murmur.

"He's coming," said the young priest, almost to himself, and Mrs. Engel saw his face whiten. The murmur rose and became a clamor: "*Viva!*" Mrs. Engel heard. "*Viva il Papa!*" The cry rose and was repeated. "*Viva il Papa!*" screamed a woman near her in the stand, and Mrs. Engel felt the crowd go mad around her. Everyone was standing, leaning forward; the shouting grew until it was a wall of sound. The Pope was there, below her, she thought, and she couldn't *see* him. Some people clambered onto the benches, to stand. She tried to climb onto hers, but there was no room there. She was in a well, she thought, a tight, dark well, while the people around her, who made the well, roared an acclamation to the Pope she couldn't see. Then the noise lessened, and a voice floated out and up. The Pope was speaking, she realized, and she strained frantically to hear him. A half-understood phrase here and there told her he was welcoming the groups below in their several languages, going from one to another quite easily. Then, almost before she could take them in, the words came in English, pure and almost unaccented: ". . . our blessing to you and all your family and friends. . . ."

"Oh, *please*," she heard herself say aloud. "I want to *see*." She actually whimpered, and, from behind her, hands clasped her waist, and she was lifted into the air. She had one dazed glimpse of the figure in white rising from the chair on the dais before she was put down again. She turned and saw who had lifted her. It was the father of the Italian family, who was standing above her on the bench. *"Mille grazie,"* she said, but he didn't hear her. He was looking out and down, his middle-aged eyes childlike with tears. The people were now getting down from the benches. Mrs. Engel felt panic. It's over, she thought. It's all over, and I've missed the blessing. But no one left, and the complete hush that Mrs. Engel had imagined would come when the Pope first entered came at last. All around her, and down in the church, the thousands dropped to their knees as one person, with a curious sound, like snow slipping from a roof. For a moment, Mrs. Engel stood alone, looking over the bowed heads before her, and now she saw the figure in white clearly. She saw the sweeping sign of the cross, and, light though the hand was that made it, it seemed to fill the length and breadth of the church. Then she, too, knelt.

The next half-hour was a blur. Mrs. Engel knew vaguely when the Pope left the dais and was carried down the nave; she followed his progress by the diminishment of the cheering. It stopped, and he was gone. Finally, Miss Murphy appeared, pale and tear-stained, her mantilla awry, her parcel of medals clutched in a death grip. Together they made their way out to the courtyard, where the car was waiting, and rode back to the hotel in shaken silence.

Mr. Engel was in the lobby, ready to take them to lunch. Miss Murphy refused. "I'm destroyed," she said. "I'll just have a cup of tea in my room above." She looked at them both. "It wasn't the way I thought it would be, it wasn't the way at all," she said. "All that pushing and shoving and screaming at him, and himself a saint!"

Mrs. Engel thought back on the shouting and the intensity and the tears. She touched Miss Murphy's hand. "Maybe that's the reason for it," she said.

Miss Murphy's eyes filled. "Well, anyway, we saw him," she said, and an unexpected humor creased her face into a smile, "in spite of our special seats."

The Engels went alone to the garden for lunch. "What did *you* do this morning?" Mrs. Engel asked after she had given an account of hers.

"I saw the Pope," said Mr. Engel.

Mrs. Engel flushed. "I don't think it's very funny to joke about it, after all I've told you."

"I'm not joking," said Mr. Engel, prodding a piece of pastry. "I went to St. Peter's and saw the Pope. Here." He took a medal from his pocket and slid it across the table to her.

She took it up. "It's a St. Christopher," she said.

"Isn't that what you wanted?"

"Of course."

"It's blessed," said Mr. Engel severely, "so don't lose it."

"But how? How did you *get* it blessed?"

"I told you. You wanted a medal, so I got one and took it to St. Peter's."

"But how did you get in? It was jammed."

"There was a crowd," said Mr. Engel judiciously, "but I went in, in back of it."

"*How* in back of it?"

"The crowd was all in the big center aisle," said Mr. Engel patiently, "but the side ones were fairly empty. I just walked up one till I got to where the Pope was speaking. When he was all through, he walked around by the railing where I was, and that's when I saw him near to."

"You mean you were *close* to him?"

"Not very—about like that." He indicated a tub of geraniums some six feet away.

"You mean without a ticket, without waiting, without *anything*, you just walked in and saw him?"

"Certainly."

Mrs. Engel drank a glass of water. "What was he like, close to? Were you impressed?"

Mr. Engel retreated from the query. "I don't know what you mean by 'impressed.'"

Mrs. Engel changed her approach. "I just mean *imagine* seeing him so *close*. What a shame you didn't have a camera."

Mr. Engel took on what his wife called his Rock of New England look. "I wouldn't have used it," he said stiffly.

"But why not?"

"It wouldn't have been respectful," said Mr. Engel.

His wife looked down at her plate, satisfied with his answer. It was how she had felt about wearing lipstick, only she couldn't explain why. She turned the St. Christopher medal in her hand; if it had been blessed, she suddenly thought, then so had Mr. Engel. She looked at him and smiled, and then put the medal into her handbag.

Mr. Engel caught the movement. "Be careful of it, now," he said. "Don't lose it."

"I won't," said Mrs. Engel. "I promise I won't."

Questions

1. How does the author achieve the gentle humor of this light-hearted story?
2. What kind of relationship exists between Mr. and Mrs. Engel?
3. Since Mrs. Engel is not a Catholic, why does the opportunity to see the Pope mean so much to her?
4. How does the author convey the atmosphere, both physical and psychological, of St. Peter's in Rome?
5. Why is the St. Christopher medal mentioned so often in "Benediction"?
6. Speaking of the crowding people around them in the balcony, Miss Murphy says to Mrs. Engel, "I'd not be surprised if they'd slept here." How do we know if she means it? What kind of a statement is it?
7. Why does Mrs. Engel have the impression "The church is full of caviar"?
8. Exactly what is the complication in this story, and what are the opposing forces that create the tension? (See p. 26.)
9. What is the dramatic irony of the story? (See p. 42.)
10. In what way does "Benediction" illustrate the humanities' concern with man's mortality and imagination?
11. Compare and contrast the marital relationship between Mr. and Mrs. Engel with that of Ivan and Masha in Chekhov's "The Lottery Ticket."

Mortality and Imagination: General Questions

1. What answers, if any, to the question, "Why must man die?" are suggested by "The Man of Adamant," "The Sisters," and "Holiday"? What answers, if any, do these stories suggest for the question "What can man do about the inevitability of death?"

2. How are man's religious faith and his attitudes toward faith revealed by "The Man of Adamant," "The Sisters," and "Benediction"?

3. Does the improbability of the action in "The Man of Adamant," "Metzengerstein," and "The Affair at 7, Rue de M——" make the themes and/or characters of the stories unbelievable? Why? Why not? Are there different degrees of believability among the three fantasies? (See p. 17.) If so, in which stories is the imaginative quality a compensating factor? What conclusions can you draw as to the capacity of man's imagination to give order and meaning to the chaos of experience, whether the experience is improbable or not?

4. How is time handled by each of the six authors in the Mortality and Imagination section of this book? Define *time* as it affects man and as these stories reflect how time affects man.

MORE STORIES ABOUT MORTALITY AND IMAGINATION

"A Municipal Report" by O. Henry
"An Occurrence at Owl Street Bridge" by Ambrose Bierce
"A Simple Heart" by Gustave Flaubert
"Goodbye, My Brother" by John Cheever
"Laughter" by Vardis Fisher
"Rip Van Winkle" by Washington Irving
"The Lesson of the Master" by Henry James
"The Lottery" by Shirley Jackson
"The Man Who Would Be King" by Rudyard Kipling
"The Pedestrian" by Ray Bradbury

Stories by Students of Short Fiction

Introduction

Most of the stories in this book are by men and women generally acknowledged to be artists of short fiction. Each of these recognized authors has mastered his art, and each has done so, in part, through prior close reading of other authors' art. Each story so far has demonstrated the qualities of universality and individuality. Some are more artistic than others, but each has merit worthy of close reading, and each gives some kind of artistic pleasure to the reader.

Not yet established as artists of short fiction are the young writers of the stories in this last section of the book. These young men and women, now in college, wrote the stories while they were seniors in high school and analyzing the stories written by artists of short fiction. The student stories have varying degrees of individuality commensurate with the young writers' varying talents and mastery of techniques of form. All their stories have the quality of universality and deal with the same universal themes that the other stories in the book do.

"Noontide of the First Day" and "Leatherback" both illustrate the theme of Man and Nature. "What Mistake?" is chiefly concerned with the Man Alone theme but also treats of Love and Hate. "Leon" and "Checking-Out" illuminate the themes of Love and Hate and Youth and Age, but "Checking-Out" emphasizes even more the highly difficult theme to illuminate well, the theme of Mortality and Imagination.

These young people's stories are included to show how an understanding of the art of short fiction can lead not only to greater pleasure in our reading of short stories, but also to the equally great pleasure of writing them and giving other readers pleasure.

Noontide of the First Day

Jean Weir

The day was as perfect-tempered as if it had begun with prayer, sung hymns all morning, and now was kneeling on the bright-hot grasses to ask grace before noontide. David dropped a pebble onto the orange sailboat he had made from a sheet of his five-cent Rainbow tablet. He broke off a nearby cat-o'-nine tail stalk to push the sinking paper out of his private pool into the white brook current.

A hairy spider, colored the same grey as David's rock, scurried out of a cleft in the stone, and he threw her into the pool with a swing of the cat-tail. She settled lightly on the surface film, not even breaking it until she began to struggle. Desperately but blindly she paddled around in swift circles. At last David rescued her with his stick and slipped her off into a hillock of tangled grass and forget-me-nots. Then he tossed the cat-o'-nine-tail stem into the air, flicking it with his fingertips so that it turned a somersault before splashing into the brook. The noise of its fall brought a sense of power to David. It was the only man-made sound he could hear.

From a grove of trees farther up the brook issued a shrill, electric buzz like the amplified squeal of fingernails on slate. It was an old July sound, one David remembered from all the summers he had known—the hot rasp of a locust. David could feel its vibrations along his arms and legs, down his back, even through his stomach, and with a fuzzy sensation in his thumbs as though a cocoon were being wound over them. He made fists, squeezing his thumbs to ring the fuzz out of them.

Then, by standing broad jumps, he sprang from rock to rock to grass clump, until he had crossed the marshy spot formed by the backwater pool and reached the lower grounds of the dry pasture slope. Like a big, squat spider, he scampered up the gentle rise, narrowly but grace-fully missing the cakes of cow manure which were drying in the sun, drawing dirt and great iridescent flies to themselves and steaming their peculiar fragrance into an air already delicious with the warm summer smells of hay, dust, pasture flowers, and juniper. His ankles bleeding a little from the scratches of the wild raspberry vines which laced the pasture, David stopped to rest under a shagbark hickory near the slope's crown.

Then, pretending he was a goat, he leaped across the tree's fat roots as he had crossed the pool on rocks and hillocks. The naked ropes of roots led to the top of the slope, the place David called the Bridge or the Cliff, depending upon what he needed it for. Here the underlying rock appeared in an outcropping of quartz-flecked grey gneiss, like a cutting tooth cradled among spongy folds of gum. The formation looked as though a slice had been taken from the hillside to reveal that face of bedrock, with sandy, pebbly banks on all other sides gently curving from the summit to the brook and swamp below. The surface of the gneiss was seamed and slanting enough for one to creep down it, using the cracks and protruding quartz for grips and footholds.

David seated himself on the rock, pressing his palms into the granite until its pattern was imprinted upon them, dangling his calves down the incline so that the sharp quartz points pricked him agreeably. Among the brook trees the locust again grated. David turned to one side to bring his legs level along the rock; then he bent his knees and stood upright.

He decided to play a game with the locust, to try to scramble through the barbed-wire fence separating his yard's soft lawn and white clover from the fat pink clover and velvet mullein leaves of the pasture before the next locust rasp. He darted toward the gate, spreading his arms like wings to sail over wild-rose bushes and buttercups, dipping his right arm low in flight when he passed a juniper clump in order to snatch a half-handful of blue needles for tossing up in rapid offering to the sun, or air, or whatever happened to want an offering at the moment.

Before David was two rose-bushes past the juniper, he heard the locust again. But now it was no longer a pungent summer sound; it was a fear, the same fear that filled him when he woke at night to sense thunder in the distance, to hear a storm crawl closer and closer like the train in his railroad dream, where he would hop off a solitary track to find that another had grown under his feet, and another and another, each with a train rushing toward him on it, until there was no sanctuary left for him.

Now it was life and death for David to be through the fence before the locust crowed again. He dropped his arms and ran fiercely, crouching a little, straining in panic even the muscles of his throat. Arriving at the two fence posts which had once marked a real gate, but now only leaned tipsily, drawn toward each other by the barbed wire criss-crossed around their upper halves, he hurtled through the gap next to the ground. Sand, shreds of withered grass, and the partly pulverized leaves from the apple tree close by clung to his jeans, like common pins to a magnet.

He ran between the two garden plots and across the lawn to the back doorway before brushing the dirt from his knees. A silver tiger kitten clawed at the cuffs of his jeans. David lifted it in his palm and cuddled its warm head under his chin. The pointed staccato rhythm of its heart struck upon his forefinger, and the vibrations made him conscious of his own pulse, which beat in a rhythm different from that of the kitten's. The discord between the two brought a faintly sick feeling to his stomach. Gently he tossed the kitten onto the grass and entered the house.

Just before he shut the door the locust shrilled again. He shivered, then walked quickly from the humid darkness of the entryway into the kitchen, where lunch was waiting.

Guest Commentary by a Teacher

Nature against man—this is the conflict at the heart of Jean Weir's story. The sensitive boy David, alone in the woods, reacts to the world about him. The sense of power that follows his play with the hairy spider and the cat-tail stalk is challenged by "an old July sound," the hot rasp of a locust, "a shrill, electric buzz like the amplified squeal of fingernails on slate."

The challenge comes again, and David makes a game of the race home before the third rasp reaches him. But it comes before he "was two rose-bushes past the juniper." And the game gives way to war; the power he had felt becomes fear, and "Now it was life and death for David to be through the fence before the locust crowed again."

The conflict is as old as man's consciousness. The persistent rasp of the locust is a fitting symbol of the nameless dreads that nature has evoked since the earliest man fled to his cave to propitiate those unseen forces before his altar of stones—since, indeed, the noontide of the first day.

Miss Weir's use of language is sensitive. The first sentence sets the tone: "The day was as perfect-tempered as if it had begun with prayer, sung hymns all morning, and now was kneeling on the bright-hot grasses to ask grace before noontide." This is heightened prose, but the consistency of language, sentence after sentence, works its magic; and the reader comes to respond as if he were reading poetry. The exact expression, the sensuous image, the flow of word-rhythms all bespeak the poet, even though the medium is prose fiction.

The matching of language with theme adds to the story. Nature's enmity is one of man's earliest experiences (it is significant that David is young). Those feelings aroused by the experience can best be reached by language that leads directly to them, words that suggest by the senses they excite. The nameless fears are, after all, nameless—they can only be suggested. Miss Weir achieved what she wanted, and her story remains a fine example of the poetry that can be made of prose.

Harold Keables
Denver South High School

Questions

1. At what point in the story does a change occur in the boy? Contrast the pace of the language before and after the change. What is the emotional effect of this change in pace? (See p. 40.)
2. Early in the story the author foreshadows the threat of nature. How does she supply this clue?
3. Besides the clarity of the imagery, the aptness of figurative language contributes to the story's poetic quality. Find examples of metaphor and simile that make the description vivid and further intensify the emotion.
4. How does David recover from his rising fears? Is nature at work in any way at the close of the narrative?
5. Contrast the actions of David with those of the boy in "Patricia, Edith and Arnold."

Leon

Carolyn Lansden

I drive a CTA bus. It's not hard, really, once you get used to steering from a position above and in front of the wheels. I don't drive a bus all the time. In the winter I'm a student at the university.

I never know what run I'm going to get until I check in at the depot. Usually I get Wacker or La Salle or Congress, but last week I got Jackson Street.

You meet all kinds of people on a bus—old women, kids, drunks, hoods, lonely people. Once I met the nicest Polish lady after I caught her accidentally in the rear door. She was so short, I swear I didn't even see her. I just closed the doors, and then some people in the back of the bus started to yell, so I opened the doors again and went to check. She just stepped down, smiled, and said, "*A dank*." A lady my busdriver friend Steve caught in his doors threatened to sue him for two thousand bucks, but another passenger told her to shut up, and she got off like a grouchy hedgehog. You meet all kinds of people on a bus.

But, anyway, this Jackson Street run goes right through the middle of the mayor's pride and joy, the new slum clearance district. A lot of people think it's a great thing and it is. But some people can't stand to live in layers, one plain apartment on top of another, with no porches to sit on at night. And many people like to own their own houses, even if it is only a dirty dump.

The new apartments keep some of the city clean, but a lot of families still live in the uncleared sections. On a hot night lots of teen gangs are prowling around, but they like alleys and stay away from the bus streets unless they feel like intimidating a driver for kicks.

Late at night, though, most people go home or somewhere to sleep, and the bus run can get pretty lonely around three in the morning. Any passenger is welcome at that time. Last Tuesday was no exception.

I pulled into a stop and waited for the light to change. There was a soft knocking at the door. I hadn't opened it because I had seen no one at the stop. But here was a little boy in dirty pants, tennis shoes, and faded green jacket, standing waiting to get onto the bus.

"What are you doing up so late, sonny?" I said. He couldn't have been more than nine. "Come sit here."

He made no answer but got in and sat in the seat across from my driver's booth.

I had never seen such beautiful eyes in my life. The black of the pupil spilled into the iris; all was one solid color, contrasted perfectly against the white.

"What's your name?" I said.

"Leon."

"Are you lost, Leon?" I asked, as if talking to my kid brother.

"No."

"Don't you think it's awfully late for you to be out?"

No answer.

"Where do you live, Leon?"

Feeling sure he was tired of questions, I asked only one more. "Would you like to wear my cap?"

Immediately he smiled, and his teeth glittered for an instant as a passing headlight reflected off them.

The stop light had changed several times during my soliloquy. I pulled away from the curb remembering that I had a strict schedule to keep.

From the corner of my eye I could see Leon looking at himself in the window or running down the aisle to jump on the last seat. He soon tired of this, and, feeling talkative, he asked, "What's in your box?"

He had pulled out the surplus Army cartridge case I used for holding my transfers, punch, time tables, and change rolls.

In a little of a hurry to make up for lost time, I made the circuit and headed back for the stop at which I had found Leon waiting. He climbed on the seat and, as if there were fifty other people on the bus, pulled the buzzer to be let off. With great ceremony, he climbed down from the seat, gave me my hat, and got off the bus. As I pulled away from the curb, I waved and watched him return the sign and fade away.

At the station after checking in, I filled out my records and counted my money. I was missing five rolls of dimes and quarters. I searched carefully all over the bus. Surely, I must have let them fall beneath my seat. I hated having to make up for the loss with my own money, but that was the rule.

The next night it rained, and Leon was waiting at the bus stop. Again he played with my equipment and talked little. That night I was missing over twenty dollars. The suspicion I had had the night before was true. Leon must have stolen it. It made me mad to think a little kid would do anything like that at such an early age and espe- cially with the same innocent look in his eyes.

I tried to think of every excuse to pardon the boy—hardened by his environment, desperate for food, forced by his parents, helping some other person in need; but all I could think of was: he's a thief.

On Thursday night I had a drunk get on who fell asleep and lay out on the back seat, snoring like an old dog. I could hardly believe it, when as I pulled up for the same stop light, Leon was waiting for his ride.

As he climbed on, I gave him the coldest stare I could muster, but he merely kept the same expression, so innocent and so young. I didn't speak, but thought of the things I would say to the boy and of the best punishment for something like this.

The drunk in the back rolled off the seat and hit his head on the floor. I stopped, got up, stared at Leon sitting primly in his usual seat, and helped the fallen man off the bus into an all-night diner for a cup of coffee.

Leon's pure gaze followed me as I returned to the bus and slowly got aboard. Suddenly I turned around to frighten him and gripped him by his narrow shoulders.

"Why did you steal from me, Leon? Don't you know that's filthy dirty money and you're nothing but a dirty, rotten little thief? How could you do that? I'm your friend. I let you on the bus free and you stole from me. You stole from your *friend*, Leon. Kids like you really *ought* to be in jail."

I waited for him to cry or run or something, but he just sat there with those innocent black eyes staring right through me as my angry words fell limp on the floor.

"I'll make it up to you," he said and left the bus.

Questions

1. Analyze, interpret, and evaluate "Leon" by answering the questions on page 43-44 in "The Art of Short Fiction."
2. The author based this story on a true incident but fictionalized it by not having it end as the incident actually did. In the true

story the boy returned to the bus driver the next day and gave him two crisp, new twenty-dollar bills, refusing to say where he had got the money. Why would "Leon" be or not be a better work of short fiction if the author had made it end as the real-life incident ended?

Leatherback

Katherine M. Kittleman

The quiet water of the Atlantic parted easily as the *Nellie G* glided along in the early morning sunlight. Soon the village became a miniature behind the boat, and once in a while the new sun would reflect its rays playfully on the windows or gay roof of one of the faraway houses. The sea was dotted with lobster boats chugging sturdily through the peaceful water. All the boats were guided by their captains in the same direction—out to sea.

The skipper of the *Nellie G,* John Christopher, stood at the wheel, maneuvering the boat without difficulty over the long ocean swells. Occasionally his hand, patterned with veins that stood out blue against his tanned skin, reached for the cup of coffee sitting on the ledge to the left of the wheel. As he concentrated on the boat's course, one of the crew, an old seaman named Stanley Gaits, walked into the scanty pilothouse to pay his respects to the skipper.

"Mornin', John. The ocean sure is beautiful this morning, isn't it?"

"Yeah, it's much better than yesterday," John said, still calculating the distance separating the *Nellie G* from her lobster buoys.

"How's Linda and the boy?" asked Stanley.

"Just fine," was the absentminded reply.

Stanley moved on through the cabin and went outside.

By the time the red and white buoys were seen bobbing on the water, the twelve-man crew had almost finished preparing the lobster pots to be lowered overboard. The high stack of cages had disappeared, and in their place, the pots were attached separately to long ropes and lay on the deck like giant lunchboxes made of wooden slats. The pots were dragged to the side of the boat and lowered into the sea.

As John straightened from his task of submerging the pots, Ben Hanson, a stocky, muscular young man, approached him. Ben, who was generally considered first mate, said with anticipation in his rough voice, "I saw something black swimming in the water. It was just going under the stern, and now it's headed north." His massive chest was heaving with excitement. "Don't you think we should go after it and see what it is?"

"How big was he?" asked John.

"He must have been at least five feet long."

"Could you tell what kind of a fish it was?"

"Not exactly. It might have been a shark, but it didn't really look like one. No, I couldn't tell what it was."

"Well, we can't do any harm in looking it over. Don, swing the boat around due north and take her slow."

A well-built man in his early forties turned and sprinted easily toward the small wooden pilothouse. His agile fingers gripped the wheel and spun it in the specified direction while Ben and John watched the surrounding waters intently.

For several minutes nothing except the turning of the *Nellie G's* engine could be heard in the morning stillness. Even the seagulls seemed to stop their shrill cries and glide silently overhead.

"There he is!" Hanson's booming voice interrupted the quietness. "Look over starboard, and you can just see his back."

"Cut engine!" John followed Ben's hand until he too could see the creature's hulk in the distance. When the boat had sidled closer, what appeared to be a large fish emerged with a movement that was almost imperceptible and lay for a few seconds, partially exposed on the surface of the sea, floating, bobbing gently, only to fall back hidden by the water.

The men stared in amazement.

"That's no shark."

"Did you see those ridges on its back?"

"I never saw a shark surface on its stomach before."

The tiny spark of an idea in the back of John's mind exploded. "Boys, I think I know what it is. It's not a fish at all. It's a turtle, a tropical sea turtle. Look at that soft shell."

"A leatherback?" one of the men asked.

"Yeah, and I wonder what it's doing up in these cold waters."

"I'd sure like to see him up close," said Ben.

"Well, let's catch him and get a better look," replied the skipper.

After John had finished speaking, the crew started preparing for the momentous task of catching the turtle. With Don guiding the boat and the skipper directing the hurried activity taking place on the *Nellie G's* decks, all thought of lobsters was forgotten. At the opportune moment Don steered the boat in closer to the turtle, which was resting quietly on the smooth surface of the ocean.

"All right, move in on him, Don," John directed. Turning to the other men, he said, "Remember to aim the harpoons at the joints of his flippers. With a harpoon ripping at his shoulder he'll tire out fast."

As Hanson picked up one of the long, deadly harpoons and inspected it reverently, his dark, wide-set eyes glistened, and his lips parted in an eager smile. He said to Gaits, who was straightening the lengths of rope attached to the spear, "Can't you just see the faces of the guys in town when we haul in the old turtle? And those tourists, by Jove, they'll be gawking for days!"

"Yep, there sure is something thrilling about an animal that size. But it's a tough job catching a sea turtle alive," Gaits replied with a far-off look in his eyes as if he were recalling experiences long cherished in his memory. His tired face lightened, and his eyes were animated with anticipation.

Now they were close behind the turtle—close enough to shoot. The twang of the fired harpoon and the snapping of the rope as it flew after the spear made Gaits quiver with delight. But as one of the harpoons was deflected off the turtle's hide and the other one embedded itself in its lower back, the startled creature reared and then disappeared into the water, leaving both harpoons broken on the surface.

There was silence.

Then Hanson spoke in amazement, "That turtle was more than five feet long. He must have been at least eight!"

He turned to the skipper who was giving orders to prepare for the second attack on the turtle. "Charlie, get the rest of the harpoons. Bailey, grab the gaff. Oh, and the lines—here, Ben, haul them out and straighten their coils. And you, Gaits, get some of the others and clear off the deck. Adams," he shouted toward the cabin, "head sou'east at two knots."

The skipper watched the waves intently as he stood amidst the confusion, absorbed in his own thoughts. "For my own satisfaction I've got to bring in that turtle no matter how I do it."

But the task proved harder than he had expected because now the turtle was on its guard. Every time the *Nellie G* closed in on it, the massive ridged back rose and by powerful flippers was carried under the water and far out of sight. This performance was repeated frustratingly for close to an hour. At last John said, "All right, Jackson, get the rifle from the cabin." The nodding of heads showed the crew's approval of the skipper's intention.

"We'll show that old leatherback that he can't get away," boasted Hanson, his eyes lighting up at the prospect of killing the turtle. "What a squall we'll stir up bringing in a haul like this."

But the enthusiastic glow and determination that had lighted Gaits's eyes, colored his sallow cheeks, and strengthened the sagging line of his mouth were gone. His gray hair was matted, and his worn sweater sagged loosely over his spare shoulders.

"Now, Ben, since you're about the best person here with a gun at long range, you'll do the firing."

"Sure, John."

Ben talked with John while the boat gained on the turtle. "Say, what are these leatherbacks good for anyway?"

The skipper thought for a minute. "Nothing that I know of. You can't eat them, and their shells aren't worth anything either. I suppose an aquarium would take them."

Soon the *Nellie G* was approaching the turtle again. Just at the proper moment Ben lifted the rifle, closed his left eye, and pulled the trigger. The mass of blood that gushed from the wound and covered the stunned turtle's neck contrasted grotesquely with its dull brown skin. And on the boat they praised Ben for his skill.

The main attraction in the busy fishing village that afternoon was the turtle. It lay in the hot sun on the wharf, still alive—for turtles die very slowly. And even though the caked blood concealed much of its small head, the turtle's fierce eyes and formidable expanse of mouth were visible to the passers-by who often gazed, slightly awed, at the sight. Its back resembled strips of tough, hard leather sewn together crudely so that the seams were uneven and bumpy, and its giant flippers lay useless by its enormous sides.

Stanley took all this in as he stood, hands in pockets, staring at the turtle until he was shaken from his contemplation by a crewman from the *Nellie G* who was sauntering down the pier with a friend. "And one bullet stunned him fast. . . . Yeah, he weighed almost two thousand pounds."

Stanley slowly walked down the wharf.

The sky was still clear and blue when the *Nellie G* chugged away from the dock the next morning. John stood at the wheel as usual, whistling softly to himself. And, as before, he was intent upon his destination. Only this time he was not headed for the lobster buoys, but a place beyond them. There was also unusual activity on the decks of the *Nellie G*, and when John stopped the boat, the crew did not fall to their customary tasks of lowering the lobster pots.

The reason for the change in routine was the turtle. It was lying in
the middle of the deck, dead, its eyes sunken far into its head and its
mouth slightly opened.

"Get that block and tackle under way, boys. We can't take all day
doing this job," said John.

The turtle was slowly lifted from the white boards with great effort
and lowered over the side into the peaceful water of the Atlantic. As
it was released, its leaden body sank beneath the surface at once.

Stanley watched until the bubbles no longer appeared, and then
he turned and walked away.

Guest Commentary by a Student

The exotic in nature holds a fascination for mankind. In "Leatherback" the turtle entrances the crew of the *Nellie G.* The captain is
dominated by a desire to capture the turtle, but his pursuit is moti-
vated not by a love of nature, but by a desire to capture and conquer
nature. He is aided in his pursuit by his first mate, who hunts the
leatherback for the same reasons. Stanley Gaits is the only member
of the crew who wants to capture the turtle, far away from its natural
haunts, for another reason: he loves nature and wants to view it
more closely in order to understand it better.

The captain pursues the turtle for a more subjective reason: "For
my own satisfaction I've got to bring in that turtle no matter how I
do it." Likewise, Ben Hanson flings the harpoon and fires the rifle
to accomplish his end of conquering nature for the sake of conquest.
He and John Christopher also seek a thrill and satisfaction from the
chase and the kill. The amoral turtle moves only to preserve its
life from the hunters of the *Nellie G.* From the conflict between
Christopher and the turtle evolves the conflict of inhumane man with
nature.

The theme of the story involves a further conflict. Stanley Gaits
wants to pursue the turtle and capture it alive. As long as the
object of the hunt seems to be merely capture, he is enthusiastically a
part of it. He wants to contemplate an object of nature alive and
firsthand, not stale and dead. His aim is not satisfaction through
conquest but satisfaction through contemplation. His attitude is
in conflict with the attitudes of Captain Christopher and his mate.
To Gaits, a creature of nature is something to be preserved; to the
others, he begins to discover, it is something to be destroyed.

The tensions aroused by this conflict of attitudes are shown by
the language of the story. The descriptions at first are sedately

flowing, but as the chase and the two conflicts begin, the language becomes more vivid. While the exotic turtle is alive, it attracts all the attention of the crew of the *Nellie G.* After it has been killed, it is merely a nuisance. The attraction which was to keep the tourists "gawking for days" is disposed of the next morning. The pace of the language slows down again accordingly.

The turtle had been the goal of a day's endeavor which would otherwise have been to obtain lobsters, which can be eaten and which bring a profit. The turtle cannot be eaten; its shell is worth nothing. Its capture had been profitless. The irony of man's empty victory over nature is apparent only to Stanley Gaits and the reader.

Warren S. Weber
Evanston Township High School '62
Wesleyan University '66

Questions

1. Dialogue is a functional literary device for revealing character. How does the author employ dialogue to develop the contrasting attitudes toward nature of Gaits and the captain?
2. How does the author capture the flavor of lobster fishing?
3. Why does she emphasize the "*quiet* water of the Atlantic," "the *peaceful* water," "the *peaceful* water of the Atlantic"?
4. Would the conflict of the story be as well developed if the narration were first person rather than third person? From which character's point of view might it have been told? (See p. 31.)
5. If the creature of nature in the story had been one more dangerous to man than the leatherback, yet equally useless, would your attitude toward the capture have been different? Why?

What Mistake?

James S. Renthal

I don't make many mistakes, in fact hardly any to speak of, because if I did I wouldn't be what I am today, second vice-president of the Dilworth Machine and Tool Company, and the name of Carleton B. Esch wouldn't mean what it does in Indianapolis. If I say so myself, and I often do, I'm one of a vanishing breed of Americans who still think that freedom and independence are not only worth dying for but living for, and it looks like that's just about the heaviest cross a man can bear these days when principles are as obsolete as an old washing machine and you're surrounded on all sides by incompetence and subversion and downright fraud. Those things creep right into your own home and make a mess of it.

That morning started like any other, only more so. In my opinion it takes a hearty breakfast to set a man up for the day, but as soon as I sat down and opened the morning paper I began to lose my appetite again. As usual the communists were pushing us around everywhere, in Laos, in South Vietnam, in Cuba, in all the places I always said they would. In Washington that boy was asking for more foreign aid which is supposed to be the answer to all our problems——not firmness, not laying down the law to a crafty peasant like Khrushchev who understands only one thing, tough talk, which anyone capable of simple reasoning knows. God almighty, we've got at least ten times the number of hydrogen bombs they have and they know it. I can remember saying, when this whole Laos business started, not to give those Reds an inch, drop the bomb on 'em, it's the only language they understand!

"Is anything wrong with your omelet, dear?"

I controlled myself. "No, there's nothing wrong with my omelet, it's about the only thing there's nothing wrong with." I didn't look at my wife. I can take just so much in the morning. It's that innocent way she has of worrying about an omelet when the house is burning down.

It was a good thing I had the foresight not to have a mouthful of egg or I would've gagged when I saw my daughter come breezing down the stairs. She was wearing a filthy sweatshirt and soiled bluejeans and torn gym shoes, and she had that quiet but defiant look that always ends up driving me to the tranquilizer bottle.

"Where do you think you're going?" I asked calmly and reasonably.

She sat down and poured herself some coffee, knowing I have firmly and repeatedly stated that a girl who will drink coffee while she's only a junior in high school will drink God knows what before she graduates.

"Just a meeting," she said.

I took a deep breath. "What kind of meeting?"

"You'll be late, Carleton——" my wife began her usual defensive maneuvers.

"I asked a simple question!" I said, with restraint. "And I expect a simple answer!"

"It's not exactly a meeting, it's a demonstration," said Laura. "As a matter of fact, it's a peace march to demonstrate public feeling in favor of banning the bomb."

I could feel the blood drain from my face. I tried to steady myself by gulping down some coffee but it only sploshed on my pants.

"Would you mind telling me," I said when I managed to compose myself, "how a girl who is the product of a good home, fine schools, a respectable community, a girl who is not really feeble-minded but only spoiled, indulged, privileged, how such a girl can be taken in by a bunch of lunatics out to destroy that home, that community, that country and everything she enjoys in it?" I paused for breath.

"On the contrary, I'm trying to——"

"Don't tell me what you're doing, I'll tell you! You're proving that your home has failed you, your school has taught you nothing! You're proving that the speech I plan to give next week to the Freedom Fighters of America doesn't go nearly far enough in demanding that this country return to the virtues——!"

She was on her feet, quivering. "The Freedom Fighters of America! Really, Father, sometimes I wonder about you!"

"Sit down, you're not going anywhere!" I shouted. I rarely raise my voice.

"It's getting late, Carleton——" my wife began again.

"I know, I know it's late! I should've strangled her in her crib before letting her grow up to become a dupe of subversives and beatnik slobs!"

"And I suppose," replied Laura, "you've got a better way, you've got security——!"

I could feel a sinus headache coming on. It was a good thing the phone rang at that moment.

It was Harry Johnson, of the Johnson and Johnson Contracting Company.

"Aren't you ever in your office?" I demanded. "I called you three times yesterday."

"Somethin' wrong over there, Mr. Esch?" he asked in that hearty voice all crooks and bunglers seem to have.

"In the first place," I said coldly, "your bricklayers and plumbers and carpenters left a mess all over the back yard. I want the place cleaned up."

"Sure thing, Mr. Esch. Trouble was, a lot of curiosity-seekers were gettin' in the way."

"And in the second place, the ceiling in the shower stall is too low!"

"You don't take a shower with your hat on, do yuh?"

"I don't like taking a shower with my knees bent," I said firmly. "What's more, Mr. Johnson, there's a leak somewhere, you better get someone here right away!"

"I'll be right over myself."

I hung up and caught a last look at Laura through the window. She was climbing into one of those little foreign cars that are a menace on the streets, and a threat to the economy, and hanging out of one window was a sign: BAN THE BOMB.

"It's getting late, Carleton——" my wife began again. I can't stand that woman's timidity.

I almost wished I didn't have to go to the office, but it was Saturday and Miss Steinhagen, my secretary, was coming in just to type my speech for the FFA meeting and run off dittos of the program with brief biographies of the speakers. Besides, Miss Steinhagen never got anything right unless I watched her every minute. I gathered my papers and stuffed them into my briefcase and started toward the garage. I was half way there when I noticed a squeaky sound as I walked. I looked down and saw that the grass was soaked, the way it gets after a heavy rain. For a moment I thought it was dew, but I knew it wasn't when I stepped in a low spot and sank in water up to my ankle.

Just ahead I could see the vent pipe coming out of the ground not far from the garage and when I noticed how wet the ground was around there, my sinus headache got really bad.

"Somethin' ain't right here," I heard Mr. Johnson say——he came up behind me, shaking his head and repeating, "By God, somethin' ain't right."

He followed me down the bulkhead to the emergency door and I heard my wife gasp behind us. We could see in through a small window and it looked like a disaster area. The furniture was submerged like sunken boats, some of the smaller pieces were floating in the dark water up near the ceiling, and all the canned food had the labels washed off.

"Ain't that somethin'!" said Mr. Johnson. "By God, it looks like the sewer is backin' up into your fallout shelter."

It was almost noon when Miss Steinhagen began running off the dittos. I must admit I was a little shaken there for a while, but it was wearing off. I picked up the first ditto and read the brief biography of myself, and I began to feel better. Carleton B. Esch, second vice-president of Dilworth Machine and Tool Company, one of the biggest manufacturers working on a government defense contract in the Indianapolis area. . . .

I sat back and relaxed for the first time that morning as I watched the carbon copies pile up.

Guest Commentary by a Student

The problems that have been caused by American materialism and the search for security compose the subject of Jim Renthal's short story "What Mistake?" Through description of action and with imagery, the author observes and judges the characters of his story who are pursuing the American dream of equal opportunity for all.

The characters are presented through the point of view of the narrator and central character, Carleton Esch. Despite this speaker's personal prejudice, the spineless, overly anxious character of his wife and the rebellious, determined nature of his daughter Laura are clearly evident to the reader. Esch's own narrow-mindedness, false egotism, and straining for security are revealed by his words of praise for himself.

Although the businessman proudly identifies himself as "one of a vanishing breed of Americans who still think that freedom and independence are not only worth dying for but living for," it is obvious that Esch is not only conservative, but also unreasonably reactionary and socially irresponsible. Instead of showing his intelligence in appraising foreign affairs in Laos and Cuba, Esch illustrates his emotional bias by calling Khrushchev a "crafty peasant," who "understands only one thing, tough talk." Esch further damns his own character by his actions. We find evidence of his unthinking, shallow nature when the pompous man continually complains of sinus headaches and dizzy spells during moments of crisis, yet is able to relax contentedly when he reads about himself as a manufacturer whose profits depend on the insecurity of a world threatened by war.

Esch proves even less compassionate toward others in his abrupt, scared response to Laura: "I should've strangled her in her crib before letting her grow up to become a dupe of subversives and beatnik slobs!"

In contrast to her father's actions, Laura's behavior is calm, intelligent, and determined. Instead of raging hotly against him as he has raged against her, she coldly responds to his rantings: "And I suppose . . . you've got a better way, you've got security—!"

Besides characterization, the author uses imagery and paradox to present the theme of the search for success by a man alone. By telling the story from the first person point of view, the author carefully paints a picture of not only the narrator's subject but also the narrator himself. Esch boldly, foolishly presents his story, generously bestowing virtues upon himself. Esch is revealed as a man whose idea of security and prosperity has been twisted until his concepts rest on a base of pure, selfish materialism.

Certain paradoxes and images also clarify and intensify the theme. The bomb becomes a symbol of man's inhumanity to man. Esch supports the bomb only because he has given up attempting to think out a problem; he is so afraid of losing his security that he falls back into reactionary ways. The Freedom Fighters and the fallout shelter also are identified as symbols of man's isolation and loss of compassion. The basic paradox is the double meaning of the word *security*. Although Esch believes that security can be attained by erecting a fallout shelter and fighting off other human beings, his security is ironically shattered by the flooding of his shelter. *Security*, therefore, is defined for the reader, not by Esch's terms, but by the implied opposite terms of love and thoughtfulness.

Katherine M. Kittleman
Evanston Township High School '62
Wellesley College '66

Questions

1. In "What Mistake?" allusions are made to current topics. Will they "date" the story? Do they detract in any way from the universality of the theme?
2. To what mistake does the title refer? Is it merely a mistake of the central character, or is it more of an ironic criticism of a society? To what extent can an author successfully use a work of art as a social commentary?
3. How does the symbol of the carbon copies of Esch's biography emphasize the irony of the story?

Checking-Out

Sarell W. Beal

The sounds of the bells and the songs of the priests commingled into one final lament. Then the service ended. The devoted began to stream out—disgorged by an over-filled church. The parishioners gathered into groups of three, four and five. The men laughed and shook each other's hands, and the women kissed each other's cheeks as their high heels clicked on the pavement.

Across the street, from the front porch of the Hotel Swain, the bell-man Neal watched with contempt.

The bunch of stumblers and mumblers, he cried to himself, look at 'em. Guided by God's words? Nuts.

A man and a woman in ill-fitting clothes and wearing lopsided smiles crossed the street, the insignificant barrier between church and hotel, in eager quest of an early Sunday dinner. Seeing them approach, Neal opened the large front door.

"Good afternoon," he said in the richly purring voice of an insincere minister.

"Yes, yes, hello there, boy." They entered without looking up.

Stuffed shirts, the bellman thought. Why should I sing the slop of politeness to them?

Neal turned on the pavement of the front porch, walking until he stood before the large colonial windows of the hotel lounge. Inside, visitors, seated on the plump cushions of the center sofas, talked before the glowing but artificial gas fireplace. The dwellers (just Mrs. Allan and Mr. and Mrs. Spense today) were sitting to the side—Mrs. Allan reading *Motion Picture Magazine* (God, she's at least 101 in the shade) —and Mr. and Mrs. Spense listening to the German music-box play Mozart's wedding march.

As the bellman watched from outside, two recently well-fed ladies who resembled fat quails stepped onto the porch.

"Oh, hello," they called. "We just loved our duckling dinner.

And we love the Hotel Swain too—it's so quaint and friendly."

Neal wondered, why do I have this job? Always having to be gracious and charming to the relics of this old dump—loving and caring like a horsetrainer, then one day being trampled to death.

He walked to the front door, opened it, and stepped into the small entryway.

Mr. Pette, the assistant manager, stood at the main desk, breathing words to the cornhusk doll of a switchboard operator. "Poor lamb, poor darling," his shifting voice intoned, "you're so tired, poor dear, and you like to be loved."

The lousy money—that's why I'm here. And who wouldn't take the dough? Ten dollar tips—if that's what they want, let 'em give it to me. I'll be anyone's little lamb for pay like that, Neal told himself.

The dining room hostess deliciously admitted the procession of people—the visitors and the dwellers—from the lounge into the luster-loveliness of the New French Cafe and Tea Room. The multi-fixtured chandelier above blessed and haloed her.

Quiet. Fantastic, salient quiet, when Neal, allowing himself the pretense of emptying the ash-trays, passed into the now deserted lounge. Completely alone, free from the fear of listening to other people, he was at ease for the first time that day. The lounge, smelling of cigar smoke, soundless and dark—the curtains drawn to protect the mahogany—resembled a tomb. Looking in the Louis XIV mirror, the boy saw his badly soiled uniform, his absurd, smiling bow-tie, and his freshly laundered white shirt.

Suddenly, tip-toeing softly, sighing rhythmically to herself, one of the old ladies of the Hotel Swain timidly sneaked in, piercing the silence with her almost noiseless shuffle. She selected a chair far from the few rays of the sun and far from the bellman.

Then, as if to make her presence known, she whispered just loud enough to be heard, "Young man, tomorrow will be my eighty-ninth birthday." She paused. "But it sounds more stimulating to say I'm going into my ninetieth year, doesn't it?"

Isn't that a one for you, Neal asked himself. "Did you say something, ma'am?" he said, trying to ruin the conversation.

He had seen this woman only when she allowed herself to be seen—like a shadow which appears but rarely and only under the right conditions. She was dressed in grey—a neutral suit that enclosed her little body like drooping plumes. Her hands were lean and unblemished, and her fingers reached as they rested. On the left side of the high-buttoned collar glistened a black pin shaped into snaky coils. The woman's face was a souvenir of what once had been, almost assuredly, the beautiful. Neal watched her indifferent eyes as they scanned each of the antiques in the room: a china replica of *The Last Supper,* a small bronze cast of Jeanne D'Arc, and the yellowed Christian Science literature leaning drunkenly in a magazine stand.

The faintly mustached assistant manager entered proudly and, effortlessly ignoring the hired help, walked in quick, smooth strides toward the old woman.

"Good afternoon, Miss Osprey, the weather's fine—there's just a touch of a smile in the temperature. Wouldn't you like to sit on the porch?"

Miss Osprey, startled and cornered, could offer no resistance. She accepted his arm with a murmured "Yes."

Neal thought of all the pitiful old people who, in renouncing a lifetime, were only forced to renew it the next moment. What use were they to anyone anyway . . . ?

The desk bell was sounding once, twice. Something urgent.

"Go to 614—there's trouble—her pet, you know," complained the office girl.

Before Neal got there, the little girl's parakeet had died. Her mother put it in a used Kleenex box and gave it to Neal. The girl was already looking in a very fine book to discover how to train a new bird.

After throwing the dead parakeet in the incinerator, Neal returned to his post at the front door. He had watched the feathery form burst into flame. It reminded him of a movie—the victorious Viking king on his funeral pyre.

A man came up. Standing next to Neal, he peered out of the glass windows. The bellman hadn't seen him before, but his tie was beaming with bright red and pink stripes—a salesman.

"Nice place, here. Good business too. And valuable stuff."

"Yes sir," Neal countered. "We have many antiques here."

"Yeh, I know—I saw them walking in the halls."

He laughed but Neal didn't. Then Neal noticed that as the man talked, he was cutting his nails with one of those press-down nailclippers. The cuticles polka-dotted the red carpet on which they dropped. Neal turned away.

He turned to the window to forget the bird and the man, and he looked across the street at the church. Without crowds of curious sinners around it, the church was a beautifully composed shrine—calm on this clear-winded, comfortably clouded day. He stepped onto the porch to inspect the house of worship more closely.

It was then that Neal heard a guttural, almost ferocious growl. He wheeled to his right. Sitting in a large summer chair like a lesser god on the throne of Buddha, Miss Osprey was confronted by a big, brown, badly scarred mongrel. Woman and dog were rigidly staring at each other, immovable and very cautious.

The bellman felt Miss Osprey's helplessness. One of *his* old ones—*his* fossils that were of no use to anyone—needed him. They could sometimes ignore him or buy him off with tips—money and sweet words—but now, supremely, one of them needed him.

Neal lunged at the dog and kicked at it wildly. Baying blasphemies at humanity, the dog bolted.

"Are you all right, ma'am?"

"Yes, of course, I'm all right, young man, because I was not afraid." Miss Osprey's grey eyes tried to hide but exposed her lie.

Oh, they're proud, aren't they—these dames that sit and sigh all day like cripples, Neal thought.

"But, lady, you might have been hurt."

"It takes a little more than a stray animal to hurt me. . . . No, don't go away, lad—I wish to talk with you."

Neal recognized the incredible strength in her weak, whispered twitter. Why did she want him?

"You had a good time last night—your eyes look tired—perhaps you went to a party?" Miss Osprey asked.

What business is it of yours? Neal thought. Then he remembered that Miss Osprey had an Ol suite in the hotel—the very best. Better humor the old girl.

Last night, now what did I do last night? Oh yeh, I walked . . . walked on and on almost to the highway. It was a nice night—it rained on and off—no one was outside—the streets were mine.

"Was the party enjoyable, young man?" Miss Osprey asked again. The tone of her voice expressed annoyance at the forced repetition.

Party, what party? Neal questioned himself.

Then the memory of the events of last night became painful like an unexpected slap in the face.

"Oh, the party," Neal said. "Yeh, it was O.K."

Miss Osprey faintly heard him. She had only asked these questions as a pretext to tell Neal something vastly more important. Her face beamed a little.

"Do you know what I had last night, young man?"

The time-worn face lost its sternness, becoming soft and pleading. The news was so extraordinary. Someone must hear.

In the sunlight, her grey suit appeared faded and threadbare. Miss

Osprey herself seemed years older, as if this were the final moment and the dramatic last words would now be said.

"I had everything, young man, everything. I was no longer away, lost in a strange land. I was home. All my friends were there and papa and mama, too. And Peter was coming. Oh, what a lovely, grand party—a heavenly, heavenly engagement party."

Her voice cracked with all the stored-up agony of years thrown away.

"But Peter never came."

Neal felt he ought to act embarrassed.

Miss Osprey, however, was not watching.

"Do you have a mother, young—what is your name, lad?"

"Neal."

"Do you have a mother, Neal?"

With hesitation, Neal answered, "Yes." Occasionally, he said to himself. On her lonely nights.

"Then be good to her. Never let her cry. And, have you ever cried, Neal?"

Neal shrugged uncertainly.

"Oh yes, I had forgotten men don't cry," she smiled. But with the memory, her smile grew bitter and without assurance.

"I must go in—a wind is coming up. You have been good to a silly old lady. Here, take this."

"No, ma'am."

The old woman returned his compliment: she carelessly tucked the quarter away.

Neal took her arm and walked her to the door. He opened it. Arm in arm, the two walked through the lobby together.

Afterward, Neal went to the main desk. Good. Mr. Pette and the cornhusk doll had gone to the dining room for dinner. Maxye was at the desk alone.

Of all the people in the Hotel Swain—the ones who came in the front door and the ones who came in the back door—Neal liked Maxye best. Once she had worn green shoes and gone dancing. Now, she wore black and worked, because her "hubby" had died.

One of the fat, flabby old nurses was chatting excitedly to her. "Yes, we're going to fly out and I'm just thrilled. I've never been on an airplane before—they say you can get sick. But my granddaughter just insisted that I come to her wedding. And, oh Maxye, you should see my dress—yellow satin and chiffon and butterflies all over. I'm just thrilled. Would you call a cab for me, Maxye, like an old dear?"

"Hello, Maxye."

Maxye turned. She wore a red sash around the plump waist of the black, shiny dress. Glass beads sparkled on her neck. And her lips were shaped, after a fashion, by a smudge of lipstick.

"Hi, Sugar," she said. "Come on in and rest your feet."

Neal obeyed.

"Well, how's my boy today?"

"Oh, I'm O.K., I guess, Maxye," Neal answered. "How are you?"

"Yeh, well I'm all right too, Sugar. Tired though—I didn't get an ounce of sleep. I had the strangest dream. Here, have some candy—sweets for the sweet—that's what they say."

"Thanks. Maxye, tell me about your dream."

"Well, it was a queer one. I wish my hubby were here—he was great at explaining things.

"You see, I was up on the railroad tracks, trying to catch a Chicago train, but the only one that would stop was one going West. So I got on, but the people ignored me and wouldn't talk, so I tried to get off. But the big black man said no. Then, after hours and hours, I landed in a station. I was all alone. The train left without me. The station was full of dark tunnels, and every time I started to walk through one of them, I got scared and couldn't do it. I always went back to where I started. I tried and tried but I could never get out. And I cried for help and no one would come." Maxye shook her head. "That sure is one to take the cake, eh, Sugar?"

Neal, a little confused, said nothing.

An old man appeared before the desk window to inquire about the mail.

"No, Mr. Whipple. Today's Sunday—no mail on Sundays," Maxye said.

"Oh, but I've been expecting some important checks."

"I'm sorry, Mr. Whipple. How are you today?"

"I'll live. I was just resting in my room—or rusting. I'm not sure which."

Mr. Whipple wandered away.

The switchboard buzzed and a little yellow light flickered on the board. Maxye plugged in a line.

"That's funny," she said, after listening on the receiver. "301 has the phone off the hook but no one answers. Probably took it off to dial a number, then started doing something else."

The buzzing continued insistently like the staccato belches of a sub-machine gun.

"Well, I can't take this racket," declared Maxye. "You'd better go up and check. Here, take a room key. 301, Miss Osprey. And, Sugar, hurry up, so we'll have more time to talk before you-know-who gets back."

Neal was not annoyed though he usually got no tips for these pesty chores. Once again he would talk with Miss Osprey. He would tell her of himself—why he disliked other people and why he took long walks. No lies—each would understand everything. Maybe she might wonder where he came from and where he was going. He would tell her. Miss Osprey was his friend.

Neal knocked three times on the door.

"Miss Osprey."

He knocked again.

"It's Neal."

He reached into his uniform to the left-hand pocket of his white shirt. He touched the room-key, pulled it out and placed it in the lock. He turned the knob.

A portion of the room was exposed: a side table bearing a silver tea service, a stiff-backed pale red velvet chair, damask draperies, a green Tiffany lamp and a large pot containing a flowering Easter lily.

Neal entered. An overturned chair rested near the opened door of the closet. Miss Osprey lay withering on the floor. Her face and her grey hair were bathed with fresh blood flowing from a deep gash in her temple. The Persian carpet was already stained.

The eyes of the young man and the eyes of the old maid met for one final moment. Her outstretched hand seemed to flutter for recognition, as if to demand life—to be removed from the dying frame.

Neal waited, watching for some movement, for anything—for the most miniscule movement of a little finger. Nothing.

Feeling faint, Neal bolted from the room.

He took the freight elevator down, then hurried to the locker room.

Minutes later, Taki, a dining room waiter, came in to offer Neal some doughnuts and coffee.

"Yes sir," he said. "Guest in 301 just passed . . . last year, 205 passed . . . year before and the year before that, guests passed on. They just rest here—tired from years of living, and then pass on."

Neal waited silently as Taki left.

Mr. Pette entered to tell the bellman either to go home or to go back to the front door but not to upset things—it was the height of the dinner hour.

Neal walked into the lobby. The chandeliers dazzled his eyes. He passed the main desk.

"Yeh, isn't it a shame," Maxye was saying, "that little one dying like that. I mothered her for two weeks when she first came. And she remembered me at Christmas."

Neal stood alone for a moment. Then in slow, unsure steps he ambled to the entryway. He opened the front door, and the wind blew in.

He looked at the people sitting and standing on the porch like so much driftwood floating down the river. One said, "Yes, dead. They think she climbed onto a chair to get something from the top shelf of the closet. Must have lost her balance and fallen backward. Horrible way to go. And the only thing on the shelf was an old picture of a young man."

Neal looked across the street toward the solemn church.

Then he began to cry.

Questions

1. Read this story once, using the suggestions listed on page 21 of the chapter "The Art of Short Fiction."

2. Read this story a second time with the attitudes listed on page 22; then answer the questions on pages 30, 39-40, and 43-44.

Biographies and Critical Bibliographies

Ryūnosuké Akutagawa

(1892-1927)

One of the most outstanding short-story writers of modern Japanese literature, Akutagawa was born in 1892 in Tokyo, where he lived until his death in 1927. Very familiar with the classical literature of China and Japan and 19th-century Western literature, he studied in the English literature department of Tokyo's Imperial University. The publication in 1915 of his first story, "Rashomon," was the start of his literary fame. He wrote steadily for twelve years after that, publishing 150 short stories in seven collections, many of which have been translated into English, French, German, and Spanish. For the English translation of "Autumn Mountain" in this anthology, we are indebted to Dr. Ivan Morris, lecturer on Japanese history and literature at Columbia University and author of *Nationalism and the Right Wing in Japan*. "Autumn Mountain" is the title of Dr. Morris's translation of Akutagawa's story originally titled "Shuzan-zu," which is also the title of an ancient Chinese painting of mysterious origin.

Major Fiction

Novel
>   *Kappa* (1947)

Short Fiction
>   *Tales Grotesque and Curious* (1930)
>   *Hell Screen and Other Stories* (1948)
>   *Rashomon and Other Stories* (1952)
>   *Japanese Stories by Ryūnosuké Akutagawa* (1962)

Critical Bibliography for "Autumn Mountain"

Morris, Ivan, "Preface," *Modern Japanese Stories: An Anthology*. Rutland, Vermont, and Tokyo, Charles E. Tuttle Co., 1962, pp. 174-175.

Yuchi, Takashi, "Comment," *Introduction to Contemporary Japanese Literature*. Tokyo, Kokusai Bunka Shinkokai (The Society for International Cultural Relations), 1939, pp. 117-123.

Sarell Wood Beal

(1945-   )

The student short story "Checking-Out," which won the first-place award in *The Atlantic Monthly's* 42nd Annual Creative Writing Contest for High School Students (1963), was written by "Woody" Beal and inspired by his experiences as a bellboy in the North Shore Hotel, Evanston, Illinois. Particularly interested in history, he notes that April 3, 1945, when he was born in Pittsburgh, was the date on which three hundred B-29's pounded Japan. He attended schools in Evanston, where, in eighth grade, he won a Scholastic Writing Competition award, and where, in 1963, he graduated from high school. His family includes his grandmother, his mother, and a college-professor brother, whose undergraduate footsteps he is following at Williams College.

Björnstjerne Björnson

(1832-1910)

Second only to his contemporary Henrik Ibsen as a dramatist, Björnson is considered by his countrymen the greatest Norwegian novelist and one of the greatest Norwegian poets. He was born in the northern mountains of Kvikne, Osterdal, the son of a pastor, and spent his childhood in Romsdal. Björnson attended the University of Oslo; later he became a drama critic and began writing his novels and tales of peasant life. He was active in politics and influential in bringing about the separation of Norway from Sweden in 1905. Before that time he had been a political exile in Germany. In addition to writing plays, he was director of the theater at Bergen for two years. One of the original members of the Nobel Committee, he himself was the third recipient of the Nobel Prize for literature, in 1903. He died on April 26, 1910, in Paris, and his body was returned in state to his own land.

Major Fiction

Novels
>*Arne* (1858)
>*A Happy Boy* (1860)
>*The Fishermaiden* (1868)
>*Flags Are Flying in Town and Port* (1884)
>*In God's Way* (1889)

Short Fiction
>"The Father" (1881)
>*Dust* (1894)
>*Mother's Hands* (1894)
>*Absalom's Hair* (1894)

Ray Bradbury

(1920-   )

Although Ray Bradbury is known primarily as a writer of science fiction, his particular flair is for imaginative themes combining advanced technology and subtle fantasy. He was born on August 22, 1920, in Waukegan, Illinois. He attended public schools in Waukegan until 1934, when the family moved to California, where he was graduated from Los Angeles High School. He sold newspapers and held other odd jobs that allowed him time to devote to the storywriting that he had been doing ever since he was twelve years old. He has written almost two hundred short stories, twenty-five radio dramas, five television dramas that have been produced, and a number of motion-picture scripts. In 1947 he married Marguerite McClure, English instructor at the University of California.

Major Fiction

Novel
>*Dandelion Wine* (1957)
>*Something Wicked This Way Comes* (1962)

Short Fiction
>*Dark Carnival* (1947)
>*The Golden Apples of the Sun* (including "The Golden Kite, the Silver Wind") (1953)
>*The Illustrated Man* (1951)

C. D. B. Bryan

(1936-   )

This new young writer was born in New York City in 1936 and attended prep schools in the South and New England before going to Yale University. In 1958 he graduated from Yale and then served three years in the Army. Returning to civilian life, he was married and with his wife, Phoebus, has been living in New York City. He is an editor of *Monocle* and a writer of short stories, several of which have appeared in *The New Yorker*. "So Much Unfairness of Things" was his first *New Yorker* story; the character P.S. in that story has appeared in subsequent stories, causing much speculation as to whether he is a fictional counterpart of Mr. Bryan himself, who desires to keep his private life private.

Major Fiction

Novels (none)
Short Fiction (not yet collected in book form)

Albert Camus

(1913-1960)

The setting of most of this French author's fiction is Algeria, where he was born on November 7, 1913, at Mondovi. His father, an agricultural worker, was killed in the Battle of the Marne in World War I. Albert Camus grew up in poverty and was seriously ill during most of his school life at a *lycée* and at the University of Algiers, where he studied philosophy. He worked as a journalist, actor, writer of fiction, and dramatist. During World War II, he joined a French resistance group in 1942, and was editor of the underground newspaper, *Combat*. His early works, especially *The Myth of Sisyphus*, expressed his Existentialist philosophy, but he regarded himself more a moralist than a philosopher and disclaimed association with the Existentialist school led by Jean-Paul Sartre. Camus' masterpiece, *The Plague*, a novel unlike his earlier works that emphasized the theme of isolation, affirms the responsibility of the individual to the community. He received the 1957 Nobel Prize for literature. On January 13, 1960, he was killed in an automobile accident.

Major Fiction (translated into English)

Novels
> *The Stranger* (1946)
> *The Plague* (1948)
> *The Fall* (1957)

Short Fiction
> *The Exile and the Kingdom* (including "The Guest") (1958)

Critical Bibliography for "The Guest"

Barnes, Hazel E., "Self-Encounter," *The Literary Possibility: A Study of Humanistic Existentialism.* Lincoln, University of Nebraska Press, 1951, pp. 254-255.

Bree, Germaine, *Camus.* New Brunswick, Rutgers University Press, 1959, pp. 133-134.

Maquet, Albert, *Albert Camus: The Invincible Summer.* New York, George Braziller, 1958, pp. 174-176.

Picon, Gaeton, "Exile and the Kingdom," translated by Josephine Valenza, in *Camus: a Collection of Critical Essays* (Germaine Bree, editor). Englewood Cliffs, N.J., Prentice-Hall, 1962, p. 156.

Thody, Philip, *Albert Camus: A Study of His Work.* London, Hamilton, 1957, pp. 90-92.

Anton Chekhov

(1860-1904)

Anton Pavlovich Chekhov (or Tchekhov, Tchehov, or Chehov), Russian playwright and short-story writer, was born on January 17, 1860, in Taganrog on the Sea of Azov. He attended the local Gymnasium and the University of Moscow, where he studied to be a doctor. He practiced medicine for only a short time. He began writing while he was still a student. In 1887 he produced his first play, *Ivanov*. His most successful plays after that were *Uncle*

Vanya, The Seagull, The Cherry Orchard, and *The Three Sisters.* He married Olga Knipper, an actress, in 1901, a year after he was elected an honorary fellow of the Academy of Science, from which he later resigned as a protest against the government's cancellation of Maxim Gorky's election. Chekhov died on July 2, 1904, at Badenweiler in the Black Forest.

Major Fiction (translated into English)

Short Fiction
> *The Black Monk and Other Stories* (1915)
> *The Bet and Other Stories* (1915)
> *Russian Silhouettes* (1915)
> *The Duel and Other Stories* (1916)
> *The Wife and Other Stories* (including "The Lottery Ticket") (1918)
> *The Portable Chekhov* (1947)

Critical Bibliography for "The Lottery Ticket"

Brewster, Dorothy, and Burrell, Angus, *Modern Fiction.* New York, Columbia University Press, 1934, p. 359.

Patricia Collinge

(1894-   )

Primarily an actress but also a writer of short stories, Miss Collinge is Mrs. James Nichols Smith in private life. She lives in New York City with her husband and spends summers on Nantucket Island. Born in Dublin on September 20, 1894, she went to schools in Dublin and made her theatrical debut at the Garrick Theater in London when she was ten years old. In the United States she has appeared in the plays *The Little Foxes, The Heiress,* and *I've Got Sixpence.* She received an Academy Award nomination for her performance of Birdie in the motion-picture version of *The Little Foxes.* Other films in which she has appeared are *Shadow of a Doubt, Teresa, Washington Story,* and *The Nun's Story.* Miss Collinge has also appeared in a number of television dramas. As a writer, she has been published in several magazines, chiefly *The New Yorker.* Her short story "Chow!" received the Italian *Premio Enit* gold medal.

Major Fiction

  Novels (none)
  Short Fiction
    The Small Mosaics of Mr. and Mrs. Engel (including "Bene-
      diction") (1959)

Joseph Conrad

(1857-1924)

  The son of a literary Polish revolutionist, Teodor Josef Konrad
Korzeniowski was born on December 3, 1857, at Berdichiev in the
Polish Ukraine. He spent a childhood in an atmosphere of political
unrest, and at eleven, an orphan, he went to school in Cracow. From
his reading he became fascinated by the sea, and he joined the French
merchant marine when he was nineteen. When his ship touched
England, he began to study English, the language which he was to
master by the time he was forty and writing fiction. He became known
as one of the greatest stylists of the language. Becoming a British
mariner and a British subject, he took the name Joseph Conrad. The
mysterious sea and fatalistic, exotic lands, including the Congo, to
which his travels took him, became the colorful background of the
books he wrote. Married, he settled in England in 1888, and was a
close friend of numerous literary figures, notably the Britisher Ford
Madox Ford and the American Stephen Crane. Conrad devoted
the remainder of his life, until August 3, 1924, to writing.

Major Fiction

  Novels
    Almayer's Folly (1895)
    Outcast of the Islands (1896)
    The Nigger of the "Narcissus" (1897)
    Lord Jim (1900)
    Nostromo (1904)
    The Secret Agent (1907)
    Under Western Eyes (1911)
    Victory (1915)

Short Fiction
>*Tales of Unrest* (1898)
>*Youth, A Narrative and Two Other Stories* (1902)
>*Typhoon and Other Stories* (1903)
>*A Set of Six* (1908)
>*'Twixt Land and Sea* (1912)
>*Within the Tides* (1915)
>*Tales of Hearsay* (1925)

Critical Bibliography for "Youth"

Gurko, Leo, *Joseph Conrad: Giant in Exile.* New York, Macmillan, 1962, pp. 79-82.

Haugh, Robert E., *Joseph Conrad: Discovery in Design.* Norman, University of Oklahoma Press, 1957, pp. 22-24.

Heiney, Donald W., *Essentials of Contemporary Literature.* Great Neck, Barron, 1954, pp. 214-215.

Jean-Aubrey, Gerard, *The Sea Dreamer: A Definitive Biography of Joseph Conrad.* New York, Doubleday, 1957, pp. 93-99.

Karl, Frederick P., *A Reader's Guide to Joseph Conrad.* New York, Noonday Press, 1960, pp. 131-133.

Krieger, Murray, "Conrad's *Youth:* A Naïve Opening to Art and Life," *College English,* Vol. 20, No. 6 (March, 1959), pp. 275-280.

Moser, Thomas, *Joseph Conrad: Achievement and Decline.* Cambridge, Harvard University Press, 1957, pp. 43-49, 128-129.

Unger, Leonard, *The Man in the Name.* Minneapolis, University of Minnesota Press, 1956, pp. 240-242.

Zabel, Morton Dauwen, "Introduction," Joseph Conrad, *Youth: A Narrative and Two Other Stories.* Garden City, Doubleday Anchor Books, 1959, pp. 1-16.

Alfred Edgar Coppard

(1878-1957)

Author of more than two hundred short stories, A. E. Coppard was born on January 4, 1878, in Folkestone, Kent County, England. He left school when he was nine years old to work as an errand boy and at various other occupations. He was a clerk in Brighton and later at Oxford. When he was forty-one, he gave up office life to concentrate on writing. In 1921 he published his first book of short

stories; a year later, a book of poetry.   Thenceforth he published
regularly, both prose and poetry, and is recognized as a great master
of the art of short fiction, primarily through folk tales, realistic stories
of humor, and fantasies.   After his death on January 13, 1957, his
autobiography, *It's Me, O Lord!* was published.   He enunciated two
major principles of short-story writing: (1) the modern short story
should conform to the folk tale's tradition of "being spoken to you
rather that at you"; and (2) unity, verisimilitude, and "completeness
of contour" are best achieved by plotting a story through the consciousness of a single character.

Major Fiction

Short Stories
> *Adam and Eve and Pinch Me* (1921)
> *Clorinda Walks in Heaven* (1922)
> *The Black Dog* (1923)
> *Fishmonger's Fiddle* (1925)
> *The Field of Mustard* (1926)
> *Silver Circus* (1928)
> *Nixey's Harlequin* (1931)
> *Dunky Fitlow* (1933)
> *Polly Oliver* (1935)
> *Ninepenny Flute* (1937)
> *You Never Know, Do You?* (including "The Fair Young Willowy
>   Tree") (1939)
> *Ugly Anna* (1944)
> *The Collected Tales of A. E. Coppard* (including "The Fair
>   Young Willowy Tree") (1952)

Stephen Crane

(1871-1900)

The tragically short life of Stephen Crane, writer of fiction, poet,
and journalist, began on November 1, 1871, in Newark, New Jersey.
The son of a Methodist minister, he attended military school and
spent a year at Lafayette College and another year at Syracuse
University.   He worked as a free-lance reporter for the New York
Herald and *Tribune*.   Although he had never been to war, the reality

of war was so vividly portrayed in his masterpiece, *The Red Badge of Courage*, that his genius was recognized, and he achieved almost instant fame. The following year, in 1896, he sailed for Cuba on a newspaper assignment. The ship sank, and because of the exposure he suffered in an open boat, his health was thereafter impaired. He was a war correspondent for the Greco-Turkish War in 1896 and the Spanish-American War in 1898. These first-hand experiences on battlefields enabled him to write other war stories, including "The Upturned Face," and to prove to himself that the psychology of combat was as he had imagined it to be when he wrote *Red Badge*. A self-imposed exile, he settled in Brede Place, Sussex, England, in 1899, but the following year, on June 5, he died of tuberculosis in Germany.

Major Fiction

Novels
> *Maggie: A Girl of the Streets* (1893)
> *The Red Badge of Courage* (1895)
> *George's Mother* (1896)

Short Fiction
> *The Little Regiment* (1896)
> *The Open Boat and Other Tales of Adventure* (including "The Upturned Face") (1898)
> *The Monster and Other Stories* (1899)
> *Whilomville Stories* (1900)
> *Wounds in the Rain* (1900)

Critical Bibliography for "The Upturned Face"

Jennings, Frank G., and Calitri, Charles J., eds., "Teacher's Guide," *Stories*. New York, Harcourt, Brace, 1957, p. 14.

Stallman, Robert W., *Stephen Crane: An Omnibus*. New York, Knopf, 1952, pp. 375-376.

Nathaniel Hawthorne

(1804-1864)

Descended on both sides from prominent New England families, Nathaniel Hawthorne was born on July 4, 1804, in Salem, Massachusetts, the only son in a family of three children. When he was four,

his father, a sea captain, died in Dutch Guiana, leaving his family poor
and dependent upon relatives. Nathaniel attended Bowdoin College
and then spent twelve years at home, reading and writing, editing
and publishing. From 1838 to 1840 he was a measurer in the Boston
Custom House. The following year he married Sophia Peabody and
lived at the Old Manse in Concord, where he associated with Emerson,
Thoreau, Margaret Fuller, and Amos Bronson Alcott and joined the
famous Brook Farm Association. A later friend and contemporary was
Herman Melville. After being a surveyor in the Salem Custom
House, Hawthorne wrote his masterpiece, *The Scarlet Letter*. In
1853, he was appointed by President Pierce to serve as United States
Consul at Liverpool. After four years there, he lived in Rome and
Florence for two years before returning to New England. He died on
May 19, 1864.

Major Fiction

Novels
The Scarlet Letter (1850)
The House of the Seven Gables (1851)
The Blithedale Romance (1852)
The Marble Faun (1860)
Short Fiction
Twice-Told Tales (including "The Man of Adamant") (1837)
Mosses from an Old Manse (1846)
The Snow-Image and Other Twice-Told Tales (1852)

Critical Bibliography for "The Man of Adamant"

Arvin, Newton, *Hawthorne*. New York, Russell and Russell, 1961, pp.
62-63.

Brennan, Joseph X., and Gross, Seymour L., "The Origin of Hawthorne's Unpardonable Sin," *Boston University Studies in English*,
Vol. 3, No. 2 (Summer, 1957), pp. 126-129.

Turner, Arlin, *Nathaniel Hawthorne: An Introduction and Interpretation*. New York, Viking, 1949, p. 89.

Waggoner, Hyatt H., *Hawthorne: A Critical Study*. Cambridge, Harvard University Press, 1955, pp. 95-100.

Shirley Jackson
(1919-)

Shirley Jackson was born in 1919 in San Francisco and grew up there and in Rochester, New York. She attended Syracuse University, where she founded, wrote for, and edited a literary magazine and where she met the man who was to become her husband in 1940, Stanley Edgar Hyman, teacher and literary critic. They live in Vermont and have had four children. Noted for her most terrifying fantasy, "The Lottery," the best-known and most popular of her short stories, Miss Jackson also is the author of a number of entertaining stories about children.

Major Fiction

Novels
> *The Road Through the Wall* (1948)
> *Hangsaman* (1951)
> *The Bird's Nest* (1954)
> *We Have Always Lived in the Castle* (1962)

Short Fiction
> *The Lottery* (1949)

James Joyce
(1882-1941)

James Joyce, one of the great writers of modern literature, experimenter in linguistic acrobatics and in stream-of-consciousness writing, especially the interior monologue, was born on February 2, 1882, in suburban Rathmines near Dublin. He studied at Clongowes Wood College, Sallins, County Kildare; Belvedere College, Dublin; and University College of Dublin, a Jesuit institution, at which he mastered almost every major modern language, as well as Latin, and read comprehensively in classic and modern literature. After he married Nora Barnacle, a Galway girl, he found a job teaching language in the Berlitz School at Trieste. The major part of his life he lived in exile from Ireland, chiefly in Rome and Paris. He supported his family by teaching and with gifts from friends who encouraged him to continue his writing. Fighting blindness, illness, and poverty, he died in Zurich on January 13, 1941.

Major Fiction

Novels
> *A Portrait of the Artist As a Young Man* (1916)
> *Ulysses* (1922)
> *Finnegans Wake* (1939)

Short Fiction
> *Dubliners* (including "The Sisters") (1914)

Critical Bibliography for "The Sisters"

Daiches, David, *The Novel and the Modern World*. Chicago, University of Chicago, 1960, p. 70 ff.

Ellmann, Richard, *James Joyce*. New York, Oxford University Press, 1959, pp. 20, 169-170.

Kaye, Julian B., "Simony, the Three Simons and Joycean Myth," in *A James Joyce Miscellany* (Marvin Magalaner, editor). New York, The James Joyce Society, 1957, pp. 21-23.

Kenner, Hugh, *Dublin's Joyce*. Bloomington, Indiana University Press, 1956, pp. 50-53.

Levin, Richard, and Shattuck, Charles, "First Flight to Ithaca," *Accent*, Vol. 4, No. 2 (Winter, 1944), pp. 80-81; in *James Joyce: Two Decades of Criticism* (Seon Givens, editor). New York, Vanguard Press, 1948, pp. 55-57.

Walzl, Florence L., "Pattern of Paralysis in Joyce's *Dubliners*: A Study of the Original Framework," *College English*, Vol. 22, No. 4 (January, 1961), pp. 221-228.

Franz Kafka

(1883-1924)

Kafka was born in Prague on July 3, 1883, to wealthy Jewish parents. The young Franz was resentful of his father's authoritarian domination yet eager for the man's approval, which he never won. A good student, he attended the Volksschule, the Alstader Ring Gymnasium, and the German University of Prague, where he received his doctorate in jurisprudence, though his chief interest was literature. In 1908 he obtained a position in the Prague office of the government accident insurance bureau, where he was successful and popular. He went to the front in World War I, and his chronically poor health broke down. He wrestled with tuberculosis the remainder of his life, moving from one sanitarium to another, till the disease ended his life on June 3, 1924. He had begun writing in 1912, and he continued to write for a span of ten years. He destroyed much of his work and extracted a promise from his close friend Max Brod never to publish the stories. To this literary executor we owe what we know of Kafka and his fiction, for after a struggle with his conscience, Brod decided to publish his friend's books after all, as well as to write the standard biography of the now great experimental Czechoslovakian author.

Major Fiction (translated into English)

Novels
>The Castle (1930)
>The Trial (1937)
>Amerika (1938)

Short Fiction
>The Great Wall of China (including "The Burrow") (1933)
>The Metamorphosis (1937)
>The Penal Colony (1948)

Critical Bibliography for "The Burrow"

Bergel, Lienhard, "The Burrow" in The Kafka Problem (Angel Flores, editor). New York, New Directions, 1946, pp. 199-206.

Fraiberg, Selma, "Dream and Creation in Kafka," Partisan Review, Vol. 23, No. 1 (Winter, 1956), p. 57.

Goodman, Paul, Kafka's Prayer. New York, Vanguard, 1947, pp. 222-227.

Hodin, J. P., "Memories of Franz Kafka," Horizon, Vol. 17, No. 97 (January, 1948), p. 38.

Muir, Edwin, "Introductory Note" to Franz Kafka, The Great Wall of China, Stories and Reflections. New York, Schocken Books, 1946.

Politzer, Heinz, Franz Kafka: Parable and Paradox. Ithaca, Cornell University Press, 1962, pp. 318-333.

Savage, D. S., "Franz Kafka: Faith and Vocation," Sewanee Review, Vol. 54, No. 2 (April-June, 1946), p. 239; in The Kafka Problem (Angel Flores, editor). New York, New Directions, 1946, pp. 334-335.

Walker, Augusta, "Allegory: A Light Conceit," Partisan Review, Vol. 22, No. 4 (Fall, 1955), pp. 484-490.

Richard M. Kain

(1908-   )

A graduate of Swarthmore College, Dr. Kain is now a professor of English at the University of Louisville. He has been a leading authority on James Joyce and other Irish subjects for more than ten years. In his research he has visited Ireland six times and has traveled to Paris and Zurich with John J. Slocum, noted Joyce collector with whom Dr. Kain also met Joyce's family and friends. A member of the James Joyce Society, he has lectured at the Yeats International Summer School at Sligo, Ireland, and at the opening of the James Joyce Museum in Dublin. He spent one year at Yale University and one summer at the British Museum doing research on Joyce and William Butler Yeats. In addition to writing numerous articles, reviews, and books on contemporary literature, he has been a visiting professor at several universities: Northwestern, Harvard, Colorado, Venice, Massachusetts, and New York. Besides *Joyce: The Man, the Work, the Reputation,* which he coauthored with Marvin Magalaner, Dr. Kain has written *Fabulous Voyager: James Joyce's "Ulysses,"* and *Dublin in the Age of William Butler Yeats and James Joyce.*

Harold Keables

(1900-   )

Creative-writing teacher of Jean Weir, author of "The Noontide of the First Day," Harold Keables is one of the most outstanding and beloved high school English instructors in the United States. He was born on January 28, 1900, in Canon City, Colorado, where he lived till the family moved in 1912 to Denver. After his graduation from the University of Denver in 1923, he married his childhood sweetheart and took her with him to his first teaching position at Cebu Junior College, a branch of the University of the Philippines, where he taught English for two years. Afterwards, for ten years he worked with his father and brother in the family restaurant in Denver. In 1935, he began teaching at Denver South High School, his alma mater, where he is still in charge of the creative writing laboratory he originated. The creative writing workshop was inspired by Dr. Keables's association with Robert Frost, Thomas Wolfe, Edward Davison, and Whit Burnett at the Writer's Workshop at the University of Colorado in 1935. Since then, more than one hundred of his students have achieved distinction for their writing. Dr. Keables himself has received national recognition: the 1959 award of the Teachers Award Foundation for Distinguished Service, the honorary degree of Doctor of Letters, in 1961, from the University of Denver, and the honorary degree of Doctor of Humane Letters from the University of Colorado in 1963, and articles about him in such publications as *Time, Life,* and *Amerika,* and *This Week.* In October, 1962, Dr. Keables received one of the newly established Yale Awards for Outstanding Secondary School Teachers; he had been nominated for the honor by former students attending Yale and by other friends in the teaching profession.

Katherine M. Kittleman

(1944-   )

The student author of "Leatherback" was born on January 21, 1944, in Evanston, Illinois, where she attended Haven School and Evanston Township High School. She is the daughter of a management consultant, and, besides her parents, her family includes an older brother and a younger sister. Miss Kittleman won a first-place award for "Leatherback" in the 1961 Scholastic Writing Competition for high school students. In her senior year at Evanston High, she took the college-level English course. When she graduated from high school, she received the Mary L. Taft Memorial Award for Excellence in English and the Senior Girls' Honor Award for general excellence. Miss Kittleman was inspired to write "Leatherback" by a family vacation at Boothbay Harbor, Maine, where she witnessed a similar episode involving a leatherback. At Wellesley College she is majoring in English.

Carolyn Lansden

(1945-   )

The author of the short-short story "Leon" was born on George
Washington's birthday in Seattle. She attended schools in Cairo and
Evanston, Illinois, and was graduated from Evanston Township High
School in 1963, ranking first in her class. She won the Boltwood-
Beardsley-Bacon Prize, the Stanford Cup for general excellence, and
the Irene Kissner Turner Memorial Prize in Latin. Her father is an
attorney, and, in addition to her mother, her family includes a younger
brother and sister. She is a student at Wellesley College.

Jack London

(1876-1916)

Novelist and short-story writer John Griffith London was born on
January 12, 1876, in San Francisco and lived part of his childhood also
in Oakland, California. He left school at fourteen in search of adventure and as a protest against the poverty around him. As a sailor on
a sealing cruise, he traveled as far as Japan, and as a railroad "hobo"
he saw much of his own country. He was a member of Kelly's Industrial Army, a California economic protest group. He spent a term in
prison for vagrancy, studied Marxian socialism, and adopted the
doctrine for his own philosophy. He attended high school for a year
and the University of California for a semester and decided to make
a career for himself as a writer. He spent a winter in the Klondike,
served as a war correspondent, traveled to the South Seas, all in order
to amass material for his fiction. London wrote fifty books in seventeen years. On November 22, 1916, he died at his ranch in Glen Ellen,
California.

Major Fiction

Novels
  The Son of the Wolf (1900)
  The Call of the Wild (1903)

The Sea Wolf (1904)
White Fang (1906)
The Iron Heel (1907)
Burning Daylight (1910)
The Valley of the Moon (1913)
Short Fiction
Best Short Stories of Jack London (1953)
Jack London's Tales of Adventure (1956)
Jack London: Short Stories (including "To Build a Fire") (1960)

Marvin Magalaner

(1920-   )

Dr. Magalaner, who was born November 6, 1920, received his bachelor's degree from The City College of New York, where he is now an associate professor of English. For four years after he graduated from college he served in the Army Airways Communications System in India. He later received his master's and doctor's degrees from Columbia University, where his dissertation on James Joyce's *Dubliners* was the start of a long, continued interest in and study of that Irish author. He has also been a lecturer in contemporary literature at Columbia. Dr. Magalaner has written two books on Joyce in addition to *Joyce: The Man, the Work, the Reputation*, which he wrote with Richard M. Kain, and from which the critical review of "The Sisters" in this book is taken. Dr. Magalaner has made two trips to Dublin to gather material on Joyce and in 1963 went to Europe on a study grant from the Ford Foundation.

Katherine Mansfield

(1888-1923)

Born in Wellington, New Zealand, on October 14, 1888, to a successful merchant, Katherine Mansfield Beauchamp had the advantages and disadvantages of life in a provincial upper-middle class. She went to London in 1903 to study at Queen's College. Returning to New

Zealand, she began to write short vignettes, which an editor accepted for publication. Encouraged by this success, she returned to London for a literary career. In 1908 she impulsively married an older man but left him the next day. Lonely and ill, her only consolation was her growing success as a short-story writer. In 1911, she published her first volume of stories and that same year met John Middleton Murry, who was to be her most important friend and associate for the remainder of her short life. He became editor of the new literary magazine *Rhythm*, whose success was due largely to Katherine Mansfield's contributions. She frequently sought refuge from her Bohemian London life at Fontainebleau, near Paris, and it was there that she died on January 9, 1923.

Major Fiction

Short Fiction
> *In a German Pension* (1911)
> *Bliss and Other Stories* (including "Feuille d'Album") (1920)
> *The Garden Party and Other Stories* (1922)
> *The Dove's Nest and Other Stories* (1923)

Critical Bibliography for the Short Stories of Katherine Mansfield

Berkman, Sylvia, *Katherine Mansfield: A Critical Study*. New Haven, Yale University Press, 1951.

Bowen, Elizabeth, ed., *Stories by Katherine Mansfield*. New York, Random House Vintage Books, 1956.

Cather, Willa, "Katherine Mansfield," *Not Under Forty*. New York, Knopf, 1936, pp. 123-147.

Daiches, David, "Katherine Mansfield and the Search for Truth," *The Novel and the Modern World*. Chicago, University of Chicago Press, 1939, pp. 65-79.

Murry, John Middleton, "Katherine Mansfield," *Katherine Mansfield and Other Literary Studies*. London, Constable, 1959, pp. 69-93.

Porter, Katherine Anne, "The Art of Katherine Mansfield," *The Days Before*. New York, Harcourt, Brace, 1952, pp. 82-87.

Schneider, Elisabeth, "Katherine Mansfield and Chekhov," *Modern Language Notes*, Vol. 50, No. 5 (June, 1935), pp. 394-397.

Guy de Maupassant

(1850-1893)

One of the creators of the short story in its modern form, Maupassant also wrote novels, but it is in the realm of short fiction that he created his masterpieces, "The Tallow Ball," "The Necklace," and "The Piece of String." He was born on August 5, 1850, in the château of Miromesnil near Dieppe. He learned Latin from his vicar and attended schools in Yvetot and Rouen, completing his formal education at Caen University. From his youth he intended to be a writer, and he learned his art from his uncle's close friend, Gustave Flaubert, the French novelist, who for seven years tutored Maupassant in the art of fiction. The young writer served as a clerk in the navy department for ten years and then was appointed to a secretarial post in the office of the minister of education. His personal life was miserable despite his growing success as an author. Convinced his failing health would lead him to an early death, he worked at his writing as though possessed. After a suicide attempt in Cannes in 1892, he was sent to a nursing home in Paris, where eighteen months later, on July 6, 1893, he died.

Major Fiction

Novels

> *Life* (1883)
> *Pierre and Jean* (1888)
> *Fair Friend* (1885)
> *Notre Coeur* (1890)

Short Fiction

> *Mademoiselle Fifi* (1882)
> *Tales of Day and Night* (1883)
> *The Sisters Rondoli* (1884)
> *Miss Harriet* (1884)
> *The Odd Number* (including "The Piece of String") (1889)
> *The Complete Short Stories of Guy de Maupassant* (1955)

Critical Bibliography for "The Piece of String"

Bement, Douglas, *Weaving the Short Story*. New York, Long and Smith, 1932, pp. 54-60.

Cross, Ethan Allan, *A Book of the Short Story.* New York, American Book, 1934, pp. 31-38.

Herman Melville
(1819-1891)

Herman Melville, third child of the eight sons and daughters of Allan and Maria Melville of New York City, was born on August 1, 1819, while his father was still a prosperous importer. His father died in 1832, deeply in debt, never to be forgiven by Herman for leaving the family in such straits. At nineteen Herman went to sea and found sailing more exciting than teaching school, which he had tried. His experiences with whaling and in the exotic Marquesas Islands were to furnish him with material for his novels. In 1844 he began writing, and his early books were successful enough so that in 1847 he married and in 1850 bought a farm near Pittsfield, Massachusetts, where he was to complete his masterpiece, *Moby Dick.* Later he suffered ill-health, wrote books that did not have popular success, journeyed to Europe and the Holy Land, and visited his friend Nathaniel Hawthorne. In 1866 Melville became a district inspector of customs in New York. The last years of his life he spent in silent obscurity, and it was not for three decades after his death on September 28, 1891, that his works began to receive the acclaim that has grown ever since for one of America's greatest writers.

Major Fiction

Novels
> *Typee* (1846)
> *Omoo* (1847)
> *Mardi* (1849)
> *Redburn, His First Voyage* (1849)
> *White-Jacket* (1850)
> *Moby Dick* (1851)
> *Pierre* (1852)
> *Israel Potter* (1855)
> *The Confidence-Man* (1857)

Short Fiction
>*The Piazza Tales* (including "Bartleby") (1856)
>*Billy Budd, Foretopman* (1924)

Critical Bibliography for "Bartleby the Scrivener"

Arvin, Newton, *Herman Melville*. New York, Sloane, 1950, pp. 242-244.

Chase, Richard, *Herman Melville: A Critical Study*. New York, Macmillan, 1949, pp. 143-148.

Felheim, Marvin, "Meaning and Structure in 'Bartleby,'" *College English*, Vol. 23, No. 5 (February, 1962), pp. 369-376.

Fogle, Richard Harter, *Melville's Shorter Tales*. Norman, University of Oklahoma Press, 1960, pp. 14-27.

Howard, Leon, *Herman Melville: A Biography*. Berkeley, University of California Press, 1951, pp. 208-209.

Kazin, Alfred, "Ishmael in His Academic Heaven," *The New Yorker*, Vol. 24, No. 5 (February 12, 1949), pp. 84, 87.

Marcus, Mordecai, "Melville's Bartleby As a Psychological Double," *College English*, Vol. 23, No. 5 (February, 1962), pp. 365-368.

Marx, Leo, "Melville's Parable of the Walls," *Sewanee Review*, Vol. 61, No. 4 (Autumn, 1953), pp. 602-627.

Miller, James E., Jr., *A Reader's Guide to Herman Melville*. New York, Farrar, Straus and Cudahy, 1962, pp. 160-161.

Olivier, Egbert S., "A Second Look at 'Bartleby,'" *College English*, Vol. 6, No. 4 (May, 1945), pp. 431-439.

Rosenberry, Edward H., *Melville and the Comic Spirit*. Cambridge, Harvard University Press, 1955, pp. 145-146.

C. E. Montague

(1867-1928)

Irish journalist, novelist, short-story writer, and literary critic Charles Edward Montague was born in Ealing, London, on January 1, 1867. As a boy Montague went to the City of London School and in 1885 to Balliol College, Oxford, where he took a first in Classical Moderations and a second in Humane Letters. He played Rugby football and rowed with the college eight. Because he had rescued a drowning man, he was awarded the Royal Humane Society's bronze medal. In 1890 he joined the staff of *The Manchester Guardian* and eight years later was assistant to the editor and proprietor, whose daughter Madeline Mr. Montague married. He lived a strenuous life, working nights at the newspaper; reading, writing, and cycling afternoons; and taking every opportunity he could for vacations in the Swiss mountains, rock climbing. When he was forty-seven and gray-haired, he dyed his hair and enlisted in the British Army as a private. He was injured in bombing practice but went to France in November, 1915, with the Royal Fusiliers, though his poor health soon sent him back home. In July, 1916, he returned to the front as an intelligence officer, guide for distinguished visitors, and assistant press censor. He retired from *The Manchester Guardian* in 1925, and lived with his wife and family at Burford, Oxfordshire, until he died on May 28, 1928, two years after the University of Manchester had honored him with a Litt.D. degree.

Major Fiction

Novels
> *A Hind Let Loose* (1910)
> *The Morning's War* (1913)
> *Rough Justice* (1926)
> *Disenchantment* (1926)
> *Right off the Map* (1927)

Short Fiction
> *Fiery Particles* (1923)
> *Action* (including "Action") (1928)

Edgar Allan Poe

(1809-1849)

Poet, critic, editor, and "father of the American short story," Edgar Allan Poe was born January 19, 1809, in Boston. Because his parents, both actors, died when Edgar was two, he was adopted by his wealthy Virginia godfather. He received a classical education in Virginia and in Scotland and England, and he attended but did not graduate from the University of Virginia and West Point. His life was a series of unfortunate disappointments due largely to his personal instability. His genius as a writer and literary theorist was recognized abroad, particularly in France. A writer from early youth, Poe also was editor of the

Southern Literary Messenger and later of *Burton's* and *Graham's* magazines, the New York *Evening Mirror,* and *The Broadway Journal.* He married his fourteen-year-old cousin Virginia Clemm, who died a year and a half before his own death, which came on October 7, 1849.

Major Fiction

Short Fiction
"A MS Found in a Bottle" (1833)
The Narrative of Arthur Gordon Pym (1838)
Tales of the Grotesque and Arabesque (1840)
The Murders in the Rue Morgue (1841)

Critical Bibliography for "Metzengerstein"

Bonaparte, Marie, *The Life and Works of Edgar Allan Poe: A Psycho-Analytic Interpretation.* London, Imago Publishing, 1949, pp. 273-282.
Smith, Grace P., "Poe's 'Metzengerstein,'" *Modern Language Notes,* Vol. 48, No. 6 (June, 1933), pp. 356-359.

Katherine Anne Porter
(1894-   )

Miss Porter was born on May 15, 1894, in Indian Creek, Texas. Her family was Catholic, and she was educated accordingly in convent schools in Texas and Louisiana. Although she began writing when she was very young, she did not publish her first fiction until 1922. She supported herself by writing book reviews, political literature, and translations and by editing the work of other writers. She has traveled widely, at one time teaching school in Mexico, and she has married twice, in 1933 to Eugene Pressly, an American diplomat in Paris, and in 1938 to Albert Erskine, Jr., a professor at the University of Louisiana and business manager of the *Southern Review.* She is a slow and careful writer and has withheld or destroyed much of what she has written. Her first novel was published in 1962, after thirty years of polishing and refining. Since 1942 she has lived in New York City. She has been a lecturer at Stanford University and a Fellow in Regional American Literature of the Library of Congress. She holds an honorary LL.D. from the Woman's College of the University of North

Carolina. Her short story "Holiday," which appears in this anthology, was originally published in *The Atlantic Monthly* in December, 1960, and has since won a first prize in the annual O. Henry Awards.

Major Fiction

Novel
>   *Ship of Fools* (1962)

Short Fiction
>   *Flowering Judas and Other Stories* (1930)
>   *Hacienda* (1934)
>   *Pale Horse, Pale Rider* (1939)
>   *The Leaning Tower and Other Stories* (1944)

James S. Renthal

(1944-   )

The youthful author of "What Mistake?" was born on April 5, 1944, in Chicago. He attended schools in Evanston, Illinois, and was graduated from Evanston Township High School. There, in his senior year—when he wrote "What Mistake?"—he took the college-level English course. He was editor-in-chief of his high school yearbook, *The Key*. His father is a free-lance writer, and his mother is an elementary school librarian. He is now a student at the University of Chicago, and he intends to continue writing as an avocation.

Mary Jane Richeimer

(1913-   )

Miss Richeimer was born in 1913 in Massillon, Ohio, and attended elementary and high schools there. She received her B.A. from Lake Erie College, where she majored in English and in library science. It was as a librarian that she earned the money with which to go to college and graduate school. She received her M.A. from Kent State University and has done additional graduate work at Teachers College of Columbia University and at Northwestern University. She taught in Massillon and at New Trier Township High School in Winnetka, Illinois, before going to Evanston Township High School, Evanston, Illinois, where she was a school librarian for several years before becoming an English teacher for freshmen and sophomores, a position she still holds. Miss Richeimer is well known for encouraging outside reading among young people and has appeared on a number of educational reading panels. She also encourages creative writing, among her pupils, many of whom have won awards in state and national contests. Her own poetry and various articles have been published in magazines, and she is the author of three books: *A Century of Education, Planning My Future,* and *Toward Adult Living.*

William B. Rood, Jr.

(1942-   )

This student literary critic was born in Evanston, Illinois, on September 1, 1942, and attended Haven School and Evanston Township High School, where he wrote the poetry that won him an award in the 39th Annual Creative Writing Contest for High School Students (1960), sponsored by *The Atlantic Monthly.* An honors student, both in high school and Northwestern University, he received his B.A. in 1964 and entered the Master of Arts in Teaching program to become a secondary school English teacher.

John Steinbeck

(1902-   )

In 1962, John Ernst Steinbeck became the sixth American writer to receive the Nobel Prize for literature, twenty-two years after he had received a Pulitzer prize for his best-known, controversial novel, *The Grapes of Wrath.* He was born in Salinas, California, on February 27, 1902, and was graduated from high school in Salinas. He attended Stanford University without taking a degree, and in 1926 went to New York City, where he worked at odd jobs while trying to establish himself as a writer of short stories. He has worked as a newspaperman, including war reporting, and his college interest in biology has led him on numerous fishing and scientific expeditions. His first three novels attracted little attention, but when his short story "The Red Pony" was published in 1933, he gained a wider audience. *Tortilla Flat* was his first popular success, and *Of Mice and Men* established him as a leading American novelist. After a trip abroad in 1937, he traveled with the migrant workers of Oklahoma and became familiar with and horrified by their plight. The result was his masterpiece, *The Grapes of Wrath*, to which have been attributed a number of legislative reforms of the social conditions of migrants and the Dust Bowl. In politics, he is an independent liberal, and though generally sympathetic to the proletariat and rural labor, he has not adhered to the platform of any one political party or social movement.

Major Fiction

Novels
>   *Tortilla Flat* (1935)
>   *In Dubious Battle* (1936)
>   *Of Mice and Men* (1937)
>   *The Grapes of Wrath* (1939)
>   *The Moon Is Down* (1942)
>   *East of Eden* (1952)
>   *Sweet Thursday* (1954)
>   *The Winter of Our Discontent* (1961)

Short Fiction
>   *The Long Valley* (1938)
>   *The Portable Steinbeck* (1943, 1946)
>   *The Pearl* (1945, 1947)

Dylan Thomas

(1914-1953)

Primarily a poet, Dylan Thomas is less well known for his fiction of fine quality. He was born on October 22, 1914, in Camarthenshire, Wales, and went to school at the Swansea Grammar School, where his father was an English master. Thomas worked briefly as a newspaperman and then turned to poetry, which was first published when he was nineteen years old. During World War II he worked for the British

Broadcasting Corporation and also served as an antiaircraft gunner. After the war he continued his writing, chiefly poetry, which was acclaimed by the critics but generally ignored by the public, who found it too obscure. He began to give readings of his own and others' verse, and the unforgettable music of his voice began to attract a following even though many did not understand the words of what he was reading. The recordings he made of his own poetry and prose are widely sold today. He made three successful lecture tours in the United States, where he was lionized. He was striken with a cerebral disease and died suddenly on November 9, 1953, in New York City.

Major Fiction

Short Stories
> *Portrait of the Artist As a Young Dog* (including "Patricia, Edith and Arnold") (1940)
> *Adventures in the Skin Trade and Other Stories* (1955)
> *A Prospect of the Sea and Other Stories and Prose Writings* (1955)

Critical Bibliography for "Patricia, Edith and Arnold"

Barrows, Herbert, *Suggestions for Teaching 15 Stories.* Boston, Heath, 1950, pp. 9-10.

Korg, Jacob, "The Short Stories of Dylan Thomas," *Perspective*, Vol. 1, No. 3 (1948), pp. 184-191.

Williams, Michael, "Welsh Voices in the Short Story," *Welsh Review*, Vol. 6, No. 4 (Winter, 1947), pp. 290-298.

William York Tindall

(1903-   )

A professor of English in the graduate school of Columbia University, Dr. Tindall has lived since 1931 in New York City. He was born on March 7, 1903, in Williamstown, Vermont. He received his bachelor's, master's, and doctor's degrees from Columbia and is a member of Phi Beta Kappa. A visiting professor at several universities, he also taught at New York University for five years. His interest in James Joyce was heightened by a visit in 1932 to Dublin. In 1954 he returned to

Ireland as a Guggenheim Fellow, and since then, he has written five critical books on Joyce, including *A Reader's Guide to James Joyce,* from which his analysis of "The Sisters" in this anthology is taken. A member of the James Joyce Society, he is also active in the Modern Language Association and the American Association of University Professors. Dr. Tindall has written books on other authors besides Joyce: D. H. Lawrence, Samuel Beckett, John Bunyan, Wallace Stevens, and Dylan Thomas.

John Updike
(1932-   )

That John Updike is "the most talented writer of his age in America . . . the most gifted writer of his generation" is the opinion of Arthur Mizener, Cornell University professor and well-known literary critic. John Updike was born on March 18, 1932, and spent his boyhood in Shillington, Pennsylvania, where he attended public schools. He graduated from Harvard College and attended the Ruskin School of Drawing and Fine Arts in Oxford, England. He was a member of the staff of *The New Yorker* from 1955 to 1957, and since that time has contributed short stories and poems to that magazine and others. At Ipswich, Massachusetts, where he lives with his wife and four children, he devotes his career full time to writing.

Major Fiction

Novels
> *Carpentered Hen* (1958)
> *The Poorhouse Fair* (1959)
> *Rabbit, Run* (1960)
> *The Centaur* (1963)

Short Fiction
> *The Same Door* (1959)
> *Pigeon Feathers and Other Stories* (1962)

Critical Bibliography for "Pigeon Feathers"

Mizener, Arthur, "Behind the Dazzle Is a Knowing Eye," *The New York Times Book Review,* March 18, 1962, Section 7, pp. 1, 29.

BIOGRAPHIES AND CRITICAL BIBLIOGRAPHIES** **473**

Warren S. Weber

(1945-   )

Author of the student commentary on his fellow student's short story "Leatherback," this young critic was born on February 4, 1945, in Evanston, Illinois, where he attended Haven School and graduated from Evanston Township High School, first in his class, winning the Boltwood-Beardsley-Bacon Prize. A student at Wesleyan University, he plans a business career but is majoring in English as preparation for an avocation as a writer.

Jean Weir

(1937-   )

"Noontide of the First Day" was a prize-winning short story in the 1955 Scholastic Writing Competition for high school students. Its author was a student in the creative writing class of Harold Keables at Denver South High School. Miss Weir was born in Boston on July 31, 1937, and spent her early school life in Shrewsbury, Massachusetts. In 1953 she moved to Denver with her mother and younger sister and brother. When she graduated from Denver South High School, she received the regional scholarship to Smith College, from which she was graduated in 1959, *summa cum laude*, Phi Beta Kappa. At Smith, Miss Weir won several prizes for Greek scholarship and the poetry prize in her senior year. She was editor of the college publication *Perspective*. On a fellowship in classical languages, she attended the University of Toronto, where in 1961 she received her master's degree. She then received a grant to study at the American School of Classical Studies in Athens for a year. During the summer of 1962 she studied further at the American Academy in Rome, and that fall returned to Toronto to begin work on her doctorate in preparation for a college teaching career in Greek and Latin.

474

Glossary

Abstract: Having the quality of being general, opposite of **Concrete,** pure idea (idealistic), apart from material objects or particular instances; such abstract ideas as vengeance, jealousy, hate, love, loyalty, etc., have their place in literature, but they are usually incorporated into concrete situations, characters, or action; the reader abstracts or generalizes from these concrete particularities the theme, the universality, of a story. (See also **Concrete, Individuality, Universality.**)

Action: What happens in the story, revealing character, determined by character, and, with character, illuminating theme. (See p. 25.)

Allegory: A set of objects that have metaphorical equivalents for each item in the set. (See p. 42.)

Ambiguity: Richness of meaning through two or more possible connotations.

Atmosphere: The emotional effect of the physical setting and external action or of the psychological aspect of character and internal action. (See p. 29.)

Central Character: The single main character or person or personification in the story, an essential element in the content of the short story.

Character: A person or personification who determines action, is illuminated by action, and combines with action to effect theme. (See p. 23.)

Climax: The turning point of the action at which the conflicting forces reach their highest point of tension and are upset, with one of the forces winning out over the other; the change of the action or of the fortunes of a character, either

through reversal or discovery or gain or loss, after which the ending or resolution is inevitable. (See p. 26.)

Concrete: Having the quality of being real (realistic), particular, specific, capable of being perceived by the senses; literature deals with the concrete rather than the abstract, the particular rather than the general. (See also **Abstract, Imagery, Individuality, Universality.**)

Conflict: The struggle, tension, or problem set up by two opposing forces early in a story for the purpose of producing suspense and change; in external action, the conflict may be between characters or between characters and their environment; in internal action, the conflict may be between opposing forces within a character himself. (See also p. 25.)

Content: The characters, action, and theme that an author blends with his material through the unifying principle of form. (See also p. 22.)

Denouement: The unraveling or falling off and ending of the action, usually after the climax, though it may coincide with the climax in certain so-called "surprise-ending" stories, such as those by O. Henry and in most short-short stories.

Development: The middle episodes of the action.

Discovery: See **Climax.**

Episode: Incident or scene in a series of incidents or scenes depicting the action; may be a physical happening, rendering of a mood, a conversation, a process of thinking or reacting on the part of a character. (See also **Initial Incident.**)

Exposition: The background information for the action of the story. (See also **Initial Incident.**)

External Action: See **Conflict.**

Fable: Fictitious tale whose purpose is to teach a moral lesson, usually with characters that are personified animals. (See also **Parable** and p. 17.)

Fiction: See page 15.

First-Person Narration: See **Point of View** and page 31.

Foreshadowing: Providing intimations of some event before it takes place. (See p. 28.)

Form: The unifying principle that achieves an organic whole of all the elements of content and material; the total effect achieved. (See also pp. 13 and 30.)

Imagery: The representation by words of a sense perception, including metaphors which indirectly identify two objects or ideas by implying a comparison between them; an author makes extensive use of imagery in order to convey concreteness and individuality.

Incident: See **Episode.**

Individuality: The uniqueness and originality that an author gives to his story; the opposite of **Universality**, which, like individuality, is essential to a work of art. (See also p. 11.)

Initial Incident: The first episode in a series of episodes that constitute the action; it completes the **Exposition**, which is the process of providing all the background information the reader needs about characters and action existing before the beginning of the story. (See also p. 26.)

Irony: A literary device that presents a contrast or discrepancy between appearance and reality, between the expected and the actual. Dramatic irony, or irony of situation, is the discrepancy between the expected and actual outcomes of an action; verbal irony is deliberate statement of the opposite of what its speaker means, though his tone of voice indicates what he does mean.

Internal Action: See **Conflict.**

Material: The language the author employs to convey his content (character, action, and theme); the material and the content are inextricably interwoven by the unifying principle of **Form.** (See also p. 13.)

Motivation: The inner drive, purpose, reason (conscious or unconcious), impulse, or intention that makes a character think, act, or react in a certain way.

Novelette: A work of short fiction, shorter than a novel, longer than a short story, demonstrating more characteristics of the short story than of the novel; between 10,000 and 20,000 words.

Pace: The speed of the movement of the action, achieved through author's sentence structure and diction, including report of action, description of scene, and summary.

Parable: A simple story whose chief purpose is a stated or implied moral lesson. (See p. 17.)

Pattern: A conspicuous, significant repetition of incidents, images, metaphors, symbols, or other literrary devices, for the purpose of illustrating the content or any of its parts.

Plot: See **Action** and **Form** and page 25.

Point of View: The "post of observation" (Henry James) or authority from which the story is narrated; the mind through which the story is presented; five major points of view are first-person central, first-person minor, third-person omniscient, third-person limited, and third-person central; one of the most important literary devices the author of fiction uses. (See also p. 31.)

Reversal: See **Climax.**

Scene: See **Episode.**

Sense Impressions: The concrete perceptions of reality that human beings make through their powers of vision, hearing, taste, smell, touch, and feelings of tension and relaxation (see **Imagery** and p. 40).

Setting: The time and place, physical background of a story.

Short-Short Story: A story of impact, about 500 to 2500 words.

Signature: An image closely associated with a particular character.

Suspense: One of the pleasures the art of fiction offers the reader; the result of conflict and the emotional desire to find out "what happened next?" Also achieved through subtle implications requiring the reader to draw his own inferences; essential to any story, to at least a small degree, in order to capture and maintain the interest of the reader.

Theme: The central idea, point, or meaning of a story; the generalization to be abstracted from the concrete situation of characters in action. (See p. 29.)

Third-Person Narration: See **Point of View** and page 34.

Tone: The attitude of the author toward his content and sometimes to the reader, as revealed explicitly or implicitly by the story.

Turning Point: See **Climax.**

Unifying Principle: See **Form** and page 13.

Unity: The feeling of wholeness, oneness, harmony of parts; an important synonym of **Form.**

Universality: The common experiences of all human beings, abstracted from their individual experiences; the reason for the pleasure of recognition and identification by a reader or viewer with a work of art. (See also **Concrete, Individuality,** and p. 11.)

Verisimilitude: The appearance of truth or reality. The term is used in relation to fiction to mean that fiction is metaphorical; it can be compared to life in some ways, but it is not the same as life. (See p. 16.)

Index

The letter *b*. before a number indicates the pages on which the reader will find the biographical sketch and the critical bibliography of the author. Other lightface numbers refer the reader to pages on which he will find helpful discussion of a story or author.

A B C D E F G H I J   0 6 9 8 7 6 5 4
PRINTED IN THE UNITED STATES OF AMERICA